Dreamland

Andri Snær Magnason

Dreamland

—————— *August* ——————

A Self-Help Manual

for a Frightened Nation

—————— *2008* ——————

Citizen-Press
London

Dreamland: a Self-Help Manual for a Frightened Nation

First published by
© Citizen Press Ltd. London, 2008

Originally published as
Draumalandið – Sjálfshjálparbók handa hræddri þjóð,
by Mál og menning, Reykjavík in 2006

Design: Börkur Arnarson
Maps and graphs: Jean-Pierre Biard
Prepress, Lauri Dammert, Art& literature Ltd.

Printed in India

A CIP record for this book is available from the British Library

First Edition

www.citizen-press.co.uk
www.andrisnaer.is

ISBN 978-0-9551363-2-0

Foreword

This book had an enormous impact in Iceland when it came out.

After Icelandic politicians had sold Icelandic nature as cheap energy to some of the industrial giants of this world without the peoples consent, the Icelandic people were upset.

We didn't get a chance to defend ourselves.
Or our nature.
We couldn't put into words our fury over the injustice of this.

Andri did.

You see, Iceland is today the largest untouched area in Europe. We were a Danish colony for 600 years. They treated us as colonizers do. We were taxed heavily and isolated from the rest of the world. Which partially turned out to be a good thing, because we missed out on the industrial revolution and once we got our independence in 1944, me and my generation and anyone younger were excited to head straight for the green revolution and keep our nature.

Instead, Iceland's politicians seem to want to catch up as quickly as possible and do what Western Europe did in 300 years to its nature in the space of five.

Andri Snær Magnason

Right now they are planning to build five of the largest aluminium factories in the world in Iceland.

Last year they built one.
Four to go?

(No more 'untouched'…)

Anyway, most Icelanders are not against dams or harnessing nature, but believe it can be done in a 'green' way, without sacrificing nature, and so the Icelandic people profit from it, not the international industrial giants.

Andri in his book not only explains the situation – what these politicians did behind the scenes – but also suggests other ways to interact with Icelandic nature and keep one's dignity.

I have a feeling this is an universal problem that our generation will find solutions to.

This book is one of these solutions.

Björk

THE SEARCH FOR REALITY

The search for reality

I was in a taxi the other day and the driver wanted to talk. 'Wasn't it you that wrote that piece in the paper yesterday?' he asked. 'Could be,' I said. 'Yeah, well,' he said. 'You were going on about some places up in the highlands that are supposed to be under threat and you were encouraging us to go there before it's too late.' 'That fits,' I answered. 'OK, you writers can write, maybe, but you're just not in touch with reality. Where are we supposed to get the money to go travelling? Do you want us back living in turf cottages again?' 'There weren't any turf cottages in the article,' I said. 'What are we actually supposed to live on? Where do we end up if people completely turn their back on progress?' he asked. 'We can't all be writers, can we?' 'No,' I answered, 'I suppose not.' 'We can't all go to university, can we? We can't all live off selling each another stocks and shares or psychoanalyzing one other!' 'Maybe not,' I said, but I couldn't seem to come up with any particularly compelling reply. 'We have to have something to live off! We need real jobs! How are we expected to live here when there's no one left except psychologists and stockbrokers? What are all these people supposed to do? What are we supposed to live on when no one wants to work in the fish?' 'People are bound to create opportunities for themselves if they study what they're interested in,' I muttered and tried to sound convincing. The taxi driver shook his head. 'Yes, and be like my cousin who went to Denmark to learn design!' 'For instance,' I said. 'Can you live off design? How are people supposed to get the money to buy all this design? What's everybody supposed to live off? You people are out of all touch with reality. You need to get real!'

So when I got out of the taxi I had a look around me to see if I could see reality and came to the conclusion that no one I know does anything that is real. No one in my household comes anywhere near reality, no one next door, no one in the family, none of my friends. There are people in computers, marketing, advertising, languages. There are stockbrokers, artists, photographers, students, kids and old age pensioners, journalists, economists, pilots, psychologists, air hostesses, ministers of the church, architects, teachers and accountants. I have one childhood friend who sells fizzy drinks, another who gets people to watch more television. That hardly counts as 'real'. An engineer with the telephone company. Is that reality? Icelandic teenagers send text messages for fifty million dollars a year. A real need? For that you could buy a year's supply of flour for the whole of Iceland. Give us this year our yearly bread, literally.

My family is made up almost entirely of doctors and nurses. Yes, fair enough, they are dealing with real problems and there's a bright future for people like them. In *Living Science* my eyes hit on the words, 'In the future it will be the healthy people that take the drugs.' It was an interesting piece about the so-called Barbie pill that makes people slim, makes their skin go brown and increases the libido. What could be better? Slim, tanned, and up for it.

My grandfather came presumably from the last generation that was born into absolute reality. His family had a clear overview of all aspects of its life and every single minute was spent in direct contact with reality. The family caught fish, collected down, burned driftwood, milked cows and herded sheep. Food was life and in a house of 1400 square feet there were twenty to thirty people, because the land yielded enough food for precisely this number. Everything was cut and dried. One sheep was a month and a bit of human survival next winter. His brother took over the farm. He bought himself a tractor and produced ten times as much food as had ever been produced there since the dawn of time. His machines cut the grass, brought in the hay and dug the ditches. 'Ha ha!' he cried. 'Plenty of food for everybody! A hundred litres of milk a day!' But his voice echoed hollowly around the house. Everyone had moved away. What did it mean? Ten times more reality, ten times fewer people.

At one time people feared that machines would steal their jobs and put us all out of work. For some, the machines seemed to promise a life of endless leisure: they would see to the fishing and haymaking, feeding the ani-

Andri Snær Magnason

mals, milking, filleting the fish and heating the houses, carrying the water and wringing out the washing. But strange to relate, rather than technological progress creating contented unemployment, allowing us to lie in bed and take it easy while the waterworks pumps and the heating utility heats and the trawling machine scoops up the catch and brings it back to land, no sooner has unemployment reached 3 per cent than the papers are full of shock!horror! headlines:

"RECESSION! CRISIS!"

'Downturn', 'recession', 'crisis' – these are charged words. They mean different things to different people. Are we talking about a crisis like the one when granny, at the tender age of eight, was forced to leave the family home in their little fishing port out on the east coast? Or does it count as a crisis when someone has to cancel his subscription for cable TV? Or when there's an overtime shortage and people have the time to meet their friends and the energy to read their children a bedtime story? Or can you call it a crisis when people don't actually notice any change in their own circumstances, for all that the papers tell them that some Central Bank indicator is showing down instead of up.

Last year my domestic electricity bills came to 400 dollars. For lighting, cooking, the washing machine, vacuum cleaner, computer and television, to name but a few. The phone bills were something over 2500 dollars, and that was before I got broadband. The crisis will have to cut pretty deep before it has any effect on anything that really matters.

'You writers are out of touch with reality,' said the taxi driver. Maybe to some extent he was right. But the truth is that the reality has been stolen from us. The machines stole it. Every day a new machine turns up to take away yet another slice of reality. And every day another machine appears that has no connection with reality whatsoever.

We can try to turn back. This summer I made an honest attempt to feed myself from what I could catch. I stood on the banks of Iceland's most renowned salmon river, Laxá in Aðaldalur, for four days and came back with one lousy sea trout. Aðaldalur in fact operates a 'catch and return' policy when it comes to salmon. I had to sell a hundred and fifty books of poetry to cover the fishing permit, or the same price as 200 kilos of filleted haddock.

'You can't live off design,' said the driver. So I decided to discard everything 'you can't live off'. I had a look around me and cut out all the fashion clothing, all films, all music, all theatre and the internet. I jettisoned football, travel and religion. I emptied out Benidorm, Disneyland and Las Vegas: people don't live off tinsel like that. Coffee is a luxury, completely surplus to requirements, despite its being by far the biggest trading commodity in the world today after oil. Whole continents, whole millions of people, live off other people's desire to drink the stuff! What kind of a reality is that? Alcohol, entirely expendable, let alone poetry or taxis. Having pared away everything unneeded from society, I was left with the following:

One 20 foot container/tent
running water
100 kilos of fishmeal
100 kilos of flour
two sheep
one sleeping bag
one thermally insulated skisuit
silence

Reality – that's about the size of it

Andri Snær Magnason

The origin of ideas

When Eve sank her teeth into the fruit of the tree of knowledge she was engulfed by a feeling unlike anything she had ever known before. It was a feeling she had no words to express; it was like a potent combination of intoxication and joy and an indescribable energy that coursed through her body. She bit into the fruit again and was filled with restlessness and longing. She looked down at Adam as he lay there stupid and naked under the trees and went off on her own into the forest. The restlessness eased when she found things and turned over stones to see underneath them, when she whistled so the notes formed a melody and when she found words to put together that rhymed.

There was no way to share with Adam the joy at even one of her thoughts. He didn't understand the rhymes or the melodies and they were precious little use if there was no one there to share them with. Eve gave him a bite from the fruit of the tree of knowledge. There was a flash in his eyes and they spent the next days in an untrammelled orgy of ideas. There was a new smell to the Creation. The world was virgin territory. The ideas set them apart from the animals, raised them above them to a higher plane. Together they were filled with will, impatience, impulsiveness and a tumultuous lust for life. They had the power to create something new out of nothing, a thing that up until now had been the prerogative of the divine.

But God saw them and was angry with them for their disobedience. Exactly why he got so angry is hard to say. Maybe he hadn't quite finished fine-tuning the human soul, smoothing away a few rough edges before he endowed it with the power of creation. Perhaps he realized that within the power of creation there lay in equal measure a power for destruction. One little idea could lay the world in ruin. The only authenticated source we have is the words of the Lord God, word for word, as spoken to Adam in the Creation story:

Because thou hast hearkened unto the voice of thy wife, and hast eaten of the tree, of which I commanded thee, saying, Thou shalt not eat of it: cursed is the ground for thy sake; in sorrow shalt thou eat of it all the days of thy life. Thorns also and thistles shall it bring forth to thee; and thou shalt eat the herb of the field. In the sweat of thy face shalt thou eat bread, till thou return unto the ground; for out of it wast thou taken: for dust thou art, and unto dust shalt thou return.

Source:
Genesis 3:17-19
King James Bible

God condemned them to live by the sweat of their face and to live only in order to die and become dust. And that is the way it was for thousands of years. Men lived and died to the rhythm of the harvests and the passing of the seasons, and it was only at a few fleeting moments in the history of mankind that people found themselves with the opportunity to put aside the toil and do what they most desired, to rise up from the dust, to get ideas, to create something from them, and so to call up again the feeling that had suffused Eve so long ago when she first bit into the fruit of the tree of knowledge. In between, life was pretty uncomplicated: men worked from dawn to dusk, sang five-hundred-year-old songs, died, and turned into dust.

Grass grows: I live.
Grass withers: I die.

Five thousand years after the Fall, twenty men were toiling in a sun-baked field. One of them scratched his head, bemoaned his lot, and decided to do something about it. He disappeared behind a knoll and came back driving a Massey Ferguson tractor. He did a few circuits of the field and after an hour he had ploughed the equivalent of a month's labour for the other nineteen. He stood up proud from his seat and called to his mates, 'That's God dealt with. You are freed from original sin. Never again shall you live by the sweat of your face. Go home and put your feet up!'

But the man failed to realize that God had reckoned on the technological advances. They hadn't had their feet up for an hour before they became restless, and ideas started buzzing around them like flies and filling them with a malaise. One of them built an extension to his house while another one put together some furniture; the third one brewed beer and the fourth made up stories and the fifth built cars and microwaves, until they were all working twice as much as ever. They drove their cars round and round and sold each other barbecues and mobile phones; they chomped on Prozac and went to erotic clubs where they spent a thousand dollars getting what up until then they had always got for free. The man on the tractor was no longer the basis for everything. His friends paid him to carry on driving his tractor round the field just for the fun of it. They wanted to maintain their links to their origins.

It was the same whatever problem got solved: man could not relax, every single solution called for something higher to aim for. It was as if the curse of toiling in the field had been nothing to do with the field as such but was some in-built dissatisfaction within man himself. God knew that, endowed with the power of creation, man would never be able to put his feet up and that every new answer only led to more complicated questions. What was life for? Why was it created? What was its purpose? The one who had created life ought to know. The purpose was the creation itself.

The day I wrote Hey Jude

Sometimes it's just as if the world is gripped by idea mania. If it isn't need or want that drives people upward and forward, it is boredom and the craving for a new idea. We crave a new song, preferably sung by a new celebrity, a new direction in art or music with a change in fashion to go with it; we desire new gadgets, new technologies, and ground-breaking advances and great leaps forward in every area of science and learning. We yearn for a new look to the car, an annual revolution in poetry and filmmaking, new gods and new religions, a new truth. But what we desire most of all is to be the person who had the idea, the person who revolutionized the world, the person who wrote the song or the poem, the person who discovered the formula or identified the disease and named it after themselves: Williams syndrome, the Van Allen belt, Maoism, Lutheranism, the House of Dior, the diesel engine, Newtonian physics, the collected works of Shakespeare.

Even if it is only a tiny minority who get to see their name become a syndrome or a brand, we all know the driving force that lies behind the ideas. The basic instinct is usually the same whatever it is that people turn their minds to. We recognize it in the state between sleep and waking, when the head fills up with images we have no real idea where they come from.

An idea is a hard taskmaster. Although those who bring ideas into the world may believe they are in some way special, they need to realize that they are not really of any unique significance. History records the victors and we are taught to look up to them. Alexander Graham Bell is remembered as the genius who invented the telephone. But in reality he changed the course of history not one jot. Two hours after Bell filed his application for a patent for the telephone, on 14 February 1876, Elisha Gray walked into the New York patent office and filed a patent for the very same idea. Technology had reached that stage. The telephone was the product of the combined thought and experiments of thousands of people all round the world. The same goes for the light bulb. Sir Joseph Swan had already invented a light bulb in 1879, the same year Edison discovered his. An idea courses through the world and infects people to stake everything they have on it. They know deep inside that if they wait the idea will move elsewhere. Or, worse still, at that very moment the same idea is probably plaguing someone else. An idea is a hard taskmaster, and he who lives under its tyranny opens the papers every morning with a knot in his stomach, in fear of discovering that somebody else has got there first.

We are too prone to see only the individual who had the idea, rather than considering its substance in the context of history. Ford is the genius who introduced the conveyor belt into automobile manufacturing. But does it matter whether Ford was a good or a bad employer, whether or not he remembered the names of his subordinates, whether he remembered the names of his own children, whether he was in any way cultured or literate? Would someone who copied everything Ford did, who adopted his philosophy of life, his way of living and how he presented himself to others, would he discover some revolutionary idea? Probably not, any more than a person becomes a doctor by dressing up in a white coat.

Anyone who toils in the sweat of their face digging up an idea and seeing it into reality knows in their heart of hearts that the idea is only a tiny fraction from within themselves. Ideas just come to people, they blow down the main street like tumbleweed. Many of the best ideas provoke scandal, derision, are said to be 'unthinkable', ridiculous; they are laughed out of court, banned or suppressed, and it takes them decades to become an accepted part of the scenery. They threaten the status quo and attack the roots and the world-view of obsolete and moribund ideologies. It is not as if everyone just said 'What a clever idea!' when women first started demanding equal rights. Many of the best ideas are there already, within reaching distance, just waiting to be grasped. They are what many people 'are just starting to think now'. A light goes on and people say, 'Now why didn't I think of that?' The necessary circuitry was already in place, inside people's heads. It just needed someone to switch on the current.

Andri Snær Magnason

Some wise man once said that the worst punishment someone who has big ideas can suffer is to see someone else turning them into reality. You might think that celebrated examples like those of Edison and Swan or Bell and Gray are exceptions, bizarre coincidences in the history of mankind. But it's probably closer to the truth to say that in this case the exception is the rule.

I remember hearing someone say that one of our poets, Vilborg Dagbjartsdóttir, had once got an idea for a poem but kept it stored away in her head. Within a month, another of our poets, Matthías Johannessen, had finished writing the thing and had had it published. I found this amusing, until I saw similar examples popping up all around me.

In 1999 I submitted an idea to the organizing committee for Reykjavík: Cultural Capital of Europe, 2000. The idea in itself was very simple – all the lights of the city would be turned off for an hour to give city dwellers the chance to see what a deep, clear starry sky looks like. Over the centuries the night sky has inspired all of mankind's biggest questions and speculations in the fields of religion, philosophy, science, art and our whole view of the world. The city dwellers of today are the first generation of humanity to have missed out on its depth and beauty. At the very same time, the very same idea landed on the desks of the city council from a different source, the astronomers Thorsteinn Sæmundsson and Gunnlaugur Björnsson. This struck me as a remarkable coincidence. Be that as it may, our idea was rejected. Towards the end of 2003 a friend of mine urged me to see if I couldn't get the proposal resurrected. In the mark II version, the idea was that all the lights in the city would be turned off and the astronomer Thorsteinn Sæmundsson would do a commentary on the night sky in a live broadcast on radio:

A poem for a city
The Lights Go Out – The Stars Come On
on a clear winter's night
all the lights in Reykjavík
will be extinguished
from eight o'clock to half past ten
an eminent astronomer

A Self-Help Manual for a Frightened Nation

will describe the heavens
live on national radio

everybody go outside
everyone invited

The idea got a positive reception from the mayor of Reykjavík, but he reckoned it would need good advance warning and so best to leave it until the winter holiday of 2005 before seeing it into reality. I had considered arranging for a weather satellite to take an aerial photograph of Iceland while the event was going on. But I felt uncomfortable about the delay, reckoned there was no time to lose. And I was right. In summer 2004 I got an email from my friend Sigurbjörg:

----------Sigurbjörg----------
Sent: 20:56:27
30/07/2004

Hi, was watching The Simpsons. Lisa got the mayor to turn out the lights in Springfield so they could see the stars!

I went into a sweat and hoped audience ratings for The Simpsons had taken a nosedive. I couldn't help thinking, 'People are going to think I stole the idea from The Simpsons?' I phoned the culture department at City Hall and said we needed to get this sorted and issue a statement, 'preferably to the international media'. Before the matter had ground its formal course through the city bureaucracy, a headline appeared on the front page of our leading newspaper, Morgunblaðið, on 21 November 2004: 'No lights over New Year?'

> If an idea by the artist Vignir Jóhannsson goes through, most of the street lights and groundlights in the southwest of Iceland will be turned off over midnight on New Year's Eve.

The idea attracted considerable attention. Vignir appeared on the New Year's current-affairs round-up on television. 'Idea of the year,' said the presenter. AAAGH!

An idea is like a babushka doll in reverse. Right inside the smallest babushka hides another, bigger one, and so on and so on, one after another. An idea is not all it appears to be: it is not enough just to think it and flirt with its surface, because an idea has many sides and many layers and more often than not its depths are unfathomable.

--- --- --

When the light bulb suddenly flashes on in your head, the time you have to do something about it is very short. In the computer business it is said that, if an idea hasn't made it through to production and onto the shelves within a year, somebody else will have developed it and got it marketed. More and more of us are now working within this reality at the same time as 'real' jobs get fewer and fewer: those that haven't fallen by the wayside of obsolescence have been eaten by machines or outsourced to China.

We cannot be absolutely sure that the guy in the mental hospital who says he wrote Hey Jude is suffering delusions. Maybe it was already out there in the air, some mysterious vibration waiting to happen, and he was already humming it to himself in the spring of 1968. All he's done is take it too personally, thought of it as part of his own individual genius. We think we know better, we think we know who wrote it. But ideas can be deceptive, uncomfortable, almost even preternatural. Sometimes one feels inclined to think that Hey Jude was echoing around in one's head long before one heard the song itself.

So what is so special about ME if this is just the way that ideas work? What is what *I* think worth if everyone else can think the same thing? And if this is the case, how can one believe in individual genius? Are people maybe not indispensable after all? Is it perhaps better just to sit back and wait? Everything's going to happen anyway.

Are you writing the book?
No, I guess I'll just wait
for the movie to come out.

Andri Snær Magnason

Grasping the idea

Everything we think is a product of the world we live in. A product of western culture, education, upbringing, international news, music, stimuli, desires, boredom, happiness, hunger, technology, greed and libido, a consequence of shortage and excess, conscience, satisfied and unsatisfied basic instincts. Our thought is a product of daily life, driving to work, driving back home, picking up the kids from school. In all probability, the solution to some problem – a service, a machine, a new technology, a lifestyle, a piece of art – that works in one place can work anywhere where people find themselves face to face with the same problems or emotions.

It is perfectly possible to get through life as a passenger on ideas and systems created by others. But people who sleepwalk through events and situations may one day find themselves in for a rude awakening. Our language doesn't offer much in the way of metaphors or expressions to help us encompass the nature of ideas, to explain how one person can think something before it becomes an accepted truth or how mass hysteria can spread through a society without anyone being able to raise a finger to stop it. Those who get sucked in scratch their heads and cannot understand how they came to be infected; and those who remained untouched feel they have the right to a smug sense of self-satisfaction, able to condemn whatever has happened and say, 'I would have never got taken in by this.'

There is no way of telling which ideas will take off, which ideas will become part of our everyday lives five years down the line, because the conditions simply aren't in place yet, the stimulus the idea springs from or the emotion that will act as its progenitor. People who get ideas first often have a lower threshold than others; their brains take in the stimulus and reach a conclusion before others are even aware of its existence. But after them, people who are fed on the same information, live in a similar environment, experience the same fashions, employ the same technologies and are witness to the same events will most likely hit on the same ideas and solutions, even the same shops and companies.

I asked my grandmother how she understood the word 'entrepreneur', how you needed to be made to be able to turn your back on everything and chase after some dimly formed desire that sparks in the breast. She said it was a vestige of the hunting instinct. The Danes, for example, had never understood the Greenlanders. When the weather was right the factories emptied and the hunters ran out onto the ice to hunt seals. When the Danes said how dare they leave the factories unstaffed they answered, 'The factory will always be here but the seals will go away.' The office will still be there but the song will go. The story will be written, the poem will be composed, the bottle opener will be designed, the company will be set up and the service will be provided. The seal will be clubbed whether you do it or not.

Things like this toughen a man up. Next time I get a big idea I intend to run out onto the ice and club that seal. I'm going to let the whole world know. Or not. I'm doing just fine as it is.

Ideas are cheap

There is a serious oversupply of ideas in the world. They are like the number of sperm cells compared with the number of women capable of bearing children. A sperm cell is not a child, and an idea on its own is not a work of art, or a new company, or the focus of the world's attention. Just a tiny little something. There wouldn't be much room for us if all the sperm cells turned into people. The idea for Hamlet is not *Hamlet*, the idea for a picture of a steamboat off Harwich is not Turner's *Snow Storm*, the idea for a car is not a car.

Everything is built on other ideas and on a foundation of thoughts and concepts that has already been laid. Idea, adaptation, fusion, parody, variation, opportunity, possibility, imitation, chance, theft, plagiarism. Hard to say what is what. It is a good thing to take what we call reality to pieces regularly and reassemble it and prioritize it as we see fit. This way we get the chance to have an influence on just about all parts of our existence – eating habits, fashions, music, education, politics, art, architecture, living conditions, and our own happiness. By thought alone it is possible to infuse worthless objects with history, significance and meaning, and so create value out of nothing. At heart, this is a question of attuning the mind and not taking the world we know already too seriously. A large part of human existence is built on pure choice and will, desires and frailties, rather than on any pressing need. Half my car is really just excess fat. Someone has sold me the idea that I need this fat, the car reinforces the way I view myself. Gives me freedom. Gives me an image. I am Toyota Avensis man (father of three, fleece jacket, baseball cap and a 20-year mortgage with the bank).

Maybe it is best not to squander one's life and creativity in a race to acquire all the trash that currently surrounds us and that clouds our minds to what really matters. To live in a society is to create a society, to be in a relationship is to create a relationship, to desire one's wife is to create desire, to bring up a child is to create a person, to live is to create a life.

Who knows what the next big idea is going to be? It might not be anything sparkling bright and new, not necessarily an Icelandic Space Institute or a mobile phone implant. It might be a revival of a very old idea, or a new way of combining existing ideas. The opportunities may even be greatest where things have been in long-term decline and the way seems only downwards. It can pay to turn over stones, open babushkas, dig up something that is there already and breathe new life into it.

Farming report

'I see no possibility for any future growth in sheep rearing over the coming years,' a senior politician was saying on the television news. I turned over in my mind whether it is thinkable that, after 1100 years of human settlement, the future for the farming communities of Iceland will be one of unbroken linear decline. Whether one single man can have so complete an insight into the possibilities of an entire sector of the economy that he can say yea or nay as to its entire future. When someone says the possibilities are nil and that all we have to look forward to is a download slope to extinction, it's tempting to take out some ideas for a bit of a shakedown.

We can start by asking, what is the name of the most famous farmer in Iceland? When I asked people this question, the answer I got most commonly was the same: Gísli of Uppsalir. It is interesting that the archetype of the oldest industry in Iceland should be an eccentric hermit who lived at the top of an isolated valley in the remotest northwest, with no machines, no electricity, and precious little contact with the world outside – an extreme Appalachian mountain man, Joe Grundy gone feral. After 1100 years of agricultural society it is this name that first occurs to people when the words 'Icelandic farmer' are mentioned. A fair exemplar of the profession? Gísli, we can suppose, was a remarkable man – the picture we got of him from the documentary about him on television says nothing about his mental accomplishments – but it is still his wild and dishevelled outer appearance that presents itself as the image of his class. Several nationally known figures are farmers, only they aren't famous for being farmers but for something else.

Aðalból, Aðalbreið, Aflsstaðir, Akbraut, Akrakot, Akrar, Akur, Akurbakki, Akurbrekka, Akureyjar, Akurgerði, Akurtraðir, Al
Arnarfell, Arnarholt, Arnarhóll, Arnarnes, Arnarnúpur, Arnarstaðakot, Arnarstaðir, Arnarstapi, Arnartunga, Arnarvati
Arnkötlustaðir, Arnórsstaðapartur, Arnstapi, Arnþórsholt, Asknes, Asparlundur, Asparvík, Atlastaðir, Atlastaðir, Auðbjarg
Augastaðir, Ausa, Austaraland, Austari-Hóll, Austari-Krókar, Austdalur, Austmannsdalur, Austurey, Axlarhagi, Á, Ábær, Á
Álftavatn, Álftavík, Álftá, Álftárbakki, Álftárhóll, Álftárós, Álftártunga, Álftártungukot, Ámá, Ámundakot, Ánabrekka, A
Árhvammur, Árkvörn, Árland, Árlundur, Ármót, Ármúli, Árnagerði, Árnahús, Árnanes, Árnastaðir, Árnes, Ártangi, Árteig
Ásbrún, Ásbúðir, Ásbyrgi, Ásfell, Ásgarður, Ásgautsstaðir, Ásgeirsbrekka, Ásgeirsstaðir, Ásgerðarstaðasel, Ásgerðarsta
Ásmundarstaðir, Ásmúli, Ásólfsskáli, Ásólfsstaðir, Ássel, Ástún, Ásunnarstaðir, Ásvöllur, Ásamýri, Árnanes, Bakkaflöt, Ba
Barðastaðir, Barðsgerði, Barðsnes, Barkarstaðasel, Barkarstaðir, Barkarstaðir, Barká, Barmar, Barnafell, Bassastaðir, B
Beggakot, Beigaldi, Beinakelda, Beinárgerði, Beingarður, Beitistaðir, Bekansstaðir, Belgsdalur, Belgsholt, Berg, Bergás, Berg
Berunes, Berustaðir, Bessahlaðir, Bessastaðir, Bessatunga, Betanía, Birkiból, Birkiflöt, Birkihlíð, Birkikinn, Birkilundur,
Bjarg, Bjargarkot, Bjargarstaðir, Bjarghús, Bjargshóll, Bjarkarland, Bjarmaland, Bjarmaland, Bjarnanes, Bjarnarey, Bjarnar
Bjálmholt, Bjóla, Bjóluhjáleiga, Björg, Björk, Björnólfsstaðir, Björnskot, Blanda, Blábjörg, Bláfeldur, Bláhvammur, Bláland, I
Bogabúð, Bogaslóð, Bogey, Bolholt, Bollakot, Bollastaðir, Borðeyrarbær, Borg, Borgarás, Borgarey, Borgareyrar, Borgarfe
Botn, Botnar, Botnastaðir, Botnsmýrar, Ból, Bóla, Bólhraun, Bólstaðarhlíð, Bólstaður, Bóndastaðir, Bóndhóll, Bót, Brag
Brautarholt, Brautarhóll, Brautarland, Brautartunga, Brávellir, Breið, Breiðaból, Breiðaból, Breiðabólstaður, Breiðadalur,
Brekka, Brekknakot, Brekkuborg, Brekkubær, Brekkugerði, Brekkuhús, Brekkukot, Brekkulækur, Brekkur, Brekkusel, B
Brimnes, Brimnesgerði, Bringa, Bringur, Bryti, Brjánslækur, Brjánsstaðir, Brjánsstaðir, Broddadalsá, Broddanes, Brokey,
Brúarhraun, Brúarhvammur, Brúarland, Brúarreykir, Brúarvellir, Brún, Brún, Brúnagerði, Brúnahlíð, Brúnalaug, Brúnas
Burstabrekka, Bursthús, Bustarfell, Butra, Búastaðir, Búð, Búðardalur, Búðarhóll, Búðarnes, Búðir, Búland, Búlandsborg,
Bæjarfljót, Bæjarsker, Bæjarstæði, Bær, Böðvarsdalur, Böðvarsgarður, Böðvarsholt, Böðvarshólar, Böðvarsnes, Böggviss
Dagverðarnessel, Dagverðartunga, Dalbrún, Dalbær, Dalgeirsstaðir, Dalhús, Dalir, Dalkot, Dalland, Dallandspartur, Dals
Digurholt, Dilksnes, Dísarstaðir, Dísukot, Djúpárbakki, Djúpidalur, Djúpilækur, Draflastaðir, Dragháls, Drangar, Drang
Dunkárbakki, Dunkur, Dúkur, Dvergabakki, Dvergasteinn, Dvergasteinskot, Dverghóll, Dvergsstaðir, Dynjandi, Dyrhólai
Dyrhólar, Efra-Bakkakot, Efra-Haganes, Efra-Haganes, Efra-Holt, Efra-Langholt, Efra-Nes, Efra-Nes, Efra-Sel, Efra-Sel, E
Brúnavellir, Efri-Dálksstaðir, Efri-Engidalur, Efri-Ey, Efri-Ey, Efri-Ey, Efri-Fitjar, Efri-Fjörður, Efri-Flankastaðir, Efri-Fljót
Efri-Hóll, Efri-Hóll, Efri-Hreppur, Efri-Hrísar, Efri-Hvoll, Efri-Hvoll, Efri-Hvoll, Efri-Kirkjuhvammur, Efri-Kvíhólmi, Efi
Skálateigur, Efri-Skálateigur, Efri-Skútá, Efri-Steinsmýri, Efri-Steinsmýri, Efri-Steinsmýri, Efri-Svertingsstaðir, Efri-Sýr
Efsta-Kot,, Efstaland, Efstalandskot, Efsta-Samtún, Efstibær, Efsti-Dalur, Efsti-Dalur, Efsti-Dalur, Egg, Egilsá, Egilssel, Egil
Eiði, Eiði, Eiði, Eiðsstaðir, Eiðsstaðir, Eilífsdalur, Einarsengi, Einarshús, Einarshöfn, Einarshöfn, Einarsnes, Einarsstaði
Einholt, Einifell, Eintúnaháls, Eiríksbakki, Eiríksbúð, Eiríksstaðir, Eiríksstaðir, Eiríksstaðir, Eiríksstaðir, Eiríksstaðir, E
Emmuberg, Engi, Engidalur, Engigarður, Engihlíð, Engihlíð, Engihlíð, Engihlíð, Engihlíð, Engihlíð, Engihlíð, Engilæku
Veturhúsum, Eskiholt, Eskiholt, Eskiholt, Espiflöt, Espigerði, Espigrund, Espihóll, Ey, Ey, Eyði-Sandvík, Eyhildarholt, Eyl
Hólshjáleiga, Eyma, Eyrarbakki, Eyrardalur, Eyrarhús, Eyrarkot, Eyrarland, Eyrarland, Eyrarland, Eyrarteigur, Eyrartún, E
Eystra-Stokkseyrarsel, Eystra-Súlunes, Eystra-Þorlaugargerði, Eystri-Dalbær, Eystri-Garðsauki, Eystri-Grund, Eystri-Hól
Eystri-Þurá, Eyvindará, Eyvindarholt, Eyvindarhólar, Eyvindarmúli, Eyvindarstaðaheiði, Eyvindarstaðir, Eyvindartunga, Ey
Suðurkot, Efri-Arnórsstaðir, Einfætingsgil, Fremri-Breiðadalur, Fagrabrekka, Fagrabrekka, Fagragerði, Fagrahlíð, Fagra
Fagridalur, Fagridalur, Fagridalur, Fagridalur, Fagridalur, Fagrifoss, Fagrihvammur, Fagrihvammur, Fagriskógur, Fagurey,
Fell, Fellsendi, Fellshlíð, Fellshlíð, Fellskot, Fellsmúli, Fellsmúli, Fellsmúli, Fellssel, Ferjubakki, Ferjubakki, Ferjubakk
Finnbogastaðir, Finnmörk, Finnsstaðasel, Finnsstaðir, Finnsstaðir, Finnsstaðir, Finnsstaðir, Finnsstaðir, Finnstunga, Fiskilækur, Fit,
Fjallalækjarsel, Fjallaskagi, Fjallssel, Fjarðarhorn, Fjarðarkot, Fjós, Fjósakot, Fjósakot, Fjósar, Fjósar, Fjósatunga, Fjöll,
Fljótsbakki, Fljótsdalur, Fljótsholt, Fljótshólar, Fljótstunga, Flóagafl, Flóðatangi, Flókastaðir, Flugumýrarhvammur, Flug
Fornhagi, Fornhagi, Fornhólar, Forni-Hvammur, Fornusandar, Fornustekkar, Forsæludalur, Forsæti, Foss, Fossabrekka, Fo
Framland, Framnes, Fremrasel, Fremri-Arnardalur, Fremri-Bakki, Fremri-Brekka, Fremri-Fitjar, Fremri-Gufudalur, Fren
Fremrikot, Fremri-Langey, Fremri-Nýpur, Fremri-Ós, Fremri-Svartárdalur, Fremri-Víðivellir, Fremsta-Fell, Fremstagil,
Furubrún, Furufjörður I, Fyrirbarð, Fremri-Hjarðardalur, Fremri-Reykjarfjörður, Galtastaðir fram, Gaddsstaðir, Gafl, Ga

óra, Andrésfjós, Apavatn, Arabæjarhjáleiga, Arabær, Arakot, Arkarlækur, Arnaldsstaðir, Arnanes, Arnarbæli, Arnardrangur, kur, Arndísarstaðir, Arney, Arngeirsstaðir, Arngerðareyri, Arnheiðarstaðir, Arnhólsstaðir, Arnkelsgerði, Arnkötludalur, kka, Auði Hrísdalur, Auðkúla, Auðnir, Auðólfsstaðir, Auðshaugur, Auðsholt, Auðsholtshjáleiga, Auðsstaðir, Auðunarstaðir, öir,, Álfgeirsvellir, Álfheimar, Álfholt, Álfhólahjáleiga, Álfhólar, Álfhóll, Álfsnes, Álfsstaðir, Álftagerði, Álftamýri, Álftanes, ‹ki, Árbót, Árbæjarhellir, Árbæjarhjáleiga, Árbær, Árdalur, Áreyjar, Árgerði, Árgil, Árgilsstaðir, Árholt, Árhólar, Árhóll, ι, Árvangur, Ás, Ásakot, Ásamýri, Ásar, Ásatún, Ásbjarnarnes, Ásbjarnarstaðir, Ásbrandsstaðamór, Ásbrandsstaðir, Ásbrú, ‹grímsstaðir, Áshildarholt, Ásholt, Áshóll, Áskot, Ásland, Áslaugarstaðir, Ásláksstaðir, Ásmundarnes, Ásmundarstaðir, akot, Bakkasel, Bakkavöllur, Bakkáholt, Bakki, Balaskarð, Baldurshagi, Baldursheimur, Bali, Ballará, Bangastaðir, Barð, taðir, Baulárvellir, Baulhólmi, Baulhús, Bálkastaðir, Bár, Bárðarbúð, Bárðarstaðir, Bárðartjörn, Bárustaðir, Bás, Básar, l, Bergsholt, Bergskáli, Bergskot, Bergsstaðir, Bergvík, Bergþórshvoll, Berjanes, Berserkjahraun, Berserkseyri, Berufjörður, Birnufell, Birnunes, Birnustaðir, Birnustaðir, Birtingaholt, Bitra, Bitrugerði, Bíldhóll, Bíldsey, Bíldsfell, Bíldsfell, Bjalli, ‹gil, Bjarnarhöfn, Bjarnarnes, Bjarnarstaðir, Bjarnastaðagerði, Bjarnastaðahlíð, Bjarnastaðir, Bjarneyjar, Bjarteyjarsandur, gur, Blesastaðir, Blikalón, Blikastaðir, Blómsturvellir, Blöndubakki, Blöndudalshólar, Blöndugerði, Blönduhlíð, Blönduholt, r, Borgargerði, Borgarholt, Borgarhóll, Borgarhöfn, Borgarhöfn, Borgarkot, Borgarland, Borgarmýrar, Borgartún, Borgir, lt, Brakandi, Brandagil, Brandaskarð, Brandsstaðir, Brandsstaðir, Brattahlíð, Brattavellir, Brattholt, Brattsholtshjáleiga, iðamýrarholt, Breiðamýri, Breiðamörk, Breiðanes, Breiðargerði, Breiðavað, Breiðavík, Breiðás, Breiðilækur, Breiðsstaðir, rekkuvellir, Brenna, Brenniás, Brenniborg, Brennigerði, Brennigerðispartur, Brennistaðir, Brettingsstaðir, Brimilsvellir, r, Brunavík, Brunnar, Brunnavellir, Brunngil, Brunnhóll, Brú, Brúar, Brúará, Brúarás, Brúarfoss, Brúarhlíð, Brúarholt, rúsastaðir, Brúsholt, Bryðjuholt, Bryggja, Bræðraá, Bræðraból, Bræðrabrekka, Bræðratunga, Buðlungavellir, Bugðustaðir, 3úlandshöfði, Búlandssel, Búrfell, Bústaðir, Búvellir, Byggðarholt, Byggðarhorn, Byrgisholt, Byrgisskarð, Byrgisvík, Bæir, r, Brúarás, Breiðholt, Búlandsnes, Daðastaðir, Dagmálaborg, Dagverðará, Dagverðareyri, Dagverðargerði, Dagverðarnes, shöfði, Dalskot, Dalsmynni, Daltún, Dalur, Daufá, Deild, Deildará, Deildarfell, Deildartunga, Deplar, Desey, Desjarmýri, Drangshlíð, Drangshlíðardalur, Dratthalastaðir Draumbær, Droplaugarstaðir, Drumboddsstaðir, Dufþaksholt, Dunhóll, Dýhóll, Dýjabekkur, Dýrastaðir, Dýrfinnustaðir, Dýrholt, Dæli, Dönustaðir, Efri-Arnórsstaðir, Efri-Dufansdalur, Eystri-arð, Efra-Vatnshorn, Efri-Ás, Efri-Ás, Efri-Brunnastaðir, Efri-Brunnastaðir, Efri-Brunná, Efri-Brú, Efri-Brúnavellir, Efri-Efri-Foss, Efri-Gegnishólar, Efri-Grímslækur, Efri-Gróf, Efri-Hamrar, Efri-Harrastaðir, Efri-Hesthús, Efri-Hlíð, Efri-Hólar, Miðbær, Efri-Mýrar, Efri-Mörk, Efri-Núpur, Efri-Rauðalækur, Efri-Rauðalækur, Efri-Reykir, Efri-Rot, Efri-Sandvík, Efri-fustaðir, Efri-Tunga, Efri-Úlfsstaðir, Efri-Vindheimar, Efri-Vík, Efri-Vík, Efri-Völlur, Efri-Þverá, Efri-Þverá, Efsta-Grund, taðir, Egilsstaðir, Egilsstaðir, Egilsstaðir, Egilsstaðir, Egilsstaðir, Egilsstaðir, Egilsstaðir, Eiðar, Eiðar, Eiðhús, Eiðhús, Eiði, Einarsstaðir, Einarsstaðir, Einarsstaðir, Einarsstaðir, Einarsstaðir, Einbúi, Einhamar, Einholt, Einholt, Einholt, Einholt, jufell, Ekkjufellssel, Ekra, Ekra, Eldjárnsstaðir, Eldjárnsstaðir, Eldleysa, Elivogar, Elliðaey, Elliðakot, Elliði, Emburhöfði, gjabakki, Engjabrekka, Engjanes, England, Enni, Enni, Enni, Enniskot, Erpsstaðir, Eskey, Eskifjarðarsel, Eskifjörður m/ darholt, Eyjanes, Eyjar, Eyjardalsá, Eyjarhólar, Eyjarkot, Eyjasel, Eyjólfsstaðir, Eyjólfsstaðir, Eyjólfsstaðir, Eyland, Eyland Cystra-Fífilholt, Eystra-Fróðholt, Eystra-Geldingaholt, Eystra-Geldingaholt, Eystra-Hraun, Eystra-Miðfell, Eystra-Seljaland, arðar, Eystri-Lyngar, Eystri-Rauðárhóll, Eystri-Reynir, Eystri-Skógar, Eystri-Sólheimar, Eystri-Torfastaðir, Eystri-Tunga, jarnarholt, Eystri-Hellur, Efra-Lambavatn, Eystri-Loftsstaðir, Efra-Lýtingsstaðakot, Efri-Rauðsdalur, Eystra-Stafnes, Efra-Fagrahlíð, Fagranes, Fagranes, Fagranes, Fagranes, Fagranes, Fagranes, Fagraneskot, Fagribær, Fagridalur, Fagridalur, urhóll, Fagurhóll, Fagurhólsmýri, Fagurhólsmýri, Fagurhólsmýri, Fallandastaðir, Fannardalur, Fáskrúðarbakki, Feitsdalur, erjubakki, Ferjubakki, Ferjukot, Ferjunes, Ferstikla, Ferstikla, Fet, Féeggsstaðir, Finnastaðir, Finnastaðir, Finnastaðir, Fitjar, Fitjar, Fitjar, Fitjar, Fitjarmýri, Fífilgerði, Fíflholt, Fíflholtsnorðurhjáleiga, Fíflholtssuðurhjáleiga, Fífustaðir, Fjall, laga, Flatatunga, Flatey, Flateyri, Flatnefsstaðir, Flautafell, Flekkudalur, Flekkuvík, Flekkuvík, Flesjustaðir, Fljótsbakki, ýri I, Flugumýri II, Flugustaðir, Flúðasel, Flúðir, Flúðir, Flögusel, Folafótur, Forna-Fróðá, Forna-Krossnes, Fornastaðir, Fossá, Fossárdalur, Fossárteigur, Fossgerði, Fosshólar, Fosshóll, Fosskot, Fossmúli, Fossnes, Fossel, Fossvellir, Frakkanes, ihlíð, Fremri-Hlíð, Fremri-Hnífsdalur, Fremri-Hrafnabjörg, Fremri-Hundadalur, Fremrihús , Arnardalur, Fremri-Hvesta, 3arminni, Friðheimar, Friðheimur, Frostastaðir, Fróðastaðir, Fróðá, Fróðholtshjáleiga, Fróðhús, Fuglavík, Furubrekka, töð, Galtafell, Galtahryggur, Galtalækur, Galtalækur, Galtará, Galtarholt, Galtarholt, Galtarholt, Galtarholt, Galtarholt,

Galtarlækur, Galtarnes, Galtartunga, Galtarvík, Galtastaðir, Gambra, Gamlabúð, Gamla-Hraun, Gamla-Hraun, Garðakot, G
Garðshorn Þelamörk, Garðsmór, Garðsstaðir, Garðsvík, Garður, Garður, Garður, Garður, Garður, Garður, Garður, Garður, G
Gauksstaðir, Gaul, Gaulverjabær, Gautastaðir, Gautastaðir, Gautavík, Gautland, Gautlönd, Gautlönd, Gautlönd, Gautsdalur, G
Geirastaðir, Geirastaðir, Geirbjarnarstaðir, Geirhildargarðar, Geirland, Geirmundarhóll, Geirmundarstaðir, Geirmundars
Geitareyjar, Geitasandur, Geitaskarð, Geitavík, Geitavík, Geitdalur, Geiteyjarströnd, Geiteyjarströnd, Geiteyjarströnd, Ge
Gemlufall, Gemlufall, Gerðakot, Gerðar, Gerðar, Gerðhamrar 1, Gerði, Gerði, Gerði, Gerði, Gerði, Gerðuberg, Gjörvidalur,
Giljaland, Giljar, Giljir, Giljur, Giljur, Gillastaðir, Gillastaðir, Gilsá, Gilsá, Gilsá, Gilsá, Gilsárstekkur, Gilsárteigur, Gilsá
Gíslakot, Gíslastaðagerði, Gíslastaðir, Gíslastaðir, Gíslholt, Gjábakki, Gjögur, Glammastaðir, Glaumbær, Gláma, Glerá, C
Glæsibær, Gnúpufell, Gnýsstaðir, Goddastaðir, Goðanes, Goðatún, Goðdalir, Goðdalur, Goðhóll, Gottorp, Góustaðir, Grafa
Grásteinar, Grásteinn, Grenivík, Grenjaðarstaður, Grenjar, Grenstangi, Grindur, Grímarstaðir, Grímkelsstaðir, Grímsey, C
Grjótgarður, Grjótlækur, Grjótnes, Grjótnes, Gróf, Grófargerði, Grófargil, Grófarsel, Gróunes, Gróustaðir, Grund, Grundará
Grænanes, Grænavatn I, Grænhólar, Grænhóll, Grænumýrartunga, Gröf, Guðlaugsstaðir, Guðlaugsvík, Guðmundarstaðir,
Gullberastaðir, Gullbrekka, Gunnarsholt, Gunnarsstaðir, Gunnbjarnarholt, Gunnfríðarstaðir, Gunnhildargerði, Gunnla
Gýgjarhólskot, Gýgjarhólskot, Gýgjarhólskot III, Göltur, Göltur, Göngustaðakot, Göngustaðir, Galtastaðir út, Galtastaðir,
Hafrafellstunga, Hafrafellstunga, Hafragil, Hafralækur, Hafralækur II, Hafranes, Hafsteinsstaðir, Hafurbjarnarstaðir, Haf
Hagi, Hagi, Hagi, Hagi, Hagi, Hagi, Hagi, Hagi, Hagi, Hagi, Hagi, Hagi, Hagi, Halakot, Halakot, Hali, Hallandi, Hallbjarnarey
Halldórsstaðir, Halldórsstaðir, Halldórsstaðir 1 Laxárd., Halldórsstaðir, Halldórsstaðir, Halldórsstaðir 2 Laxárd., Halldórsstað
Hallfríðarstaðir, Hallgeirsey 1, Hallgeirseyjarhjáleiga, Hallgeirsstaðir, Hallgilsstaðir, Hallgilsstaðir, Hallgilsstaðir, Hallgilss
Hallsstaðir, Hallsteinsnes, Hallstún, Hamar, Hamar, Hamar, Hamar, Hamar, Hamar, Hamar, Hamar, Hamar, Hamar, Ha
Hamraendar, Hamraendar, Hamraendar, Hamraendar, Hamrafell, Hamrafoss, Hamragarðar, Hamragerði, Hamrahlíð, Ha
Hamrar, Hamratunga, Hanhóll, Harastaðir, Harastaðir, Harastaðir, Harðbakur I, Harðbakur II, Harrastaðir, Haugabrekka,
Haukadalur, Haukagil, Haukagil, Haukatunga, Haukholt, Haukholt, Hauksstaðir, Hauksstaðir, Hausastaðakot, Hausastað
Hábær, Háfshjáleiga, Háfshóll, Háfur, Háholt, Háhóll, Háhóll, Hái-Múli, Hái-Rimi, Hái-Rimi, Hákonarstaðir, Hákonarstaðir
Hámundarstaðir, Hámundarstaðir, Hánefsstaðir, Hánefsstaðir, Háreksstaðir, Háreksstaðir, Hárlaugsstaðir, Hárlaugsstaði
Heggstaðir, Hegrabjarg, Heiðarbót, Heiðarbraut, Heiðarbrekka, Heiðarbrún, Heiðarbrún, Heiðarbrún, Heiðarbær, Heiðar
Heiðarsel, Heiðarsel, Heiðarsel, Heiði, Heiði, Heiði, Heiði, Heiði, Heiði, Heiði, Heiði, Heiði, Heiði, Heiðmörk, Heiðmörk, H
Helgafell, Helgafell, Helgafell, Helgafell, Helgafellseyjar, Helgastaðir, Helgastaðir, Helgastaðir, Helgastaðir, Helgastaðir, He
Hella, Hella, Hellar, Hellatún, Hellatún, Hellir, Hellir, Hellisfjarðarsel, Hellisfjörður, Hellisfjörubakkar, Hellisholt, Hellish
Hellur, Hellur, Helluvað, Helluvað, Helluvað, Helluvað I, Helluvað II, Helmingasandur, Hemla, Hemla, Hemra, Hemrumörk
Hestgerði, Hestheimar, Hesthöfði, Hestur, Hestur, Hestur, Heydalir, Heydalsá 1 og 2, Heydalur, Heydalur, Heyholt, Heykl
Hítará, Hítardalur, Hítarnes, Hítarneskot, Hítarvatn, Hjallakrókur, Hjallaland, Hjallaland, Hjallanes, Hjallanes, Hjallar,
Hjaltastaðir, Hjaltastaðir, Hjaltastaður, Hjarðarból, Hjarðarból, Hjarðarból, Hjarðarból, Hjarðarbrekka, Hjarðardalur, Hjar
Hjarðarholt, Hjarðarholt, Hjarðarhvoll, Hjarðarland, Hjarðarnes, Hjarðarnes, Hjarðartunga, Hjarðartún, Hjartarstaðir, H
Hlaðhamar, Hlaðir, Hlaðseyri, Hleiðargarður, Hleiðargarður, Hleinargarður, Hlemmiskeið, Hlemmiskeið 1, Hlemmiskeið,
Hlíð, Hlíð, Hlíð, Hlíð, Hlíð, Hlíð, Hlíð, Hlíð, Hlíð, Hlíð, Hlíð, Hlíð, Hlíð, Hlíð, Hlíð, Hlíð, Hlíð, Hlíð 2 og 3, Hlíðar
Hlíðarendi 2 Þrastahlíð, Hlíðarfoss, Hlíðarfótur, Hlíðargarður, Hlíðargerði, Hlíðarhagi Hlíðarfell, Hlíðarholt, Hlíðarholt, H
Hnappavellir, Hnappavellir 7, Hnaukar, Hnaus, Hnausakot, Hnausar, Hnausar, Hnausar, Hnausar, Hnefilsdalur, Hnitbjörg, H
Hof, Hof, Hof, Hof, Hof, Hof 1 Eystribær, Hof 1 Heimahof Austurhús, Hof, Hof, Hof, Hof 2 Lækjarhús, Hof, Hof 4 Kotið, Hof
Hofteigur, Hoftún, Hoftún, Hokinsdalur, Holt, Holt, Holt, Holt, Holt, Holt, Holt, Holt, Holt, Holt, Holt, Holt, Holt, Holt, H
Horn, Horn, Horn, Hornsstaðir, Hólabak, Hólabrekka, Hólabrekka, Hólabrekka, Hólabær, Hólagerði, Hólagerði, Hólagerð
Hólar, Hólar, Hólar, Hólar, Hólar, Hólar, Hólar í Hjaltadal, Hólar Laxárdal, Hólar Reykjadal, Hólavatn, Hólavellir, Hólkot, H
Hólmar, Hólmasel, Hólmatunga, Hólmavað, Hólmi, Hólmlátur, Hólmur, Hólmur, Hólmur, Hólsgerði, Hólsgerði, Hólshjále
Hrafnabjörg, Hrafnabjörg, Hrafnabjörg, Hrafnabjörg, Hrafnabjörg, Hrafnabjörg 1, Hrafnabjörg, Hrafnabjörg, Hrafnabjör
Hrafnkelsstaðir, Hrafnkelsstaðir, Hrafnkelsstaðir 3, Hrafnseyri, Hrafnsgerði, Hrafnsstaðakot, Hrafnsstaðir, Hrafnsstaði
Hrappsstaðir, Hraukbæjarkot, Hraukbær, Hraukur, Hraun, Hraun, Hraun, Hraun, Hraun, Hraun, Hraun, Hraun, Hraun, Hr
Hraungerði, Hraungerði, Hraungerði, Hraunháls, Hraunhlaða, Hraunholt, Hraunhólar, Hraunkot, Hraunkot, Hraunkot, H

, Garðar, Garðar, Garðar, Garðey, Garðhús, Garðhús, Garðsá, Garðsendi, Garðsengi, Garðshorn, Garðshorn Kræklingahlíð, rður, Garður, Garður, Garður, Garður, Garður, Garpsdalur, Gata, Gata, Gata, Gata, Gata Safamýri, Gauksmýri, Gauksstaðir, namar, Gautsstaðir, Gautsstaðir, Gásaeyri, Gásir, Gegnishólapartur, Geirakot, Geirakot, Geirastaðir, Geirastaðir, Geirastaðir, arstaðir, Geirólfsstaðir, Geirshlíð, Geirshlíð, Geirsstaðir, Geitaberg, Geitafell, Geitafell, Geitagerði, Geitagerði, Geitagil, ls, Geithellar, Geithellar, Geitland, Geldingaá, Geldingaholt, Geldingaholt I, Geldingaholt II, Geldingalækur, Geldingsá, aðir, Gestsstaðir, Geysir, Gil, Gil, Gil, Gil, Gil, Gilá, Gileyri, Gilhagi, Gilhagi, Gilhagi, Gilhagi, Gilhagi, Giljahlíð, Giljaland, Gilsfjarðarbrekka, Gilsfjarðarmúli, Gilslaug, Gilsstaðir, Gilsstaðir, Gilsstaðir, Gilsstreymi, Gíslabali, Gíslabær, Gíslakot, ttingsnes, Glitstaðir, Gljákot, Gljúfur, Gljúfurá, Gljúfurárholt, Gloppa, Glóra, Glúmsstaðasel, Glúmsstaðir, Glúmsstaðir, lur, Grafargerði, Grafargil, Grafarkot, Grafarkot, Grafarnes, Granastaðir , Grandi, Grasgeiri, Grashóll, Gráhella, Grásíða, shús, Grímsland, Grímsnes, Grímsstaðir, Grímstunga, Grísará, Grísartunga, Gríshóll, Grjót, Grjótá, Grjóteyri, Grjóteyri, undarhóll, Grundarkot, Grundarland, Grunnavatn, Grýta, Grýtubakki , Grænaborg, Grænahlíð, Grænahraun, Grænamýri, önabær, Guðnastaðir, Guðrúnarstaðir, Guðrúnarstaðir, Gufuá, Gufudalur, Gufudalur, Gufuhlíð, Gularás, Gularáshjáleiga, lfsvík, Gunnsteinsstaðir, Guttormshagi, Gvendareyjar, Gvendarnes, Gvendarstaðir, Gýgjarhóll, Gýgjarhóll, Gýgjarhóll, Hafnardalur, Hafnareyjar, Hafnarhólmur, Hafnarhólmur, Hafnarland, Hafnarnes 1, Hafnarsel, Hafnir, Hafnir, Hafrafell I, r, Hafursstaðir, Hafursstaðir, Hafursstaðir, Hafursstaðir, Hafþórsstaðir, Hagakot, Haganes, Hagasel, Hagavík, Hagi, Hagi, ðir, Hallbjarnarstaðir, Hallbjarnarstaðir, Hallbjarnarstaðir, Hallbjarnarstaðir, Halldórsstaðir, Halldórsstaðir, Halldórsstaðir, órsstaðir 4 Laxárd., Halldórsstaðir Reykjadal, Hallfreðarstaðahjáleiga, Hallfreðarstaðir, Hallfreðarstaðir, Hallfríðarstaðakot, ar, Hallkelshólar, Hallkelsstaðahlíð, Hallkelsstaðir, Hallland, Halllandsnes, Hallormsstaður, Hallskot, Hallskot, Hallsstaðir, nar, Hamar 1, Hamarland, Hamarsheiði, Hamarsheiði, Hamarshjáleiga, Hamarsholt, Hamarssel, Hamborg, Hamraborg, ot, Hamrar, Hamrar, Hamrar, Hamrar, Hamrar, Hamrar, Hamrar, Hamrar, Hamrar, Hamrar, Hamrar, Hamrar, Hamrar, r, Haugur, Haugur, Haukaberg, Haukaberg, Haukabrekka, Haukadalur, Haukadalur, Haukadalur, Haukadalur, Haukadalur, borg, Háabrekka, Háafell, Háafell, Háafell, Háagerði, Háagerði, Háagerði, Háa-Kotey, Hábær, Hábær, Hábær, Hábær 1A, Hákot, Hákot, Háleggsstaðir, Háls, Háls, Háls, Háls, Háls, Háls, Háls, Háls, Háls, Háls, Hálsar, Hálshús, Hámundarstaðir 1, gur, Hátún, Hátún, Hátún, Hátún, Hátún, Hátún, Hátún, Hávarðarkot, Hávarðsstaðir, Hávík, Heggsstaðir, Heggsstaðir, Heiðarbær, Heiðarbær, Heiðargarður, Heiðargerði, Heiðarholt, Heiðarhús, Heiðarhöfn, Heiðarmúli, Heiðarsel, Heiðarsel, bær, Heimabær, Heimabær, Heimabær, Heimabær 5, Heimabær, Arnardal, Heimaland, Heinaberg, Helgadalur, Helgafell, atn, Helgavatn, Helgá, Helguhvammur, Helguhvammur, Helgusandar, Helgustaðir, Helgustaðir, Hella, Hella, Hella, Hella, ellnasel, Hellubær, Helludalur, Helludalur, Helludalur, Helluland, Helluland, Helluland, Helluland, Hellur, Hellur, Hellur, rgilsey, Herjólfsstaðir, Herjólfsstaðir, Herjólfsstaðir, Hermundarfell, Hermundarstaðir, Herríðarhóll, Hesjuvellir, Hesteyri, Heylækur, Heylækur, Heynes, Heysholt, Héðinshöfði, Héðinshöfði, Héraðsdalur, Héraðsstaðir, Hillur, Hindisvík, Hítará, Hjallholt, Hjalli, Hjalli, Hjalli, Hjalli, Hjalli, Hjallkárseyri, Hjaltabakki, Hjaltadalur, Hjaltastaðahvammur, Hjaltastaðir, , Hjarðargrund, Hjarðarhagi, Hjarðarhagi, Hjarðarhagi, Hjarðarhagi, Hjarðarhagi, Hjarðarhlíð, Hjarðarholt, Hjarðarholt, igueyri, Hjálmárströnd, Hjálmholt, Hjálmholt, Hjálmsstaðir, Hjálmsstaðir, Hjörleifshöfði, Hjörsey, Hjörsey, Hlaðhamar, emmiskeið 5, Hlemmiskeið 6, Hléberg, Hléberg, Hlégarður, Hlégarður, Hléskógar, Hlíð, Hlíð, Hlíð, Hlíð, Hlíð, Hlíð, Hlíð, líðarból, Hlíðarendakot, Hlíðarendi, Hlíðarendi, Hlíðarendi, Hlíðarendi, Hlíðarendi, Hlíðarendi, Hlíðarendi, Hlíðarendi, ús, Hlíðarhús, Hlíðartunga, Hlíðartún, Hlíðartún, Hlíðskógar, Hlöðunes, Hlöðutún, Hlöðutún, Hnappavellir, Hnappavellir, r, Hnjótur, Hnjúkahlíð, Hnjúkar, Hnjúkur, Hnjúkur, Hnjúkur, Hnúkur, Hnúkur, Hof, Hof, Hof, Hof, Hof, Hof, Hof, Hof, Hof, ell, Hofgarðar, Hofsá, Hofsárkot, Hofsnes, Hofsstaðasel, Hofsstaðir, Hofsstaðir, Hofströnd, Hofsvellir, Hofteigur, Hofteigur, ot, Holtakot, Holtasel, Holtastaðir, Holtsfit, Holtskot, Holtsmúlapartur, Holtsmúli, Holtsmúli, Holtsmúli, Holtssel, Horn, kot, Hólakot, Hólakot, Hólakot, Hólakot, Hólakot, Hólaland, Hólalandshjáleiga, Hólar, Hólar, Hólar, Hólar, Hólar, Hólar, ólkot, Hólkot, Hólkot, Hólkot, Hóll, Hóll Haukadalur, Hóll í Firði, Hóll í Þorgeirsfirði, Hólmahjáleiga, Hólmakot, Hólmar, shús, Hólshús, Hólshús, Hólsland, Hólssel, Hraðastaðir, Hraðastaðir, Hraðastaðir, Hraðastaðir, Hraðastaðir, Hrafnabjörg, afnagil, Hrafnagil, Hrafnagil, Hrafnhólar, Hrafnhóll, Hrafnkelsstaðir, Hrafnkelsstaðir, Hrafnkelsstaðir, Hrafnkelsstaðir, ntóftir, Hranastaðir, Hrappsey, Hrappsstaðasel, Hrappsstaðir, Hrappsstaðir, Hrappsstaðir, Hrappsstaðir, Hrappsstaðir, n, Hraun í Keldudal, Hraunból Sléttaból, Hraunbrún, Hraunbú, Hraunbær, Hraunbær, Hraundalur, Hraunfell, Hraungerði, t, Hraunkot, Hraunprýði, Hraunsás, Hraunsfjörður, Hraunshjáleiga, Hraunsholt, Hraunshóll, Hraunshöfði, Hraunsmúli,

Hraunsmúli, Hraunsnef, Hrauntangi, Hraunteigur, Hrauntunga, Hrauntún, Hrauntún, Hreðavatn, Hreggsstaðir, Hreiðars:
Hringsdalur, Hringver, Hringver, Hringverskot, Hrífunes, Hrísakot, Hrísakot, Hrísakot, Hrísar, Hrísar, Hrísar, Hrísar,
Hrollaugsstaðir, Hrosshagi, Hrossholt, Hróaldsstaðir, Hróaldsstaðir, Hróarsdalur, Hróarsdalur, Hróarsdalur, Hróarsholt,
Hrólfsstaðir, Hrólfsstaðir, Hruni, Hruni, Hruni 2A, Hrútafell 1, Hrútafellskot, Hrútatunga, Hrútatunga, Hrútey, Hrútham
Hunkubakkar, Huppahlíð, Huppahlíð, Huppahlíð, Hurðarbak, Hurðarbak, Hurðarbak, Hurðarbak,.Hurðarbak, Hurðarbak
Húsar, Húsar, Húsatóftir, Húsatóftir, Húsatóftir, Húsatún 1, Húsavík, Húsavík, Húsey, Húsey, Húsey, Húshólmi, Hvalgrafir,
Hvammsdalskot, Hvammsdalur, Hvammsgerði, Hvammshlíð, Hvammsvík, Hvammur Hjalteyri, Hvammur II, Hvammur í L
Hvassafell, Hvassafell II, Hvassahraun, Hvassahraun, Hverabakki, Hverabakki, Hveratún, Hveravellir, Hveravík, Hverhóla:
Hvítárhlíð, Hvítárholt, Hvítárvellir, Hvítárvellir, Hvíteyrar, Hvítidalur, Hvítidalur, Hvítsstaðir, Hvoll, Hvoll, Hvoll, Hvoll, H
Miðnes, Hæringsstaðahjáleiga, Hæringsstaðir, Hæringsstaðir, Hærukollsnes, Hæsti-Hvammur 1, 2 og 3, Höfðabrekka, Hö
Innstibær, Höfði, Höfði 2 Miðbær Narfanes, Höfði 3 Ystibær, Höfn, Höfn, Höfn, Höfn, Höfn, Högnastaðir, Högnastaðir, Högr
Hörgsdalur, Hörgshlíð, Hörgsholt, Hörgsholt, Hörgshóll, Hörgsland, Hörgsland, Hörgslandskot, Höskuldarnes, Höskul
Heklumörk, Hafnarsel, Höfðatún, Innri-Drápuhlíð, Innri-Fagridalur, Innri-Gröf, Innri-Hjarðardalur, Innri-Hænuvík, Innri
Ingaeyjar, Ingimarsstaðir, Ingjaldshóll, Ingjaldsstaðir, Ingólfsfjörður, Ingólfshvoll, Ingunnarstaðir, Ingunnarstaðir, Ing
Skeljabrekka, Innri-Veðrará, Innstaland, Innsta-Tunga, Irpuholt, Innri-Kóngsbakki, Innri-Lambadalur 1, Innri-Látravík,
Jarðlangsstaðir, Jarlsstaðir, Jarlsstaðir, Jarlsstaðir, Jata, Jódísarstaðir, Jódísarstaðir, Jólgeirsstaðir Ás, Jónasarvöllur, Jónsnes
Kaldakinn, Kaldá, Kaldá, Kaldárbakki, Kaldárholt, Kaldárhöfði, Kaldbakur, Kaldbakur, Kaldbakur, Kaldrananes, Kalm
Kambsstaðir, Kambsstaðir, Kambur, Kambur, Kambur, Kambur, Kambur, Kambur, Kampholt, Kanastaðir, Kappeyri, Kap
Katlagil, Katrínarkot, Kaupangsbakki, Kaupangur, Kálfadalur, Kálfafell, Kálfafell, Kálfafell, Kálfafell, Kálfafell 3 Sólvangur,
Kálfárdalur, Kálfárvellir, Kálfborgará, Kálffell, Kálfholt, Kálfhóll, Kálfhóll, Kálfsá, Kálfsárkot, Kálfshamar, Kálfsstaðapartu
Kársstaðir, Keflavík, Keflavík, Keflavík, Keflavík, Keisbakki, Kelda, Keldhólar, Keldnakot, Keldudalur, Kelduland, Keldulan
Ketilhúshagi, Ketilseyri, Ketilsstaðir, Ketilsstaðir, Ketilsstaðir, Ketilsstaðir, Ketilsstaðir, Ketilsstaðir, Ketilsstaðir, Ketilsst
Kirkjuból, Kirkjuból, Kirkjuból, Kirkjuból, Kirkjuból, Kirkjuból, Kirkjuból, Kirkjuból, Kirkjuból á Bæjarnesi, Kirkjuból á L
Kirkjubær, Kirkjubær, Kirkjubær, Kirkjubær, Kirkjubær, Kirkjufell, Kirkjuferja, Kirkjuferjuhjáleiga, Kirkjuholt, Kirkjuhól
Kirkjuskarð, Kirkjuskógur, Kista, Kistufell, Kífsá, Kílakot, Kílhraun, Kjalardalur, Kjalarland, Kjalvararstaðir, Kjalvegur,
Kjartansstaðir, Kjartansstaðir, Kjarvalsstaðir, Kjóastaðir, Kjóastaðir, Kjóastaðir, Kjólsvík, Kjós, Kjölur, Kjörseyri, Kjörs
Klausturhólar, Klaustursel, Kleif, Kleif, Kleif, Kleifar, Kleifar, Kleifar, Kleifar, Kleifar, Kleifar á Selströnd, Kleifar í Kaldbak
Klettakot, Klettakot, Klettar, Klettsstía, Klettur, Klettur, Klif, Klifmýri, Klifshagi, Klifshagi, Kljá, Kljáströnd, Klón, Kluf
Klængssel, Klömbrur, Klömbur, Klöpp, Knappsstaðir, Knarraberg, Knarrareyri, Knarrarholt, Knarrarhöfn, Knarrarnes,
Kolgrafarsel, Kolgrafir, Kolgrímastaðir, Kolgröf, Kolkuós, Kollabúðir, Kollabúðir, Kollabær, Kollabær, Kollafjörður, Kolla
Kolsholt, Kolsholt, Kolsholtshellir, Kolsstaðir, Kolsstaðir, Kolugil, Kolviðarhóll, Kolviðarnes, Kolþernumýri, Komma, Kor
Kotströnd, Kotungsstaðir, Kotvöllur, Kóngsstaðir, Kópareykir, Kópsvatn, Kópsvatn, Kóreksstaðir, Krakavellir, Kraunastaði
Kross, Kross, Kross, Kross, Kross, Kross, Kross, Kross, Kross, Kross, Kross 1A, Kross, Krossaland, Krossanes, Krossane
Krossdalur, Krosseyri, Krossgerði, Krossgerði, Krosshjáleiga, Krossholt, Krosshóll, Krosshóll, Krosshús, Krossnes, Kross
Krókur, Krókur, Krókur, Krókur, Krókur, Krókur, Krókur, Krókur, Krókur, Krókur, Krókur, Krókur, Krókur, Krókur, Krónustað
Kúskerpi, Kúskerpi, Kúvíkur, Kvennabrekka, Kvennahóll, Kverkártunga, Kverná, Kverngrjót, Kvistás, Kvisthagi, Kvisthagi,
Kvígindisfjörður, Kvígsstaðir, Kvísker, Kvíslar, Kvíslarhóll, Kvíslhöfði, Kvoslækur, Kyljuholt, Kýrholt, Kýrunnarstaðir,
Lambastaðir, Lambastaðir, Lambatungur, Lambey, Lambeyrar, Lambeyri, Lambhagi, Lambhagi, Lambhagi, Lambhúshól
Langamýri, Langamýri, Langamýri, Langanesmelar, Langavatn, Langárfoss, Langekra, Langeyjarnes, Langholt, Langholt,
Laufás, Laufás, Laufás, Laufhóll, Laufskálar, Laufskálar, Laufskálar, Lauftún, Laug, Laugaból, Laugaból, Laugaból, Laug
Laugar, Laugar, Laugar, Laugar, Laugarás, Laugarás, Laugarbakkar, Laugarbakkar, Laugarbakkar, Laugarbakkar, Lauga
Laugarholt II, Laugarhvammur, Laugarlandssel, Laugarmýri, Laugarteigur, Laugarvatn, Laugasel, Laugasteinn, Laugavelli
Laxárbakki, Laxárdalur, Laxárhlíð, Laxárholt, Laxárholt, Laxárnes, Laxárnes, Laxfoss, Laxholt, Laxholt, Laxnes, Laxr
Leiðólfsstaðir, Leiðvöllur, Leifshús, Leifsstaðir, Leifsstaðir, Leifsstaðir, Leifsstaðir, Leifsstaðir, Leifsstaðir, Leifsstaðir II, L
Leiti, Leiti, Lerkihlíð, Lerkihlíð, Leyningur, Leyningur, Leynir, Leynir, Leysingjastaðir, Leysingjastaðir, Leysingjastaðir,
1A, Lindarbær 1B, Lindarbær 1C, Lindarbær, Lindarholt, Lindarhóll, Lindarhvoll, Lindartún, Litla-Ármót, Litla-Ásgeirs

rsstaðir, Hreiðarsstaðir, Hreiður, Hreiðurborg, Hreimsstaðir, Hreimsstaðir, Hrepphólar, Hreppsendaá, Hrifla, Hringsdalur, Irísar, Hrísbrú, Hrísdalur, Hrísdalur, Hrísgerði, Hrísholt, Hríshóll, Hríshóll, Hríshóll, Hrísnes, Hrjótur, Hrollaugsstaðir, arslækur, Hróarsstaðir, Hróarsstaðir, Hróbjargarstaðir, Hróðnýjarstaðir, Hrófá, Hrófá, Hrófá, Hrófberg, Hrólfsstaðahellir, Hrútsholt, Hrútsholt II, Hrútsstaðir, Hrútur, Hryggir, Hryggstekkur, Hryggur, Hrærekslækur, Hugljótsstaðir, Hundastapi, ikur, Húnakot, Húnsstaðir, Hús, Hús = Brekkugerðishús, Húsabakki, Húsabær, Húsafell, Húsafell, Húsagarður, Húsanes, nes, Hvalnes, Hvalnes, Hvalsá, Hvalseyjar, Hvalshöfði, Hvalsker, Hvalsnes, Hvammeyri, Hvammkot, Hvammkot, Hvammkot, brekka, Hvannatún, Hvanná, Hvanná, Hvanndalir, Hvanneyri, Hvannstóð, Hvarf, Hvarf, Hvarfsdalur, Hvassafell, Hvassafell, 't, Hvilft, Hvítahlíð, Hvítanes, Hvítanes, Hvítanes, Hvítanes, Hvítanes, Hvítárbakki, Hvítárbakki, Hvítárbakki, Hvítárdalur, l, Hvoll, Hvolsbrún, Hyrningsstaðir, Hæðarendi, Hæðargarður, Hægindi, Hækingsdalur, Hæll, Hæll, Hæll, Hæll, Hæll, Hæll abrekka, Höfðahús, Höfðatún, Höfðatún, Höfði, Höfði, Höfði, Höfði, Höfði, Höfði, Höfði, Höfði, Höfði, Höfði, Höfði, Höfði 1 aðir, Hölkná, Höll, Höllustaðir, Höllustaðir, Höllustaðir, Hömluholt, Hörðuból, Hörðuskáli, Hörgá, Hörgsdalur, Hörgsdalur, aðasel, Höskuldsstaðir, Höskuldsstaðir, Höskuldsstaðir, Höskuldsstaðir, Höskuldsstaðir, Höskuldsstaðir, Höskuldsstaðir,)a, Iða, Iðunnarstaðir, Illugastaðir, Illugastaðir, Illugastaðir, Illugastaðir, Illugastaðir, Illugastaðir, Indriðakot, Indriðastaðir, varir, Ingveldarstaðir, Ingveldarstaðir, Innra-Leiti, Innri-Bugur, Innri-Hólmur, Innri-Kleif, Innri-Múli, Innri-Ós, Innri- Íbishóll, Ímastaðir Innribær, Ímastaðir Ytribær, Írafell, Írafell, Ísabakki, Ísólfsstaðir, Jaðar, Jaðarkot, Jafnaskarð, Jarðbrú, aðalsstaðir, Kaðalsstaðir, Kagaðarhóll, Kalastaðakot, Kalastaðir, Kaldaðarnes, Kaldakinn, Kaldakinn, Kaldakinn, Kaldakinn, instunga, Kambakot, Kambfell, Kambshjáleiga, Kambshóll, Kambshóll, Kambsmýrar, Kambsnes, Kambsnes, Kambssel, arlsbrekka, Karlsskáli, Karlsstaðir, Karlsstaðir, Karlsstaðir, Kastalabrekka, Kasthvammur, Katadalur, Katanes, Katastaðir, fafellsstaður, Kálfagerði, Kálfanes, Kálfanes, Kálfanes, Kálfanes, Kálfaströnd, Kálfaströnd, Kálfatjörn, Kálfavík, Kálfárdalur, ilfsstaðir, Káragerði, Kárahlíð, Káranes, Káraneskot, Kárastaðir, Kárastaðir, Kárastaðir, Kárastaðir, Kárdalstunga, Kárhóll, unes, Keldunúpur, Keldur, Keldur, Kelduskógar, Kelduvík, Kerhóll, Kerlingardalur, Kerlingardalur, Kerlingarey, Keta, Keta, ir, Ketilsstaðir, Ketilsstaðir, Ketilvellir, Kiðaberg, Kiðafell, Kiðey, Kiðey, Kimbastaðir, Kinn, Kinn, Kinnarstaðir, Kirkjuból, jl í Bjarnard, Kirkjuból í Korpudal, Kirkjuból í Staðardal, Kirkjubrú, Kirkjubæjarklaustur, Kirkjubæjarklaustur, Kirkjubær, xjuhvammur, Kirkjuhvammur, Kirkjulækjarkot, Kirkjulækjarkot, Kirkjulækjarkot, Kirkjulækur, Kirkjulækur, Kirkjulækur, aransstaðir, Kjaransstaðir, Kjarlaksstaðir, Kjarlaksvellir, Kjarnholt, Kjarnholt, Kjarnholt, Kjarni, Kjarr, Kjartansstaðakot, Klafastaðir, Klakkseyjar, Klambrasel, Klasbarði, Klauf, Klauf, Klauf, Klaufabrekknakot, Klaufabrekkur, Klausturbrekka, ýðisfirði, Kleifarkot, Kleifarstekkur, Kleifastaðir, Kleifárvellir, Kleppjárnsreykir, Kleppjárnsstaðir, Kleppustaðir, Klettaborg, lukkuland Hólakot, Klungurbrekka, Klúka, Klúka, Klúka, Klúka, Klúka, Klúkur, Klyftasandur, Klyppsstaðir, Klængshóll, rr, Kolbeinsá, Kolbeinsá, Kolbeinsskeið, Kolbeinsstaðir, Kolbeinsstaðir, Kolbeinsvík, Kolfreyja, Kolfreyjustaður, Kolgerði, Kollavík, Kollsá, Kollsá, Kollsá, Kollslækur, Kollsstaðagerði, Kollsvík, Kollugerði, Kollugerði, Kolmúli, Kolmúli, Kolsholt, sá, Kornsárselsland, Kornvellir, Kot, Kot, Kot, Kotamýrar, Kotferja, Kotferja, Kothvammur, Kotlaugar, Kotleysa, Kotmúli, a, Kringla, Kringla, Kringlumýri, Kristnes, Krithóll, Krithóll II, Krithólsgerði, Kroppsstaðir, Kroppsstaðir, Kroppur, Kross, ssanes, Krossar, Krossar, Krossastaðir, Krossavík, Krossavík, Krossavík, Krossavík, Krossárbakki, Krossbær, Krossdalur, -, Krókar, Krókar, Krókasel, Krókengi, Króksfjarðarnes, Króksstaðir, Króksstaðir, Króksstaðir, Króktún, Króktún, Krókur, Kröggólfsstaðir, Kumbaravogur, Kumblavík, Kurfur, Kussungsstaðir, Kúðá, Kúðá, Kúfhóll, Kúfustaðir, Kúgil, Kúludalsá, Kvíabekkur, Kvíabóll, Kvíabryggja, Kvíar, Kvíarholt, Kvíarhóll, Kvígindisdalur, Kvígindisdalur, Kvígindisdalur, Kvígindisfell, lt, Kötlustaðir, Kerhólar, Lambadalur, Lambafell, Lambalækur, Lambanes, Lambanes, Lambanes-Reykir, Lambastaðir, ambleiksstaðir, Landakot, Landakot, Landamót, Landamótssel, Landbrot, Langagerði, Langagerði, Langahlíð, Langahlíð, lt, Langholt, Langholtskot, Langholtspartur, Langhús, Langhús, Langibotn, Langsstaðir, Laufahlíð, Laufás, Laufás, Laufás, .augaból, Laugafell, Laugafell, Laugagerði, Laugahlíð, Laugaland, Laugaland, Laugaland, Laugaland, Laugaland, Laugar, ka, Laugarbær, Laugardalshólar, Laugardalur, Laugardælir, Laugarholt, Laugarholt, Laugarholt, Laugarholt, Laugarholt, gavellir, Laugavellir, Lautarhús 1, Lautir, Laxaborg, Laxabrekka, Laxamýri, Laxamýri, Laxárbakki, Laxárbakki, Laxárbakki, Lágafell, Lágafell, Lága-Kotey, Lágar, Lágarkot, Lágidalur, Láginúpur, Lágmúli, Látur, Látur, Leiðarhöfn, Leiðarhöfn, .eirhöfn, Leirlækur, Leirubakkahóll, Leirubakki, Leirulækjarsel, Leirulækur, Leirur, Leirur, Leirvogstunga, Leirvogsvatn, ð, Lindarbakki, Lindarbakki, Lindarberg, Lindarbrekka, Lindarbrekka, Lindarbrekka, Lindarbrekka, Lindarbær, Lindarbær -Borg, Litla-Breiðavík-L Vík, Litla-Breiðuvík, Litla-Brekka, Litla-Brekka, Litla-Brekka, Litla-Brekka, Litla-Búrfell, Litla-

Drageyri, Litla-Eyri, Litla-Fell, Litla-Fellsöxl, Litla-Fjall, Litla-Fjarðarhorn, Litla-Fljót, Litla-Fljót, Litlagerði, Litla-Giljá, L
Litla-Holtsland, Litla-Hraun, Litla-Hraun, Litla-Hvalsá, Litlaland, Litlaland, Litlanes, Litla-Sandfell, Litla-Sandvík, Litla-S
Bakki, Litli-Bakki, Litli-Botn, Litlibær, Litlibær, Litlibær, Litlidalur, Litlidalur, Litli-Dalur, Litli-Dalur, Litli-Dunhagi, Lit
Kálfalækur, Litli-Klofi, Litli-Kroppur, Litli-Lambhagi, Litli-Langidalur Fremri, Litli-Langidalur Ytri, Litli-Laugardalur, L
Reykir, Litlu-Reykir, Litlu-Skógar, Litlu-Tjarnir, Litlu-Tungueyjar, Litluvellir, Ljárkot, Ljárskógar, Ljónsstaðir, Ljósaland,
Ljótunnarstaðir, Ljótunnarstaðir, Ljúfustaðir, Loftsalir, Lokinhamrar, Lokinhamrar, Lómatjörn, Lón, Lón, Lón, Lón, Lón
Lundur, Lundur, Lundur, Lundur, Lundur, Lundur, Lundur, Lykkja, Lykkja, Lyngás, Lyngás, Lyngás, Lyngbrekka, Lyng
Lýtingsstaðir, Lýtingsstaðir, Lækjamót, Lækjamót, Lækjamót Hörgsholt, Lækjarbakki, Lækjarbakki, Lækjarbakki, Lækjar
Lækjarhvammur, Lækjarhvammur, Lækjarkot, Lækjarmót, Lækjarmót, Lækjarmót, Lækjarós, Lækjarskógur, Lækjartún, L
Lönd, Löngudælaholt, Litla-Vallá, Lyngbær, Magnússkógar, Magnússkógar 1B, Magnússkógar, Malarás, Malarrif, Manheim
Mánavík, Máná, Máná, Mánárbakki, Máskelda, Máskot, Mássel, Másstaðir, Másstaðir, Mávahlíð, Mávahlíð, Meðaldalur, M
Hattardalur II, Meiri-Hlíð, Meiri-Tunga, Meiri-Tunga, Meiri-Tunga, Meiri-Tunga, Melaberg, Melabúð, Melaleiti, Melanes, M
Melgraseyri, Melhagi, Melhóll 1 Undirhraun, Melhóll 2 Undirhraun, Melhvammur, Melkot, Melkot, Melrakkaey, Melrakka
Merkigil, Merkihvoll, Messuholt, Meyjarhóll, Meyjarland, Miðbýli, Miðbæli, Miðbælisbakkar, Miðbær, Miðdalsgröf, Miðdal
Miðfell, Miðfell, Miðfell, Miðfell, Miðfell 5, Miðfell 6, Miðfjarðarnes, Miðfjarðarnes, Miðfjarðarnes, Miðfjarðarnessel, Miðfjör
Miðhálsstaðir, Miðhlíð Innri, Miðhlíð Ytri, Mið-Hóll, Miðhóp, Miðhraun, Miðhraun, Miðhús, Miðhúsagerði, Miðhúsasel, Mið
Mór, Mið-Mörk, Mið-Samtún, Miðsitja, Miðskáli, Miðskáli 2, Miðsker, Miðskógur, Miðströnd, Miðtún, Miðtún, Miðvellir, Miðve
Mikligarður, Mikligarður, Miklihóll, Minna-Hof, Minna-Hof, Minna-Holt, Minna-Hraun, Minna-Knarrarnes, Minna-Mosfell
Minni-Grindill, Minni-Hattardalur, Minni-Mástunga, Minni-Núpur, Minni-Ólafsvellir, Minni-Reykir, Minni-Vatnsleysa, M
Moldnúpur, Morastaðir, Mosdalur, Mosfell, Mosfell, Mosfell, Mosfell, Moshlíð, Mosvellir, Móabúð, Móafell, Móakot, Móakot, M
Mógilsá, Mói Meðalfell, Móskógar, Móskógar, Munaðarnes, Munaðarnes, Munaðarnes, Munaðarnes, Munaðstunga, Mundak
Múli, Múli, Múli, Múli, Múli, Múli, Múli, Múli, Múli, Múli Hof, Mykjunes, Mykjunes, Myrká, Myrkárbakki, Myrkárdalur, Myrk
Brún, Mýrarhús, Mýrarkot, Mýrarkot, Mýrarlón, Mýrartunga, Mýrartunga, Mýrdalur, Mýri, Mælifell, Mælifell, Mælifellsá, M
Mörk, Mörk, Mörk, Mörk, Mörtunga, Mörtunga, Miðhjáleiga, Neðri-Arnórsstaðir, Neðri-Breiðadalur, Neðri-Breiðadalur, N
Neðri-Kverná, Neðra-Lambavatn, Neðra-Lýtingsstaðakot, Nabbi, Narfakot, Narfastaðir, Narfastaðir, Narfastaðir, Narfeyri, N
Nautaflatir, Nauteyri, Nátthagi, Neðra-Apavatn, Neðra-Haganes, Neðra-Haganes, Neðra-Nes, Neðra-Nes, Neðra-Sel, Neðr
Brunná, Neðribær, Neðribær, Neðri-Dalur, Neðri-Dalur, Neðri-Dalur, Neðri-Dalur, Neðri-Dálksstaðir, Neðri-Engidalur, Neð
Hundadalur, Neðri-Hundadalur, Neðrihús, Neðri-Hvesta, Neðri-Lækjardalur, Neðri-Miðbær, Neðri-Mýrar, Neðri-Núpur, Ne
Neðri-Þverá, Neðstaland, Neðstibær, Neðsti-Hvammur, Neðsti-Hvammur, Neðsti-Hvammur, Nefbjarnarstaðir, Nefsholt, Ne
Nessel, Nethamar, Nikulásarhús, Nípá, Nípugarðar, Nípukot, Nípur, Njarðvík, Njálsstaðir, Njálsstaðir, Nollur, Norðtunga, N
Norður-Foss, Norðurgarðar, Norður-Garður, Norðurgröf, Norður-Götur, Norðurhagi, Norðurhjáleiga, Norðurhlíð, Norður-
Nónbjarg, Núpakot, Núpar, Núpar, Núpar 1, Núpar, Núpsdalstunga, Núpshlíð, Núpskatla I, Núpskatla II, Núpsstaðir, Núps
Nýibær, Nýibær, Nýibær, Nýibær, Nýibær, Nýibær, Nýibær, Nýi-Bær, Nýi-Bær, Nýi-Bær, Nýi-Bær, Nýi-Hóll, Nýjabúð, Nýja-Búð
Neðra-Suðurkot 3, Oddagarðar, Oddakot, Oddar, Oddastaðir, Oddgeirshólar, Oddgeirshólar, Oddgeirshólar, Oddgeirshóla
Ormarsstaðir, Ormarsstaðir, Ormskot, Ormskot, Ormsstaðir, Ormsstaðir, Ormsstaðir, Ormsstaðir, Ormsstaðir, Orrahóll, O
Ós, Ós, Ós, Ós, Ós, Ós Kirkjuból, Ósabakki, Ósabakki, Ósabakki, Ósar, Ósbotn, Ósbrekka, Ósbrekkukot, Óseyrarnes, Ósey
Páfastaðir, Pálmholt, Pálmholt, Pálsgerði, Pálshús, Pálssel, Pétursborg, Pétursbúð Bjarg, Pétursey, Pétursey, Péturshól
Purkugerði, Pyttagerði, Raftholt, Ragnheiðarstaðir, Raknadalur, Randversstaðir, Rangalón, Rangá, Rangá, Rangá, Ranga
Rauðamýri, Rauðanes, Rauðanes, Rauðanes, Rauðaskriða, Rauðaskriða, Rauðaskriða, Rauðavík, Rauðá, Rauðbarðaholt,
Rauðsstaðir Borg Dynjandi, Rauðuskriður, Raufarfell, Raufarfell, Ráðagerði, Ráðagerði, Ráeyri, Refshöfði, Refsmýri, Ref
Reyðarvatn, Reykholt, Reykhólar, Reykhóll, Reykhóll, Reykhús, Reykir, Reykir, Reykir, Reykir, Reykir, Reykir, Reykir, R
Reykjahlíð, Reykjahlíð, Reykjahlíð, Reykjahlíð, Reykjahlíð, Reykjahvoll, Reykjakot, Reykjaland, Reykjalundur, Reykjan
Reykjavellir, Reykjavellir, Reynhólar, Reynifell, Reynihagi, Reynihlíð, Reynikelda, Reynir, Reynisbrekka, Reynisdalur, Reyn
Reynivellir, Réttarholt, Réttarholt, Réttarholt, Réttarholt, Réttarnes, Rif, Rifgirðingar, Rifkelsstaðir, Rifkelsstaðir, Rifsha
Rugludalur, Runnar, Runná, Rúfeyjar, Rútsstaða-Norðurkot, Rútsstaðir, Rútsstaðir, Rútsstaðir, Rútsstaðir, Röðull, Syðri-B
Rauðimelur, Sakka, Sakka II, Saltvík, Saltvík, Samkomugerði, Samkomugerði, Samtún, Sandar, Sandar, Sandar, Sandasel, Sa

a-Gröf, Litla-Gröf, Litla-Háeyri, Litla-Heiði, Litla-Hildisey, Litlahlíð, Litla-Hlíð, Litla-Hlíð, Litla-Hlíð, Litla-Hof, Litla-Holt, nsvað 1, Litlaströnd, Litla-Strönd, Litla-Tunga, Litla-Tunga, Litla-Tunga, Litla-Vatnshorn, Litla-Þúfa, Litli-Árskógur, Litli-li-Garður, Litli-Garður, Litli-Hamar, Litli-Háls, Litli-Hóll, Litli-Hóll, Litli-Hvammur, Litli-Hvammur, Litli-Kambur, Litli-itli-Múli, Litli-Ós, Litli-Saurbær, Litli-Saurbær, Litlu-Hámundarstaðir, Litlu-Hólar, Litlu-Ketilsstaðir, Litlu-Laugar, Litlu-saland, Ljósavatn, Ljótarstaðir, Ljótarstaðir, Ljótshólapartur, Ljótshólar, Ljótsstaðir, Ljótsstaðir, Ljótsstaðir, Ljótsstaðir 2, .unansholt, Lunansholt, Lundar, Lundar II, Lundarbrekka, Lundarbrekka, Lundarbrekka, Lundarbrekka, Lundey, Lundur, ll, Lynghagi, Lyngholt, Lyngholt, Lyngholt, Lyngholt, Lyngholt, Lyngholt, Lynghóll, Lýsudalur, Lýsuhóll, Lýtingsstaðir, brekka, Lækjarbugur, Lækjarbær, Lækjardalur, Lækjarfell, Lækjargarður, Lækjarholt, Lækjarhvammur, Lækjarhvammur, avellir, Læknesstaðir, Læknesstaðir, Lækur, Lækur, Lækur, Lækur, Lækur, Lækur, Lækur, Lækur, Lögmannshlíð, Lölukot, .óll, Marbæli, Marbæli, Marðarnúpur, Maríubakki, Markaskarð, Markúsarsel, Marteinstunga, Málmey, Mánafoss, Mánaskál, ell, Meðalheimur, Meðalheimur, Meðalnes, Meðalnes, Meiðavellir, Meiri-Bakki, Meiri-Garður, Meiri-Hattardalur I, Meiri-lar, Melar, Melar, Melar, Melar, Melar, Melar, Melar, Melar, Melar, Melar, Melavellir, Melavellir, Melbreið, Melbær, Melgerði, nes, Melstaður, Melstaður, Meltún, Melur, Melur, Melur, Melur, Melur, Melur, Merki, Merki, Merki, Merkigarður, Merkigil, Miðdalur, Miðdalur, Miðdalur, Miðdalur, Mið-Dalur, Miðdalur, Miðengi, Miðengi, Miðey, Miðeyjarhólmur, Miðfell, Miðfell, Mið-Fossar, Mið-Fossar, Miðgarðar, Miðgarðar, Mið-Garðar, Miðgarður, Miðgerði, Miðgerði, Miðgil, Miðgrund, Mið-Grund, Hvammur 2 Suðurbær, Miðjanes, Mið-Kárastaðir, Miðkot, Miðkot, Miðkot, Miðkot, Miðkriki, Miðland, Mið-Meðalholt, Mið-vík, Miklaholt, Miklaholt, Miklaholt I, Miklaholt II, Miklaholtshellir, Miklaholtssel, Mikley, Miklibær, Miklibær, Mikligarður, Minni-Akrar, Minni-Bakki, Minni-Borg, Minni-Borg, Minni-Borg, Minni-Brekka, Minni-Bær, Minni-Dalir, Minni-Garður, ni-Vogar, Minni-Þverá, Mjóaból, Mjóanes, Mjóanes, Mjóanes, Mjóidalur, Mjósyndi, Molastaðir, Moldbrekka, Moldhaugar, erg, Móberg, Móberg, Móbergssel, Móeiðarhvoll, Móeiðarhvoll, Móeiðarhvolshjáleiga, Mófellsstaðakot, Mófellsstaðir, Mógil, Mundakot II, Munkaþverá, Múlakot, Múlakot, Múlakot, Múlakot, Múlakot, Múlapartur, Múlastaðir, Múlastekkur, Múli, Múli, ·, Mýlaugsstaðir, Mýnes, Mýrakot, Mýrakot, Mýrar, Mýrar, Mýrar, Mýrar, Mýrar, Mýrar, Mýrar, Mýrar, Mýrar, Mýrar, Mýrar og , Möðrudalur, Möðrufell, Möðruvellir, Möðruvellir, Möðruvellir, Möðruvellir, Möðruvellir, Möðruvellir, Mörk, Mörk, Mörk, r, Norður-Bæjarsker, Neðri-Bær, Neðri-Dufansdalur, Neðra-Flagbjarnarholt, Neðri-Hjarðardalur, Neðri-Hjarðardalur 3–4, Naust, Naust, Naustabrekka, Naustakot, Naustanes, Naustavík, Naustavík Vargsnes, Naustvík, Nautabú, Nautabú, Nautabú, Vatnshorn, Neðri-Mið-Hvammur, Neðri-Ás, Neðri-Ás, Neðri-Ás, Neðri-Bakki, Neðri-Brekka, Neðri-Brunnastaðir, Neðri-Flankastaðir, Neðri-Foss, Neðri-Gufudalur, Neðri-Harrastaðir, Neðri-Háls, Neðri-Hóll, Neðri-Hreppur, Neðri-Hrísar, Neðri-Neðri-Sandvík, Neðri-Skálateigur, Neðri-Svertingsstaðir, Neðri-Torfustaðir, Neðri-Tunga, Neðri-Vindheimar, Neðri-Þverá, aðir, Nes, Nes, Nes, Nes, Nes, Nes, Nes, Nes, Nes, Nes, Nesbakki, Neshjáleiga, Nesjar, Nesjar, Nesjavellir, Neskot, Nessandur, r-Bár, Norður-Botn, Norðurbrún, Norðureyri, Norður-Eyvindarstaðir, Norðurfjörður, Norðurfjörður, Norður-Flankastaðir, urkot, Norðurkot, Norðurkot, Norðurkot, Norður-Nýjabær, Norður-Reykir, Norður-Reykir I, Norður-Skálanes, Norður-Vík, ipur, Núpur, Núpur, Núpur, Núpur, Núpur, Núpur, Núpur, Núpur 2 Rani, Núpur, Nykhóll, Nýhöfn, Nýhöfn, Nýibær, da, Nýlenda í Hvalsneshverfi, Nýlenda í Stafneshverfi, Nýlendi, Nýrækt, Næfurholt, Neðri-Rauðdalur, Neðri-Reykjarfjörður, i, Oddi, Oddi, Oddsmýri, Oddspartur, Oddsstaðir, Oddsstaðir, Oddsstaðir, Oddsstaðir, Oddsstaðir, Ofanleiti, Ormarslón, ıstaðir, Otradalur, Orustudalur, Ófeigsfjörður, Ófeigsstaðir, Ófeigsstaðir, Ólafsdalur, Ólafsey, Ólafsgerði, Ólafsvellir, Ós, Ós, ði, Ósgröf, Óskot, Ósland, Ósland, Óslandspartur, Óspakseyri, Óspaksstaðasel, Óspaksstaðir, Óttarsstaðir, Ósavatn, Papey, r, Prestsbakki, Presthólar, Presthvammur, Prestsbakkakot, Prestsbakki, Prestshús, Prestshús, Prestshús, Pula, Purkey, Rannveigarstaðir, Rauðaberg, Rauðaberg, Rauðaberg, Rauðaberg, Rauðafell, Rauðafell, Rauðafell, Rauðafell, Rauðalækur, nolt, Rauðhólar, Rauðhús, Rauðilækur, Rauðiskógur, Rauðkollsstaðir, Rauðnefsstaðir, Rauðsbakki, Rauðseyjar, Rauðsgil, ir, Refsstaðir, Refsstaðir, Refsstaðir, Refsteinsstaðir, Reiðholt, Rein, Reistarnes, Reyðará, Reyðará, Reyðarfell Húsafell, ·ykir, Reykir, Reykir, Reykjabakki, Reykjaborg, Reykjaból, Reykjadalur, Reykjadalur, Reykjadalur, Reykjaflöt, Reykjahlíð, eykjarfjörður, Reykjarfjörður, Reykjarhóll, Reykjarhóll, Reykjarhóll, Reykjarhóll 1, Reykjarvík, Reykjasel, Reykjavellir, sholt, Reynisholt 2, Reynisholt, Reynisholt 5, Reynishólar, Reynisstaðir, Reynistaðir, Reynivellir, Reynivellir, Reynivellir, , Riftún, Rimahús, Rimakot, Rimi, Rimi, Ríp, Ríp, Ríp, Rjóður, Rjúpnafell, Rjúpnavellir, Rof, Rofabær, Rofhagi, Róðuhóll, -Einarslón, Syðri-Fjörður, Stóra-Gata, Syðri-Haukatunga, Syðri-Haukatunga, Syðri-Ingveldarstaðir, Syðri-Klömbur, Syðri-Sandbrekka, Sanddalstunga, Sandeyri, Sandfell, Sandfell, Sandfell, Sandfellshagi, Sandfellshagi, Sandhaugar, Sandhólaferja,

Sandhólar, Sandhólar, Sandhólar, Sandhóll, Sandhóll, Sandhóll, Sandlækjarkot, Sandlækjarkot, Sandlækur, Sandlækur, Sa
Sauðafell, Sauðanes, Sauðanes, Sauðanes, Sauðanes, Sauðanes, Sauðanes Engidalur, Sauðá, Sauðárhæðir, Sauðhagi, Sau
Saurbær, Saurbær, Saurbær, Saurbær, Saurbær, Saurbær, Saurbær, Saurbær, Saurbær, Saurbær, Saurbær, Saurbær, Saurba
Sámsstaðir, Sámsstaðir, Sámsstaðir, Seftjörn, Seglbúðir, Seglbúðir II, Sel, Sel, Sel, Sel, Sela-Kirkjuból, Sela-Kirkjuból, Se
Selfoss, Selhagi, Selhagi, Selholt, Seljabrekka, Seljahlíð, Seljaland, Seljaland, Seljaland, Seljaland, Seljaland, Seljalandssel, S
Selland, Sellátranes, Sellátrar, Sellátur, Sellón, Selnes, Selpartur, Selskarð, Selsker, Selsstaðir, Selsund, Selvellir, Selvíku
Siglunes 7, Siglunes 8, Sigluvík, Sigluvík, Sigmundarhús, Sigmundarstaðir, Sigmundarstaðir, Signýjarstaðir, Sigríðarstaðir,
Sitjandi, Síða, Síða, Síðumúlaveggir, Síðumúli, Sílalækur, Sílastaðir, Síreksstaðir, Sjávarborg I, Sjávarborg II, Sjávarborg
Skallhóll, Skammadalshóll, Skammbeinsstaðir, Skammbeinsstaðir, Skammbeinsstaðir, Skammbeinsstaðir, Skammidalur,
Skarðdalskot, Skarðdalur, Skarðsá, Skarðsá, Skarðshamrar, Skarðshlíð, Skarðshlíð, Skarðshlíð, Skarðssel, Skarðstorfa, Sk
Skálanes, Skálar, Skálar, Skálará, Skálatangi, Skálatún, Skálavík, Skálavík I–II, Skálá, Skáldabúðir, Skáldalækjarey, Ská
Skálmarbær, Skálmardalur, Skálmarnesmúli, Skálmholt, Skálmholtshraun, Skálpagerði, Skálpastaðir, Skálpastaðir, Sk
Skeggjastaðir, Skeggjastaðir, Skeggjastaðir, Skeggjastaðir, Skeggsstaðir, Skeggsstaðir, Skeið, Skeið, Skeið, Skeiðflöt, Skeið
Skinnar, Skinnastaðir, Skinnastaðir, Skinnastaðir, Skipagerði, Skipagerði, Skipagerði, Skipalækur, Skipalækur, Skipanes,
Skjaldabjarnarvík, Skjaldarkot, Skjaldarstaðir, Skjaldartröð, Skjaldfönn, Skjaldvararfoss, Skjaldþingsstaðir, Skjálg, Skjöldól
Skorrastaður, Skorravík, Skoruvík, Skottastaðir, Skógar, Skógar, Skógar, Skógar, Skógar, Skógar, Skógar, Skógar, Skógar, Sk
Skógskot, Skógsmúli, Skógsnes, Skrapatunga, Skrauthólar, Skriða, Skriða, Skriðnafell, Skriðnesenni, Skriðuból, Skriðufell,
Skuggahlíð, Skuggahlíð, Skurðbær, Skutulsey, Skúfslækur, Skúfslækur II, Skúfsstaðir, Skúfur, Skúmsstaðir, Skúmsstaði
Sleðbrjótur, Sleðbrjótur, Sleggjulækur, Sleitustaðir, Sleitustaðir, Slétta, Slétta, Slétta, Sléttaból, Sléttaból, Sléttárdalur, Slé
Smiðshús, Smjördalir, Smjörhóll, Smyrlaberg, Smyrlabjörg 1–2, Smyrlabjörg, Smyrlahóll, Snartarstaðir, Snartarstaðir, Snar
Snorrastaðir, Snotra, Snotrunes, Snotrunes, Snóksdalur, Snóksdalur, Snæbjarnarstaðir, Snæbýli, Snæbýli, Snæfjöll, Snæ
Sólbakki, Sólberg, Sólberg, Sólborgarhóll, Sólbrekka, Sólbrekka, Sólbyrgi, Sóleyjarbakki, Sóleyjarvellir, Sólheimagerði, Sóll
Sólheimatunga, Sólheimatunga, Sólstaðir, Sólvangur, Sólvangur, Sólvangur, Sólveigarstaðir, Sólvellir, Sólvellir, Sólvellir, Só
Staðarbakki, Staðarbakki, Staðarbakki, Staðarfell, Staðarfell, Staðarflöt, Staðarholt, Staðarholt, Staðarhóll, Staðarhóll, Sta
Staður, Stafafell, Staffell, Staffell, Stafholt, Stafholtsey, Stafholtsey, Stafholtsveggir, Stafn, Stafn, Stafn, Stafn, Stafnsholt,
Stangarás, Stangarholt, Stapadalur, Stapar, Stapasel, Stapi, Stapi, Stardalur, Starkaðarhús, Starmýri, Starmýri, Starmýri, S
Steinavellir, Steiná, Steiná II, Steiná III, Steinárgerði, Steindalur, Steindórsstaðir, Steindyr, Steindyr, Steinholt, Steinholt, S
Steinskot, Steinskot, Steinsnes, Steinsstaðir, Steinsstaðir, Steinsstaðir II, Steinstún, Steintún, Steintún, Steintún, Stekk
Stekkjarholt, Stekkjarhóll, Stekkjarmelur, Stekkjarvellir, Stekkur, Stiklur, Stífla, Stíflisdalur, Stíflisdalur, Stokkahlaðir, Sto
Syðri, Stóra-Borg Ytri, Stóra-Borg Ytri, Stóraból, Stóra-Breiðuvík, Stóra-Breiðuvíkurhjáleiga, Stórabrekka, Stóra-Brekka,
Stóra-Grund, Stóra-Gröf, Stóra-Gröf syðri, Stóra-Gröf ytri, Stóra-Gröf ytri, Stóra-Háeyri, Stóra-Heiði, Stóra-Hildisey, Stóra-
Stóra-Knarrarnes, Stóralág, Stóra-Mástunga, Stóra-Mástunga, Stóra-Mörk, Stóra-Mörk, Stóra-Mörk, Stóra-Rimakot, Stó
Stóra-Steinsvað, Stóra-Tunga, Stóra-Tunga, Stóra-Tunga, Stóra-Vatnshorn, Stóra-Vatnsleysa, Stóra-Vatnsskarð, Stóra-Vatn
Dalur, Stóri-Dunhagi, Stóri-Galtardalur, Stóri-Grindill, Stóri-Hamar, Stóri-Hamar, Stóri-Háls, Stóri-Kambur, Stóri-Kálfala
Stóri-Moshvoll, Stóri-Moshvoll, Stóri-Múli, Stóri-Núpur, Stóri-Núpur, Stóri-Núpur, Stóri-Ós, Stóri-Saurbær, Stóri-Skógu
Stóru-Reykir, Stóruskógar, Stóru-Tjarnir, Stóru-Tungueyjar, Stóruvellir, Stóru-Vellir, Stóru-Vogar, Strandarbakki, Stranda
Streiti, Strjúgsá, Strjúgsstaðir, Strýta, Strýta, Strönd, Strönd, Strönd, Strönd, Strönd, Strönd Rofabær, Stuðlafoss, Stuðla
Bær, Stöð, Stöðlakot, Stöðlar, Stöðulfell, Stöng, Suður-Bár, Suðureyri, Suður-Foss, Suðurgafl, Suðurgafl, Suðurgafl Víkurm
Suðurreykir, Suðurreykir, Suður-Vík, Sultir, Sumarliðabær, Sumarliðabær, Sumarliðabær, Sumarliðabær, Sund, Sunnuda
Sunnuhvoll, Surtsstaðir, Súluholt, Súluholt, Súluholtshjáleiga, Syðri-Súluvellir, Svaðastaðir, Svalbarð, Svalbarð, Svalba
Svartagil, Svartárkot, Svarthamar, Svartinúpur, Sveðjustaðir, Svefneyjar, Sveinagarðar, Sveinatunga , Gestsstaðir, Sveinbja
Sveinsstaðir, Sveinsstaðir, Sveinungseyri, Sveinungsvík, Svelgsá, Svertingsstaðir, Sviðholt, Sviðningur, Sviðningur, S
Svínaskálastekkur, Svínaskáli, Svínaskógur, Svínavatn, Svínavatn, Svínavatn II, Svínárnes, Svínhagi, Svínhólar, Svínhóll, S
Hvarf, Syðra-Kálfsskinn, Syðra-Kolugil, Syðra-Langholt, Syðra-Langholt, Syðra-Langholt, Syðra-Langholt 2A, Syðra-Lan
Syðra-Skörðugil, Syðra-Vallholt, Syðra-Vallholt, Syðra-Vatn, Syðri-Ánastaðir, Syðri-Ánastaðir, Syðri-Bakki, Syðri-Bakki,
Syðri-Ey, Syðri-Fljótar, Syðri-Gauksmýri, Syðri-Gegnishólar, Syðri-Gróf, Syðri-Gróf, Syðri-Grund, Syðri-Grund, Syðri-Gr

Sandur, Sandur, Sandur, Sandur, Sandur Hólshjáleiga, Sandvík, Sandvík, Sandvík, Sandvíkurpartur, Sandvíkursel, Sarpur,
t, Sauðhús, Sauðhúsnes, Sauðhúsvöllur, Sauðlauksdalur, Saurar, Saurar, Saurar, Saurar, Saurar, Saurar, Saurbrúargerði,
urbær, Saurhóll, Saurlátur, Saursstaðir, Saxhóll, Sámsstaðir, Sámsstaðir, Sámsstaðir, Sámsstaðir, Sámsstaðir, Sámsstaðir,
4, Selalækur, Selá, Selá, Selárbakki, Selárdalur, Selárdalur, Selárdalur, Selárvellir, Selás, Seldalur, Selfell, Selfoss, Selfoss,
nes, Seljanes, Seljar, Seljar, Seljateigshjáleiga, Seljateigur, Seljatunga, Seljavellir, Seljavellir, Selkot, Selkot, Selland, Selland,
rg, Setberg, Setberg, Setberg, Setberg, Setbergseyjar, Setberg, Siglunes, Siglunes, Siglunes, Siglunes, Siglunes 4–5 og 6,
Sigríðarstaðir, Sigtún, Sigtún, Sigtún, Sigtún, Sigtún Syðri-Grenivík, Sigurðarstaðir, Sigurðarstaðir, Silfrastaðir, Silfurtún,
, Sjónarhóll, Sjöundastaðir, Skaftafell, Skaftárdalur, Skaftárdalur, Skaftárdalur, Skaftholt, Skagnes, Skagnes, Skallabúðir,
karð, Skarð, Skarð, Skarð, Skarð, Skarð, Skarð, Skarð, Skarð, Skarð, Skarð, Skarð, Skarð, Skarð Dísastaðasel, Skarðaborg,
hóll, Skarfsstaðir, Skatastaðir, Skák, Skákarey, Skál, Skálabrekka, Skálabrekka II, Skálafell, Skálafell, Skálakot, Skálanes,
ısstaðir, Skáldsstaðir, Skáley, Skáleyjar, Skáleyjar, Skálholt, Skálholtsvík, Skálholtsvík, Skálholtsvík, Skálholtsvík, Skáli,
ur, Skárastaðir, Skefilsstaðir, Skeggjabrekka, Skeggjastaðir, Skeggjastaðir, Skeggjastaðir, Skeggjastaðir, Skeggjastaðir,
holt, Skeiðháholt, Skeljavík, Skeljavík, Sker, Skerðingsstaðir, Skerðingsstaðir, Skerðingsstaðir, Skerðingsstaðir, Skinnalón,
kipholt, Skipholt, Skipholt, Skiphylur, Skíðastaðir, Skíðastaðir, Skíðbakki, Skíðbakki 1A, Skíðbakki, Skíðbakki, Skíðsholt,
lfsstaðir, Skjöldólfsstaðir, Skjöldur, Skollagróf, Skoreyjar, Skorhagi, Skorholt, Skorrastaður, Skorrastaður 1A, Skorrastaður,
ógar, Skógar, Skógar, Skógar, Skógarberg, Skógargerði, Skógarhlíð, Skógarhólar, Skógarsel, Skógarsel, Skógarsel, Skóghlíð,
ðuklaustur, Skriðukot, Skriðuland, Skriðuland, Skriðuland, Skriðusel, Skriðustekkur, Skrúður, Skuggabjörg, Skuggabjörg,
ıstaðir, Skútustaðir, Skútustaðir, Skyggnir, Skyggnisholt, Skyttudalur, Skörð, Skörð, Slakki, Sleðbrjótssel, Sleðbrjótssel,
ıstaðir, Slýjar, Smáhamrar, Smáhamrar, Smáragil, Smáragrund, Smárahlíð, Smáratún, Smáratún, Smiðjuhóll, Smiðsgerði,
tartunga, Sneis, Snjallsteinshöfði, Snjallsteinshöfði 1A, Snjallsteinshöfði, Snjóholt, Snorrastaðir, Snorrastaðir, Snorrastaðir,
ıvammur, Snældubeinsstaðir, Snæringsstaðir, Snæringsstaðir, Sogn, Sogn, Sogn, Sólbakki, Sólbakki, Sólbakki, Sólbakki,
ólheimar, Sólheimar, Sólheimar, Sólheimar, Sólheimar, Sólheimar, Sólheimar, Sólheimar, Sólheimar, Sólheimar, Sólheimar,
ómastaðir, Spágilsstaðir, Sperðill, Sperðlahlíð, Spjör, Sporður, Spóastaðir, Spóastaðir, Spónsgerði, Staðarbakki, Staðarbakki,
óll, Staðarhóll, Staðarhólseyjar, Staðarhraun, Staðarhús, Staðarhöfði, Staðarsel, Staðarstaður, Staðartunga, Staður, Staður,
ıley, Stakkaberg, Stakkadalur, Stakkahlíð, Stakkamýri, Stakkanes, Stakkar, Stakkavík, Stakkhamar, Stakkhamrar, Stallar,
ıpastaðir, Steðji, Steðji, Stefánsstaðir, Steig, Steinaborg, Steinadalur, Steinanes, Steinar, Steinar, Steinar, Steinar 2, Steinar,
ıóll, Steinkirkja, Steinkot, Steinmóðarbær, Steinn, Steinnes, Steinnýjarstaðir, Steinsholt, Steinsholt, Steinsholt, Steinsholt,
kholt, Stekkjadalir, Stekkjarból, Stekkjardalur, Stekkjarflatir, Stekkjarflatir, Stekkjarhjáleiga, Stekkjarholt, Stekkjarholt,
ıalækur, Stokkhólmi, Stokkseyri, Stóra-Ármót, Stóra-Ásgeirsá, Stóra-Ávík, Stóra-Borg, Stóra-Borg, Stóra-Borg, Stóra-Borg
óra-Drageyri, Stóra-Fellsöxl, Stóra-Fjall, Stóra-Fjall II, Stóra-Fjarðarhorn, Stórafljót, Stóragerði, Stóra-Gerði, Stóra-Giljá,
Hof, Stóra-Hof, Stóra-Hof, Stóra-Holt, Stóra-Holt, Stóra-Hraun, Stóra-Hvalsá, Stóra-Hvalsá, Stóra-Hvarf, Stóra-Knarrarnes,
ra-Sandfell, Stóra-Sandvík, Stóra-Sandvík, Stóra-Sandvík, Stóra-Sandvík, Stóra-Sandvík 5, Stóra-Sandvík 6, Stóra-Seyla,
ífa, Stóra-Þverá, Stórhóll, Stórhóll, Stórhóll, Stóri-Ás, Stóri-Bakki, Stóri-Botn, Stóri-Dalur, Stóri-Dalur, Stóri-Dalur, Stóri-
alækur, Stóri-Klofi, Stóri-Kroppur, Stóri-Lambhagi, Stóri-Lambhagi, Stóri-Lambhagi, Stóri-Langidalur, Stóri-Laugardalur,
Stórólfsvöllur, Stóru-Akrar, Stóru-Akrar, Stóru-Dalir, Stóru-Hámundarstaðir, Stóru-Laugar, Stóru-Reykir, Stóru-Reykir,
arhöfuð, Strandhöfn, Strandsel, Straumfjarðartunga, Straumfjörður, Straumnes, Straumur, Straumur, Straumur, Straumur,
r, Sturluflöt, Sturluhóll, Sturlureykir, Sturlureykir, Stúfholt, Stúfholt 2 Austurbær, Stærri-Árskógur, Stærri-Bær, Stærri-
, SuðurGötur, Suður-Hvammur, Suðurkot, Suðurkot, Suðurkot, Suðurkot í Vogum, Suður-Mosi, Suður-Nýibær, Suðurreykir,
Sunnuflöt, Sunnuhlíð, Sunnuhlíð, Sunnuhlíð, Sunnuhlíð, Sunnuholt, Sunnuhvoll, Sunnuhvoll, Sunnuhvoll, Sunnuhvoll,
albarðssel, Svalhöfði, Svalvogar, Svanavatn, Svanavatn, Svangrund, Svanshóll, Svansvík, Svarðbæli, Svarfhóll, Svartagil,
bjarnargerði, Sveinseyri, Sveinseyri, Sveinseyri, Sveinshús, Sveinskot, Sveinsstaðir, Sveinsstaðir, Sveinsstaðir, Sveinsstaðir,
ðar, Svignaskarð, Svínabakkar, Svínadalur, Svínadalur, Svínafell, Svínafell, Svínafell 2, Svínafell, Svínafell, Svínanes,
nd, Syðra-Brekkukot, Syðra-Dalsgerði, Syðra-Fell, Syðra-Fjall, Syðra-Fjall, Syðra-Garðshorn, Syðra-Gil, Syðra-Holt, Syðra-
gholt, Syðra-Laugaland, Syðra-Lágafell, Syðra-Lágafell, Syðra-Lón, Syðra-Malland, Syðra-Sel, Syðra-Sel, Syðra-Skógarnes,
óri-Brekka, Syðri-Brekkur, Syðri-Brekkur, Syðri-Brekkur, Syðri-Brennihóll, Syðri-Brú, Syðri-Brúnavellir, Syðri-Bægisá,
ólfsá, Syðri-Hagi, Syðri-Hofdalir, Syðri-Hóll, Syðri-Hóll, Syðri-Hóll, Syðri-Hóll, Syðri-Hóll, Syðri-Hraundalur, Syðri-Húsabakki, Syðri-

Jaðar, Syðri-Kambhóll, Syðri-Kárastaðir, Syðri-Knarrartunga, Syðri-Kvíhólmi, Syðri-Langamýri, Syðri-Leikskálaá, Syðri-M.
Syðri-Reykir, Syðri-Reykir, Syðri-Sandhólar, Syðri-Sauðadalsá, Syðri-Skjaldarvík, Syðri-Skógar, Syðri-Steinsmýri 1–2, S
Varðgjá, Syðri-Vellir, Syðri-Vigdísarstaðir, Syðri-Villingadalur, Syðri-Vík, Syðri-Vík, Syðri-Völlur, Syðri-Völlur, Syðri-Þverá.
Fossar, Syðstu-Garðar, Syðstu-Kárastaðir, Sýrnes, Sæberg, Sæberg, Sæból, Sæból, Sæból, Sæból 2 Grund, Sæból, Sæból
Sævarland, Sævarland, Söðulsholt, Sölkutóft, Sölvabakki, Sölvaholt, Sölvanes, Sörlagarðar, Sörlastaðir, Sörlastaðir, Sörlat
Teigaból, Teigagerði, Teigagerði, Teigakot, Teigar, Teigarhorn, Teigasel, Teigasel, Teigskógar, Teigur, Teigur, Teigur, Te
Tjaldanes, Tjaldanes, Tjaldanes, Tjaldbúðir, Tjaldhólar, Tjaldurseyjar, Tjarnagerði, Tjarnaland, Tjarnarkot, Tjarnarkot, T
Tobbakot, Tobbakot, Torfabær, Torfalækur, Torfalækur, Torfastaðir, Torfastaðir, Torfastaðir, Torfastaðir, Torfastaðir, Torfa
Tókastaðir, Tómasarhagi, Tóveggur, Traðarholt, Traðarkot, Traðir, Traðir, Traðir, Traustholtshólmi, Tréstaðir, Trostansfjö
Tunga, Tunga, Tunga, Tunga, Tunga, Tunga, Tunga 1 Neðri-Tunga, Tunga í Fáskrúðsfirði, Tunga í Firði, Tunga í Valþ
Tunguhlíð, Tunguhlíð, Tungukot, Tungukot, Tungulækur, Tungunes, Tungunes, Tungusel, Tunguvellir, Tún, Tún, Tún
Undirfell, Undirveggur, Undraland, Unhóll, Unhóll 1A, Unhóll, Unnarholt, Unnarholtskot, Unnarholtskot, Unnarsholtsko
Urðarbak, Urðarteigur, Urðir, Urriðaá, Urriðafoss, Urriðakot, Urriðavatn, Urriðavatn, Utanverðunes, Uxahryggur, Uxahryg
Útgarðar, Úthlíð, Úthlíð, Úthlíð, Útibleiksstaðir, Útibær, Útkot, Útnyrðingsstaðir, Útskálahamar, Útstekkur, Útverk, Útvíl
Vaðlar, Vaðnes, Vaðstakksey, Vaglagerði , Grundarkot, Vaglar, Vaglar, Vaglir, Vaglir, Vaglir, Vagnbrekka, Vakursstaðir, Va
Valdastaðir, Valdasteinsstaðir, Valhöll, Vallakot, Vallanes, Vallanes, Vallanes, Vallarhjáleiga, Vallarhjáleiga, Vallarhús, Vall
Valþjófsstaðir III, Valþjófsstaður, Valþjófsstaður, Valþúfa, Vargsnes Naustavík, Varmadalur, Varmadalur 1, Varmagerði, Varma
Vaskárdalur, Vatn, Vatn, Vatnabúðir, Vatnadalur, Vatnagarður, Vatnahjáleiga, Vatnahverfi, Vatnsbakkaheiði, Vatnsdalsgerði,
Vatnsfjarðarsel, Vatnsfjörður, Vatnshamrar, Vatnshlíð, Vatnsholt, Vatnsholt, Vatnsholt, Vatnsholt, Vatnsholt, Vatnshorr
Vatnsskarðshólar, Vatnsskógar, Vattarnes, Vattarnes, Veðramót, Veðramót, Veðramót, Veðramót, Veðramótspartur, Vegatu
Vermundarstaðir, Vestaraland I og III, Vestaraland II, Vestaraland IV, Vestari-Hóll, Vestari-Krókar, Vestra-Fíflholt, Vestra-
Dysjar, Vestri-Garðsauki, Vestri-Grund, Vestri-Leirárgarðar, Vestri-Rauðárhóll, Vestri-Reynir, Vestri-Skógtjörn, Vestri-Tung
Vetleifsholt, Veturhús, Veturhús, Veturliðastaðir, Végeirsstaðir, Vésteinsholt Brautarholt, Viðborð, Viðborðssel, Viðborðsse
Vindás, Vindás, Vindbelgur, Vindfell, Vindheimar, Vindheimar, Vindheimar, Vindhæli, Virkishólasel, Víðar, Víðastaðir, Víð
Víðiholt, Víðihólar, Víðihólmi, Víðiker, Víðilækur, Víðimelur, Víðimýrarsel, Víðimýri, Víðimörk, Víðines, Víðines, Víðines,
Vífilsstaðir, Víganes, Vígholtsstaðir, Víghólsstaðir, Vík, Vík, Vík, Vík, Vík, Vík, Vík, Vík, Víkingavatn, Víkingavatn, Víkingssta
Vogar Innsti-Vogur, Vogar, Vogar, Vogar, Vogar, Vogatunga, Vogsósar, Vogsósar, Vogur, Vogur, Vogur, Vogur, Voladalur, Volas
Votamýri, Votamýri, Votilækur, Votmúli, Votmúli, Vælugerðiskot, Vökuland, Völlur, Völlur, Vörðubrún, Vörðufell, Vörðu
Hænuvík, Ytri-Ingveldarstaðir, Ytri-Klömbur, Ytri-Kóngsbakki, Ytri-Lambadalur, Ytri-Látravík, Ytri-Súluvellir, Ytri-Tindst
Ysti-Hvammur, Ysti-Mór, Ysti-Skáli, Ysti-Skáli 2, Ysti-Skáli, Ystu-Garðar, Ytra-Áland, Ytra-Bjarg, Ytra-Brekkukot, Ytra-Dal
Laugaland, Ytra-Lágafell, Ytra-Leiti, Ytra-Lón, Ytra-Malland, Ytra-Malland, Ytra-Seljaland, Ytra-Skógarnes, Ytra-Skörðugi
Brekkur, Ytri-Brekkur, Ytri-Brennihóll, Ytri-Bugur, Ytri-Bægisá, Ytri-Bægisá, Ytri-Dalbær, Ytri-Ey, Ytri-Garðar, Ytri-Greni
Ytri-Hóll, Ytri-Hóll, Ytri-Hóll, Ytri-Hólmur I, Ytri-Hólmur II, Ytri-Hrafnabjörg, Ytri-Hraundalur, Ytri-Húsabakki, Ytri-Jaða
Melrakkadalur, Ytri-Múli, Ytri-Mælifellsá, Ytri-Neslönd, Ytri-Nípur, Ytri-Ós, Ytri-Rauðimelur, Ytri-Reistará, Ytri-Reykir,
Sólheimar 3A, Ytri-Svartárdalur, Ytri-Tjarnir, Ytri-Tunga, Ytri-Tunga, Ytri-Tunga 1A, Ytri-Urriðaá, Ytri-Valdarás, Ytri-Var
Þambárvellir, Þangskáli, Þaravellir, Þerney, Þernunes, Þernuvík 1, Þiðriksvellir, Þiljuvellir, Þinganes, Þingdalur, Þingey, Þ
Þjóðólfshagi, Þjóðólfshagi, Þjóðólfstunga, Þjórsárholt, Þjórsártún, Þjótandi, Þorbergsstaðir, Þorbjargarstaðir, Þorbjarn
Þorgeirsstaðir, Þorgerðarstaðir, Þorgilsstaðir, Þorgrímsstaðir, Þorgrímsstaðir, Þorgrímsstaðir, Þorkelsgerði, Þorkelsgerði
Runa, Þormóðsdalur, Þormóðsey, Þormóðsholt, Þormóðsstaðir, Þormóðsstaðir II, Þorp, Þorsteinsstaðakot, Þorsteinsstað
Þórðarkot, Þórðarstaðir, Þóreyjarnúpur, Þórisdalur, Þórisholt, Þórisstaðir, Þórisstaðir, Þórisstaðir, Þórisstaðir, Þórisstað
Þórufell, Þórukot, Þórunnarsel, Þórunúpur, Þórunúpur, Þórustaðir, Þrasastaðir, Þrastarhóll, Þrastarlundur, Þrastarlund
Þröm, Þröm, Þuríðarstaðir, Þuríðarstaðir, Þurranes, Þursstaðir, Þúfa, Þúfnavellir, Þúfukot, Þúfur, Þúfur, Þverá, Þverá í H
Þverhamar 1, Gljúfraborg, Þverhamar 2A, Þverhamar 2B, Þverhamar, Þverhamar 4 Holt, Þverhamar 5, Þverholt, Þverlæku
Þúfa, Þúfa, Ægissíða, Ærlækjarsel, Ærlækur, Æsustaðir, Ögmundarstaðir, Ögur, Ögur, Ölduhryggur, Ölfusvatn, Ölkelda, Þ
Öndólfsstaðir, Öndverðarnes, Öndverðarnes, Öndverðarnes, Öngulsstaðir, Önnupartur, Önundarholt, Önundarhorn, Örlygs

Melrakkadalur, Syðri-Mælifellssá, Syðri-Neslönd, Syðri-Rauðalækur, Syðri-Reistará, Syðri-Reykir, Syðri-Reykir, Syðri-Reykir, Syðri-Tjarnir, Syðri-Tunga, Syðri-Tunga, Syðri-Urriðaá, Syðri-Úlfsstaðahjáleiga, Syðri-Úlfsstaðir, Syðri-Valdarás, Syðri-Syðsta-Grund, Syðsta-Mörk, Syðsta-Samtún, Syðsti-Hóll, Syðsti-Hvammur, Syðsti-Kambhóll, Syðsti-Mór, Syðsti-Ós, Syðstu-æla, Sælingsdalstunga, Sælingsdalur, Sænautasel, Sætún, Sæunnarstaðir, Sævarendi, Sævarendi, Sævarendi, Sævarland, nrar, Syðri-Hamrar, Skammidalur 1, Tandrastaðir, Tangaland, Tangi, Tannanes, Tannastaðir, Tannstaðabakki, Tannstaðir, igur, Teigur, Teigur, Teigur, Teygingalækur, Tindar, Tindar, Tindar, Tindrastaðir, Tindstaðir, Tindur, Tindur, Tíðagerði, rnarland, Tjarnir, Tjarnir, Tjarnir, Tjörvastaðir, Tjörn, Tjörn, Tjörn, Tjörn, Tjörn, Tjörn, Tjörn, Tjörn Holtar, Tobbakot, ðir, Torfastaðir, Torfastaðir 5, Torfgarður, Torfmýri, Torfnes, Torfufell, Torfunes, Torfur, Torfustaðir, Torta, Tóarsel, Tóftir, ð, Tröð, Tröð, Tröð, Tröllatunga, Tumabrekka, Tumakot, Tumastaðir, Tunga, Tunga, Tunga, Tunga, Tunga, Tunga, Tunga, agi, Tungufell, Tungufell, Tungufell, Tungufell, Tungufell, Tungugerði, Tungugröf, Tunguháls, Tunguháls, Tunguheiði, insberg, Túnsberg, Tyrðilmýri I og II, Tyrfingsstaðir, Ufsir, Unaðsdalur, Unalækur, Unaós Heyskálar, Unastaðir, Undhóll, psalir, Uppsalir, Uppsalir, Uppsalir, Uppsalir, Uppsalir, Uppsalir, Uppsalir, Uppsalir, Uppsalir, Uppsalir, Uppsalir, Uppsalir, Úlfarsá, Úlfarsfell, Úlfarsfell, Úlfarsfell, Úlfljótsvatn, Úlfsá, Úlfsbær, Úlfsstaðir, Úlfsstaðir, Úlfsstaðir, Úlfsstaðir, Útey, Útey, ar, Vestri-Hellur, Vestri-Loftsstaðir, Vestri-Óttarsstaðir, Vestra-Stafnes, Vað, Vað, Vað, Vaðall, Vaðbrekka, Vaðlakot, Vaðlar, kursstaðir, Valabjörg, Valadalur, Valagerði, Valagil, Valbjarnarvellir, Valbjarnarvellir, Valdalækur, Valdarássel, Valdastaðir, lholt, Vallholt, Vallnatún, Valshamar, Valshamar, Valshamar, Valshamarseyjar, Valstrýta, Valþjófsstaðir I, Valþjófsstaðir II, d, Varmaland, Varmaland, Varmalækur, Varmalækur, Varmalækur II, Varmavatnshólar, Varmidalur, Varmidalur, Varmilækur, , Vatnsdalur, Vatnsdalur, Vatnsendi, Vatnsendi, Vatnsendi, Vatnsendi, Vatnsendi, Vatnsendi, Vatnsendi, Vatnsendi, Vatnsendi, atnshóll, Vatnshóll, Vatnskot, Vatnskot, Vatnskot, Vatnsleysa, Vatnsleysa, Vatnsleysa, Vatnsleysa, Vatnsleysa, Vatnsnes, Veiðileysa, Veiðilækur, Veigastaðir, Veigastaðir, Veisa, Veisusel, Vellir, Vellir, Vellir, Vellir, Vellir, Vellir, Vellir, Vellir, Vellir, -Geldingaholt, Vestra-Miðfell, Vestra-Stokkseyrarsel, Vestra-Stokkseyrarsel, Vestra-Súlunes, Vestra-Þorlaugargerði, Vestri-urbotn, Vesturhlíð, Vesturhlíð, Vesturholt, Vesturholt, Vesturholt, Vesturhópshólar, Vesturkot, Vestur-Meðalholt, Vetleifsholt, ðvík, Viðvík, Vigur, Villingadalur, Villingaholt, Villinganes, Villingavatn, Vilmundarstaðir, Vindás, Vindás, Vindás, Vindás, stunga, Víðidalstunga, Víðidalur, Víðidalur, Víðifell, Víðigerði, Víðigerði, Víðigerði, Víðigerði II, Víðihlíð, Víðihlíð, Víðiholt, , Víðirhóll, Víðivallagerði, Víðivellir, Víðivellir, Víðivellir, Vífilsdalur, Vífilsmýri 1 Ystibær, Vífilsmýri, Vífilsnes, Vífilsstaðir, rbakki, Víkurgerði, Víkurkot, Víkurpartur, Voðmúlastaðamiðhjáleiga, Voðmúlastaðir, Vogalækur, Vogar, Vogar, Vogar, Vogar, olt, Vonarland, Vorsabæjarhjáleiga, Vorsabæjarhóll, Vorsabær, Vorsabær, Vorsabær 1, Vorsabær, Vorsabær, Vorsabær, Vorsalir, n, Ytri-Bálkastaðir, Ytri-Drápuhlíð, Ytra-Einarslón, Ytra-Fagridalur, Ytri-Gröf, Ytri-Hjarðardalur, Ytri-Hjarðardalur, Ytri-rá, Yrjur, Ysta-Bæli, Ystabæliskot, Ystabælistorfa, Ystafell, Ystafell, Ystafell, Ysta-Gerði, Ystagil, Ysta-Kot, Ysta-Vík, Ysti-Hóll, l, Ytra-Fell, Ytra-Fjall, Ytra-Garðshorn, Ytra-Gil, Ytra-Holt, Ytra-Hraun, Ytra-Hvarf, Ytra-Kálfsskinn, Ytra-Krossanes, Ytra-il II, Ytra-Skörðugil III, Ytra-Vallholt, Ytra-Vatn, Ytri-Ánastaðir, Ytri-Ásar, Ytri-Ásláksstaðir, Ytri-Bakki, Ytri-Brekkur, Ytri-lækur, Ytri-Gunnólfsá, Ytri-Gunnólfsá, Ytri-Hagi, Ytri-Hlíð, Ytri-Hlíð, Ytri-Hofdalir, Ytri-Hóll, Ytri-Hóll, Ytri-Hóll, Ytri-Hóll, ðir, Ytri-Kleif, Ytri-Knarrartunga, Ytri-Kot, Ytri-Langamýri, Ytri-Leikskálaá, Ytri-Lyngar, Ytri-Lyngar, Ytri-Másstaðir, Ytri-i, Ytri-Skeljabrekka, Ytri-Skjaldarvík, Ytri-Skógar, Ytri-Skógar, Ytri-Sólheimar, Ytri-Sólheimar 2–4, Ytri-Sólheimar, Ytri-, Ytri-Vigdísarstaðir, Ytri-Villingadalur, Ytri-Víðivellir, Ytri-Víðivellir, Ytri-Vík, Ytri-Þóreyjarnúpur, Ytri-Þurá, Þambárvellir, yrasel, Þingholt, Þinghóll, Þinghóll, Þinghóll, Þingmúli, Þingnes, Þingnes, Þingskálar, Þingvellir, Þingvellir, Þjóðólfshagi, randsstaðir, Þorbrandsstaðir, Þorfinnsstaðir, Þorfinnsstaðir, Þorfinnsstaðir, Þorgautsstaðir, Þorgautsstaðir, Þorgeirsfell, orkelshóll, Þorlákshöfn, Þorláksstaðir, Þorleifskot, Þorleifsstaðir, Þorleifsstaðir, Þorleifsstaðir, Þorljótsstaðir, Þorljótsstaðir, ðir, Þorsteinsstaðir, Þorsteinsstaðir, Þorvaldseyri, Þorvaldsstaðir, Þórarinsstaðir, Þórarinsstaðir, Þórdísarstaðir, Þórðarkot, ðir, Þóroddsstaðir, Þóroddsstaðir, Þóroddsstaðir, Þórormstunga, Þórólfshvoll, Þórólfsstaðir, Þórseyri, Þórsmörk, Þórsnes, r, Þrándarholt, Þrándarholt, Þrándarkot, Þrándarlundur, Þrándarstaðir, Þrándarstaðir, Þríhyrningur, Þrúðardalur, Þröm, Skíðadal, Þverá í Svarfaðardal, Þverárdalur, Þverárkot, Þverárskógur, Þverbrekka, Þverdalur, Þverfell, Þverfell, Þverhamar, vottá, Þvottáreyjar, Þykkvabæjarklaustur, Þykkvibær, Þykkvibær, Þykkvibær, Þyrill, Þæfusteinn, Þönglabakki, Þönglaskáli, ey, Ölvaldsstaðir, Ölvaldsstaðir, Ölvaldsstaðir, Ölversholt, Ölversholt, Ölversholt, Ölversholt, Ölversholtshjáleiga, Ölvisgerði, Ölviskross, lalur, Öskubrekka, Ösp, Öxará, Öxl, Öxnafell, Öxnalækur, Öxney, Öxnhóll.

Can you name anything you have ever eaten in this country that you can link directly to someone special, some person of genius? Where is the Björk of the Icelandic farming community? The Magnus Magnusson of the mutton hotpot, or the Eidur Gudjohnsen of the smoked leg of lamb? Ask yourself, What is the most famous farm in Iceland? There are lots to choose from, lots whose names are familiar. But it is generally a historical fame, the home of some hero in a saga, or the site of a famous battle, or a centre of learning from long ago – Hlíðarendi, Flugumýri, Oddi.

Farm names around the country – most of them anyway – do not mean very much to a modern-day Icelander unless they are associated in his mind with some story from the past, or a famous writer, or his own family origins. You drive along the national ring road and shoot past farm after farm, through district after district whose very existence is founded entirely on the production of food, and food never enters your mind. From along that road comes some of the finest food in the world. So why do you never find your mouth watering? Think of Pavlov's dogs and conditioned reflexes. Pavlov rang a bell when the dogs were fed. In the end they started salivating just at the sound of the bell. So how come we don't slaver ourselves half our way round the country? You drive through the southern lowlands, up through the north of the country, the west, out along Snæfellsnes. Every 500 metres you hurtle past a sign with the name of a farm on it, but for some reason none of them has any resonance, none of them means a thing. The names flash past, wonderful, poetic and strange: Syðri-Núpur, Granastaðir, Grenjaðarstaðir, Skjöldólfsstaðir. Not a trickle of saliva anywhere…

How come we don't say as we drive past Rauðinúpur on Melrakkaslétta, about as far north as you can get in Iceland, just below the Arctic Circle, 'Do you remember that lamb we had for Christmas 2001?' Why is there nowhere that we long to knock at the door and give someone a big hug in the farmyard to say thank you for the food? Why do we never fall in love with some farmer, some farm or district just for the food they produce? Why don't we refuse to use any butter except Sveinbjörn of Hvoll's to cook our lobster in, even if it costs fifty dollars a kilo and no one else can taste any difference? Or on special occasions treat ourselves to a glass of milk that costs as much as red wine because the cow that produced it grazes alternate days on sea grasses and marshland and has its fodder mixed with Iceland moss or some other special ingredient that the farmer has persuaded me improves my quality of life, is even the key to longevity?

The media present us with endless stories of the problems of rural Iceland – depopulation, decay, hopelessness manifesting itself in a variety of ways. 'Should we be paying to keep these people going?' asks one. 'Do you want to turn our country into a wasteland?' says another. 'Will no one come and save us?' says a third. Given the circumstances, there are many who just resign themselves to the whims and authority of the politicians. Government attempts to create jobs have as often as not been half-apologetic and of little apparent relevance to what the people of the country do best. 'In some restaurant over in France, my meat is the most expensive thing on the menu.'

At one time we heard a lot of grumbling about competition from factory farms churning out cheap pork and chicken meat. So the question is worth asking, What is lamb? A lamb is a summer on the moors of Arnarvatnsheiði, buttercups and forget-me-nots, the trill of the plover and the rasp of the snipe, the babbling brook and the midnight sun. And what is pork? Pork is the stench of farts and claustrophobia, three months in a cramped sty, swill and alienation. If you were a cannibal, which would you rather eat, a lean mountain guide or a lifer from Alcatraz? How much ought the difference to be reflected in króna per kilo?

Pork is excellent in its way, but there is obviously no real comparison. It is almost like saying the ptarmigan is in competition with the chicken. An extreme example? The ptarmigan lives in the same surroundings as the lamb, and much the same length of time if it gets shot in its first autumn. The chicken lives in the

CONTENTED COWS MAKE CREAMY MILK FOR HAPPY CUSTOMERS

RAUÐINÚPUR

FARM — MELRAKKASLETTA

SINCE 2006

A Self-Help Manual for a Frightened Nation

same conditions as the pig. One Icelandic summer – how does that compare for value to three months in a battery cage?

When I go to the shop and buy a saddle of lamb, I do not get the name of the farmer that raised it or the name of the farm it came from. No farms or farmers appear on the label. No names are used for branding. Not even the part of the country where the lamb frolicked its summer on the heath. I cannot buy an 1100-year-old tradition or a millennium of human habitation in some place, no round-ups or sheep pens or lambing sheds. I can't invite my guests for a taste of Njáll's Country, to lamb that chewed the flowers where Gunnar slew his ambushers at the bloody battle of Knafahólar, or that spent its life under the rocks of Hraundrangar where our national poet Jónas Hallgrímsson walked with staff in hand and knapsack on his back. I feel no overwhelming urge to read my guests his Homecoming as they tuck into their meat soup. Possibly some kind of advertising image springs up in your mind – 'Natural Goodness' or the like – but images like these are used equally for selling washing powders, Chevrolet TrailBlazers and exterior house paint: the word nature doesn't mean a thing any more.

No. This is more like the way it goes. You drive to the supermarket and pick out a pink saddle of lamb from a heap lying in a freezer cabinet and sealed in thick polythene wrapping marked with the logo of some agricultural co-operative. On the label are the words 'Saddle of lamb in bag'. A bored teenager runs it through the barcode reader at the checkout. You go home and cook it or dump it in the deepfreeze and forget about it for the next two years. The lamb may be excellent, but nothing of where it came from comes with it to the dining table – no labelling, no picture of a mountain, farm, person or culture – and as a result we lose valuable lines of contact, opportunities to have for once a trace of transparency in our lives, a slender thread connecting one person to another. A farm as a brand name maybe smacks of market orientation, the cheap sell. But brand names are central to the development of specialism and cuisine. Most of us recognize the difference between Coke and Pepsi, Diet Coke and Pepsi Max, but no one recognizes the difference between lamb from the Westfjords and lamb from the Eastfjords, between mountain lamb and valley lamb, inland lamb and shoreline lamb.

Andri Snær Magnason

If we had a similar system for writers, people would go to the shop and buy themselves a pound of text. The reader would never know where the text originally came from or the name of any of the authors. If a writer wanted to produce and sell more than a thousand copies he would have to buy some quota from another writer with excess to spare.

Words like 'market' and 'marketing' and 'promotion' may be banal, but they spring from the human compulsion to endow things with significance and create values from things that maybe have no inherent value of their own. Do you throw out that old vase because it is so tacky? Or do you put it up for auction and get ten thousand dollars for it? It can be a very fine line between the two. It depends entirely on the significance a person ascribes to the thing and the significance society ascribes to it. Significance lies in the eye of the beholder and is a fundamental property of human thinking. Man is ready to wage war and lay down his life for mere significances, perceived meanings, of no tangible value to anyone.

I have taken the kids to the round-up and stood about awkwardly, gawped like an idiot and tried not to get in the way, forgetting that we are part of the context. The round-up is there because of us. Nobody came over to us and said, 'What do you think of this one then? She's out of Lucky from Ljótsstaðir, spent the whole summer up under the crags at Hrólfsskálaklettur. You'll get the saddle by home delivery straight from the slaughterhouse. I'll keep the leg back and smoke it for you for Christmas dinner in the traditional way. I'll send you an email after lambing and you can order one for autumn. You'll have to pay before the sheep go up to the mountains, demand's been so great. I can't afford to let the sheep get too many or else they start going too far up onto the moors.'

If the meat is good a link has been forged and customers will may make a detour next summer for the sole purpose of camping in the valley and getting an extra leg for the barbecue, so long as everything hasn't been sold out already. And in the end the Christmas lamb has become something more than just the cheapest offer at the supermarket; it has become part of your summer holiday, or an autumn break or a trip out in spring at lambing. The meat acquires a context and significance that up till now has been denied to us. So is the lamb a mark of our alienation, or have we finally brought ourselves into contact with reality?

When whole regions of the country are viewed only in terms of raw-material prices and cost of living, economic efficiency can steamroller its way across the stage and say, 'We need to shut down here, merge there, lay this man off and reduce labour costs, preferably by bringing in people from poorer countries abroad.' Economic efficiency is technical and measurable, but it has no creative eye for the potential, significance or value of things or the ways in which people's perceptions and thinking may change. It would never occur to economic efficiency to double the value of lamb by selling people walking holidays, round-ups, the mountains, the name of the farm, the poet and the beauty – and the fact that what we have here is a small family farm producing tiny quantities of premium meat at very high prices in a thousand-year-old tradition. Economic efficiency would never consider the possibility of marketing meat by earmark – 'slit front right' and the like. A few tons of prime Icelandic lamb could pave the way for a restaurant, for winter breaks, walks, horse-riding, hotel accommodation and computerization. The product could become the major attraction of the countryside, and the highest farm in the valley with its stony meadows and barren slopes would cease to be the least economically viable unit, remote from the beaten track, and become the most valuable, the closest to the moors and mountains, in demand as a place to stay and visit. Tens of thousands of us drive the ring road - past rivers teeming with trout, farms producing succulent lamb and creamy milk, ports where they land some of the freshest fish in the world - and all you can get the whole way is hamburgers.

Economic efficiency claims to be scientific only by ignoring factors that have yet to acquire an image or special status, and are consequently seen as having no value. Economic efficiency measures the underexploitation of production potential, a machine working at half capacity, but it does not measure 'underexploitation of image potential'. The Icelandic countryside is very high on 'image capital' that is there to be realized and put to work, but which it is equally possible to rationalize so thoroughly that nothing remains to be used.

Andri Snær Magnason

My country grandmother from the far northeast once told me that thirty years ago Rauðinúpur on Melrakkaslétta made the best butter in Iceland. People fought over this butter at the co-op in Kópasker. On one occasion she struck lucky: there on the shelf was butter marked Rauðinúpur. She was just about to grab it when the shop assistant stopped her and told her she couldn't have it. It was reserved. She had to make do with butter from another farm that was famous for its rancid taste and the loose hairs that had to be pulled out of it. The price was the same: the farmer from Rauðinúpur got no reward for being best, and this created problems for the co-op. In the end the matter was resolved once and for all by stopping the labelling of butter from Rauðinúpur specially and putting everything in the same packaging. No butter is produced at Rauðinúpur nowadays. A long tradition was broken and presumably the knowledge died along with the people who had made the butter. It doesn't make much sense producing milk at the extreme edge of the habitable world, but butter and cheese are another matter. Extravagantly priced organic arctic butter for export to the most expensive restaurants in the world? It might just work. Rauðinúpur rates very high on image capital: the shore, the ocean, driftwood, volcanic craters, bird cliffs, puffins, arctic terns and gannet colonies, Arctic Circle, midnight sun and northern lights, and the birthplace of our first real novelist Jón Trausti.

A no-risk institutionalization has resulted in the loss of all kinds of special peculiarities and individualities, all kinds of potentials, without new ones coming up to fill their place. A myriad of ideas and opportunities that might have clustered around these peculiarities have withered on the vine. Lovely ancient place names that might have been turned into valuable brand names have been mercilessly wiped off the map in the name of administrative efficiency and replaced by sesquipedalian monstrosities. This urge to smother diversity extends to the most unbelievable areas, local traditions, quirks and customs. Regional, local, family or individual peculiarities have been blotted out. At a market in Toronto in Canada I saw some sheep cheese which cost 50 Canadian dollars for 100 grams. That is 500 dollars a kilo. Half a million dollars a ton.

God only knows what wonderful idiosyncrasies, what bits of local colour have died out, and with them the potential for all sorts of new jobs and industries. How did cheese from Skaftafell in the south differ from cheese from Strandir in the northwest? Maybe one of them was green and looked full of mould. Come to think of it, it was precisely that that made the 500-dollar cheese in Canada so expensive. Sheep were milked for a thousand years and sheep curds – *skyr* – was one of the staples of our national diet. They make it out of cow's milk nowadays. Sheep skyr? There's maybe jobs in that. But how many of us nowadays know that such a thing ever existed?

The problem is, the rules have got so complicated you need to be a lawyer to work out what you can do and what you can't. It's generally simplest to assume the latter. So people have their self-evident human right to sell their meat and their milk taken away from them under the pretext of protecting public health. If you go on a farmhouse holiday today the milk on your cornflakes comes out of a packet, and you get vacuum-wrapped slices of smoked lamb from a big food-processing co-op and processed cheese on blotting paper factory bread, devoid of any connection with the lambs bleating out there on the mountain or the cows lowing in the farmyard. As things stand, farmers are permitted to slaughter meat for their own use and to feed it to their children. They can invite friends round to dinner to eat it. But they can't sell it. They can milk by hand from the teat straight into their own children's mouths but not into tourists. A huge part of their lives has been straitjacketed within narrow definitions and predetermined roles. Knowledge from one area is easy to adapt to others and countless jobs that might have been created in this way have been lost through the constraints and the bureaucracy. A farmer with a customer list for his meat or vegetables and a boy around the house up to maintaining a high-spec website could transform himself into something quite new, given the kind of changed world we now live in. Even a bone-idle computer nerd with an allergy to grass, farm animals and work could act as the seed for a new enterprise that would be of more value than the farm itself.

An idea does not need to be complicated: it can simply be an adaptation from one existing setting to another. Maybe it is enough simply to translate the Parma district of Italy or the wine-growing regions of France and California into Icelandic. But the rules are so complicated and the red tape so convoluted that almost any idea is bound to get strangled within them.

With the rural communities of this country deprived of the right to create identity – the power to create value for their products, environment and lifestyle – their connection with the people who buy and eat their meat has been ruptured and the rift between town and country grows ever deeper. The city expands and its inhabitants service service companies, produce packaging, run advertising agencies, while the country remains stuck in its hidebound reality. Machines and technical advances have made human hands obsolete, but having one's hands free does not mean that our countryfolk can spend their time developing goods or packaging, producing finished products, improving links with consumers, or turning to something quite different entirely. In the closed system we have today there is simply no need for any new people in the country. The city sucks away its strength and the country shrinks in on itself. The state attempts to divert money and employment to rural areas through 'job creation schemes' aimed at making up for the damage done by technological progress. So we set up a tree farm and dream of future victories against the fir forests of Lithuania and of exporting timber to Canada and Finland by the year 2060.

Last summer I heard an interview with a member of our new breed of Icelandic lumberjacks. They had just started cutting down the first trees on a tree farm. 'How's it going?' asked the interviewer. 'Fine,' said the man, 'only we've got a problem with the produce.' 'What do you mostly do?' asked the interviewer. 'We were doing fence posts in quite a big way but now you can get them cheaper from abroad.' 'So what then?' 'Now it's mostly woodchip,' said the man. 'And what do you do with the woodchip?' 'The government buys it and uses it for forest trails.'

There is a strong tendency in people to identify with physical labour as it used to be, the workshop, the factory, and all the things that were seen as 'proper work', and as a consequence to undervalue the kinds of jobs that have emerged in recent decades: jobs founded on specialist knowledge in areas like travel and tourism, marketing, food sciences and cookery, salesmanship, nature and the environment, history and languages. This isn't true in all cases, but a recent survey by the Icelandic Institute for Regional Research in Akureyri seems to indicate that community spirit in the rural areas of Iceland is generally lower than in towns. Farmers appear to take the most negative view of innovation of any class in society, seeing it as largely irrelevant to their own lives and conditions. 'This way of thinking creates the danger that

Source:
Elín Aradóttir and
Kjartan Ólafsson (2004):
*Community spirit and
innovation: research
into selected rural areas,*
Institute for Regional
Research: Akureyri,
p. 115.

49.

agriculture and those working in it will fall out of step with trends in national working life and national outlook, that the sector will stagnate and those involved in it become a kind of marginal group with little opportunity to influence outside events.'

A child from the town can decide to become a doctor, an accountant, a cell biologist or a nuclear scientist, but it is as if people have to be born farmers. Farming is not like any other profession but a hereditary condition. If you can't go into the cowshed and put a name to every single implement you see there, however ancient, and every part of a cow's anatomy from its tail to its horns, that is something to be ashamed of. 'No, sorry, you're clearly not born to be a farmer.' A town dweller can live wherever he likes in the world. But if a farmer moves he's abandoning his farm, abdicating responsibility, denying his heritage.

To most Icelanders, the countryside is nothing more than an expensive and inefficient way of producing a few, specified raw materials. Perhaps it is a leftover from the way we were taught geography in school – Sweden produces iron ore, Argentina produces beef. Or maybe something we inherited from our Danish colonial masters, who saw Iceland as a source of cheap raw materials for their home market. But it is worth considering just how deep this preoccupation with raw materials runs in our thinking, how much influence it has had on the politics of Iceland over the years, whether the catchphrase of the day – 'We want an aluminium plant' – isn't a consequence of this way of thinking. The same man who saw no future for the farming communities of the country went on to speak in so many words of the number of 'impoverished farmers' living within a radius of such-and-such of a proposed aluminium works. Simple jobs in a factory would be ideally suited to people like this.

A fair exchange, variety of work and a first-hand intimacy with local conditions and animal husbandry in a beautiful landscape, for the mechanical routine of factory labour? Or polar opposites? Why on earth should anyone want an aluminium plant? Are these factories under some huge pressure to keep up with an insatiable demand for loft ladders and microscooters? Is there a shortage of cans to fill with Coke? No, it isn't that. We just want an aluminium plant – simple. We want to work. We can't live on image. You don't get any added value from an aluminium plant by saying that its aluminium happened to be produced in a fjord of outstanding natural beauty, or that the valley where Hrafnkell the Priest rose to power and fell from grace was drowned out of existence for the express purpose of producing it.

There are a vast number of people around the world who want to eat meat but have concerns about how it is produced – contamination, the use of drugs and growth hormones, and animal welfare in ever more intensive factory farms. This is a major subject for debate in many countries. Many people consider it a senseless misuse of nutrition to be running corn through animals rather than eating it directly, people who see the animal as an un-necessary middleman. A lamb converts grass into meat, a cow converts grass into meat and milk. A necessary process. Ridiculous? No more ridiculous than much else we read and hear. If people find themselves losing out to competi-tion from 'profitability', giant factory farms, what should they do? Should they set out to increase their 'profitability'? Or should they throw in their lot with those concerned about factory farming and the mechanistic misuse of ani-mals and trade on the fact that their animals are names and not just numbers? If 'profitability' is the only criterion, all we need do is set up a couple of giant cowsheds for the whole country, with a hundred workmen, a factory manager and a technician, and that should see to the entire protein production of the Icelandic countryside. That's if people aren't willing to make do with a hun-dred kilos of fishmeal.

Freed from the suffocating systematization, the countryside would have every chance of becoming a prime attraction for tourism in its own right, up there with the highlands and Gullfoss and Geysir. Picture in your own mind the popularity of signposted walks from farm to farm, from valley to valley, up and over the mountains, with the prospect of a hearty meal at the next farm to draw you forward.

Changes in the law now allow people to process and sell their own pro-duce. But it seems that most people regard this as a 'fluffy extra' rather than as something that might lie at the heart of the future of the countryside. There are ideas in the air – every day throws up new ones – that make whole para-graphs of what I am writing obsolete. But even so it is the old familiar refrain we hear most often: 'Can we justify the cost of preserving this?' ask the sharp young men in suits from Reykjavík. 'Are you just going to abandon us?' ask the countryfolk.

This little exercise in ideas is of course far removed from reality. Without doubt it is irrational and uneconomic when viewed through the eyes of a mechanistic system of strategic planning that would stack the entire nation neatly into a single tall block of flats. On each floor there would be a number of dwelling units, 85 sq ft, with blue or pink overalls, one size fits all. In each sty there could be three taps: hot water, cold water and a nozzle for milk mixed with fishmeal. And on the roof there would be an illuminated beacon:

HERE IS
REALITY
NO MORE, NO LESS

Integrating happiness

Some of my best friends are economists. As part of their training, their brains get completely reprogrammed. The Christian values and childhood beliefs and everything they were taught when they were young as being right and true are removed and replaced by a new understanding of the laws of the universe. Their sense of justice and understanding of life are transformed into something completely new and unrecognizable. Simultaneously, they acquire a fluency in all the words that bombard us every day from the financial markets, many of them brand spanking new in the language – beyond me to name them all – and it is amazing to see how much use they get out of their new terminological armoury in their everyday lives.

When I ask, 'How was it at the club?' they tell me there are diminishing marginal benefits from going to the club. In human language, what 'diminishing marginal benefits' appears to mean here is that the more often they go to the club the less fun they have. One of them says he happened to find himself in Café Reykjavík the other day and another says, 'Café Reykjavík represents a convergence of *adverse selection* on the matrimonial market.' Except it sounds better in plain language: 'dregchoice' has a certain something that 'adverse selection' rather lacks.

So I was sitting in a coffee bar the other day with some friends and the conversation turned to happiness. And one of them says, 'Sometimes I wish I could *integrate* happiness.' This was lost on me. It's been a long time since I was integrating functions in maths classes back in school. But I could see that the others around the table understood perfectly what he was on about and a light came on in every window of their souls – 'integrating happiness'. I felt a moment's envy: 'integration', a word redolent of wholeness, completeness, beauty.

Behind this simple word, which I didn't understand, lay a deep store of experience accumulated in their minds; the word existed against a background of calculations, theorems, graphs, bar charts and the years that had gone into learning how to integrate and then applying the method to real examples in the real world. Finally, once they understood the word inside out, once they'd got the deep structure of their learning taped, then as if by magic their learning became inextricably merged with their emotional beings. The term broke out of its isolation in the brain and in metaphorical fashion linked itself with the most beautiful word in the heart, and a new concept came into being: integrating happiness.

So I was full of optimism for the future of the language, until I went to a bewildering confirmation party that shattered my complacency. It was a fairly big gathering, with several generations of the family come together. An Icelandic confirmation: a formal social rite of passage, best clothes, an overdose of coffee and cakes, skis and MP3 players to persuade the new young adult of the benefits of going through with it, and an absolute minimum of religion. The conversation is generally pretty lively when the family gets together and I was looking forward to it. But when it came to actually communicating one with another, things started to get complicated.

My uncle had been working for a bank that had been privatized and then merged with a bigger bank that had then been taken over by a third bank. As a result he had been working for four different employers in the last three years. He had just got himself a new job with the Bank of Iceland, but now it was changing its name to Glitnir, and there were rumours that it was about to be taken over by the bank he had been working for in the first place. He told us he was thinking of buying a summer cottage in the country, in the Westfjords. After many hours of deliberation, a government committee had come up with a proposal for local administration boundary changes, under which this part of the country would be merged with the three adjacent counties. All four of them would now go under a single name – 'Vesturbyggð', the Western Settlement. Trouble is, Vesturbyggð means something to Icelanders with any interest in history, and a lot of Icelanders have an interest in history. Vesturbyggð was one of the medieval Viking settlements in Greenland. So here the conversation ended, not quite sure whether uncle wasn't buying his house in a part of Greenland that had been abandoned to the Inuit some time in the fourteenth century.

Andri Snær Magnason

I have an aunt who is a nurse, and who under normal circumstances can be relied on to say something worth listening to on the subjects of life, death, God and the health service. But now she wasn't even sure where she worked any more. The City Hospital had just joined up with the National Hospital to become the National University Hospital, leaving them with two buildings at different sites bearing the same name. But people still use the old names, and so does my aunt when she wants people to understand where she works or where they are supposed to go for treatment. And this was enough to keep the conversation occupied for another half an hour.

Then, like a true Icelander, my mother mentioned the weather. Only the conversation never actually got as far as the weather. The Icelandic Meteorological Office had just changed the gradings for wind speeds from the traditional Beaufort scale, force 1 to 12, over to metres per second. In the old currency, when there was a force 8 on its way, that meant something nasty. Now it's just a stiff breeze.

Those with some opinion they wanted to express on the future of the world ran up against the family pedant, who was set on arguing the toss over whether the new century had begun in the year 2000 or 2001. When the conversation turned to stocks and shares, things appeared to sort themselves out, until it became perfectly clear that no one understood a word of what anyone else was saying. I watched on as a highly intelligent relative of mine reeled off verbatim a whole paragraph I had read the week before in the business section of the newspaper. He was clearly trying to make the best of a bad job; it wasn't something he'd thought up himself, just something he'd learned off pat.

The 13-year-old at the centre of the festivities finally decided he'd had enough of this palaver and attempted to steer the conversation towards something more interesting. In his innocence he asked, 'Dad, where did you and mum first meet?' A far-off glint appeared in the father's eyes as his mind turned back through the years. 'Yes, I was with a group of friends and we went to Óðal down in town. Your mum used to go there a lot. A great dancer, she was.' The teenager blushed crimson. 'What? Mum used to dance at Óðal!?' Generation misunderstanding. Did dad honestly not realize that what he remembered as a popular disco was now the most infamous strip joint in the country? The new member of the Church of Iceland stormed out and locked himself in his room. And that, more or less, was the end of the party.

I thought about this on the way home. Hadn't things come to a pretty pass when my mother couldn't even talk intelligently about the weather? I found my brain whirring with conspiracy theories. In whose interests could it be to obfuscate everything we talk about these days, so that the conversation remains permanently marooned on the surface? What were the forces behind all this? What kinds of things was it NOT possible to talk about while we were all tangled up in the basic terms and concepts?

Things have not improved since. When the new prime minister took office, the first thing he did was to change one of the central figures engraved on the minds of all Icelanders. He sent a crew of scientists up to the top of Iceland's highest mountain, Hvannadalshnjúkur in the Vatnajökull ice cap, to verify its precise height. According to the new measurement, Iceland's highest peak has shrunk from 2119 metres down to… I forget what. I don't know how high it is anymore. A fixed point in the life of the nation now calls for a whole discussion on surveying techniques and mountain elevations. The new height has no bearing on any fundamental issue, involves no scientific revolution, no change in our way of thinking. But the next time mountains turn up in conversation, all the talk will no doubt get sucked down into this plughole of the prime minister's creation: the debate over the height of Hvannadalshnjúkur.

But possibly this cuts rather deeper. For a large part of the population, Icelandic elementary-school education revolved precisely around consigning to memory figures like 2119. The height of Hvannadalshnjúkur was used as an index to measure children's intelligence. Those who managed to consign to memory the figure 2119 demonstrated that they had the ability to become a doctor or a lawyer when they grew up. Óli from the remedial class wrote 2112 in an exam and failed and finished up in the gutter. It's an uncomfortable thought, seen this way. Maybe Óli was right all along. Maybe he could have made it after all?

I considered how much this might be a conscious matter. In whose benefit was it to cut adrift our reference points so that we couldn't talk to each other any more? I can't talk about kids in school without having to specify that 7th grade is actually called 8th grade and that year 9 is really year 10, i.e. the year you take your public examinations as was. Can it be an intentional ploy? Is it as simple as that? Do you just have to change a few placenames, undermine the concepts, do away with old words and replace them with specialized

Andri Snær Magnason

technical terms, and then fill the media with 'scandal of the week' and 'breaking news', and you can keep people eternally trapped on the surface and so irrevocably cut off from the heart of things?

Instead of standing with their feet planted foursquare in life and society and passing on their wisdom and experience to others, our oldest generation is in a state of disorientation and confusion. What do old people do? They listen to the weather forecast. They listen to the news. They come from somewhere out in the country. They go into hospital. And then all of a sudden the place they grew up in is called something completely different from what it was called for a thousand years and you can't find it in the phone book any more. You don't know which National Hospital you're supposed to be going to, because now there are three of them. The weatherman says it's too windy to go outside, terrifying figures inundate us daily, 12-14 metres a second. A force-12 wind? Isn't that a hurricane? The country is lying under a deep depression with a name worse than millibars – hectopascals, was it? They sound scary. Do words matter? Why not go the whole hog and merge Reykjavík's three biggest suburbs, Árbær, Breiðholt and Kópavogur, and call it Kóparholtabær? Then we'd all be lost and never find our way anywhere any more.

I turned on the radio to try and make sense of the world and got the FM 957 jingle, followed by:

> Woman's voice: The planet is yours to inherit.
> Old man: ...we're all going to hell in a handcart...
> Woman: You will guide mankind into a new age.
> Old man: ...global warming, pollution, destruction of vegetation, droughts, floods, hunger, war...
> Woman: Ha ha ha ha ha ha, but don't let's worry about that for now! Enjoy the present while it's here...
> Old man: ...while it's here...
> Woman: ... with your favourite music station, FM 957...

The guiding principle of the new generation seemed to be a kind of Descartes in reverse: I don't think, therefore I am. After the jingle and the intro came tittle-tattle. Grown-up men of thirty phoned in with salacious comments about Jennifer Lopez, without a trace of shame. The world of Hello and the gossip mags. The future is later, the past never was. In the news there was something about scientists removing a tumour with sound waves. If we the brain is a tumour, the FM 957 jingle was probably the cure.

The now is the new eternity, without history, without direction. So far as I recall, most former generations have grown up with some kind of aim in life. The only real semblance of any aim that cropped up on FM 957, any future to look forward to, came in the title of a book, *How can Iceland become the richest country on earth?* But countries do not have a will, a purpose; it is individuals that have will. Each individual has to set their own aim: how can I become the richest person in the family... in the neighbourhood... in my circle of friends?

Whole generations looked forward to the utopian year 2000 as their symbol of the future, and now we no longer have a date to hang our imaginations and long-term goals on. The future was eight years ago. If my daughter lives to be as old as my grandfather, she will still be alive in the year 2093. The date is unimaginable.

In George Orwell's novel *1984* the totalitarian authorities create a new language called Newspeak. The purpose of Newspeak is to limit vocabulary, and with it thought. The idea is that once Newspeak has established itself thoughtcrime, as it is called, will become impossible because the words on which subversive ideas are founded will have been eradicated. I spent a whole day listening to the radio, tuning my ear to the words people were using: great, cool, fun, amazing, crazy, wicked. The morning program was really cool, mid-day was just great, and the afternoon was amazing. Everyone they interviewed got sucked into some kind of compulsive funfest. Nothing specially new in that, but it made me wonder whether there might be some conscious power out there that was trying to eliminate the possibility of not being constantly cheerful. When Gallup phones round to work out the happiest country in the world the answer comes back automatically: Mum died the other day but apart from that things are just great. The audience was mostly youngsters and among them there was no possibility of assembling a glossary of human mentality except from a wafer-thin range on the scale of cheerfulness. There was no kind of previously prepared or articulated thought, no words for adolescent feelings or emotions, love and its pains, loneliness, loss and regret, happiness and hopes, no vocabulary that touched on science, literature, ideals, the world and its beliefs and religions – in fact anything that really matters or gives some pointer to possible directions in life. Was someone genuinely set on wiping out the possibility of not being cheerful?

I'm not sure what effect this has – you can't of course lay the language solely at the door of the media – but I saw a report that said that young boys had almost entirely stopped reading books and newspapers. I met a teacher who told me he was getting more and more boys who could only read a hundred words a minute. Not so long ago that would have been classed as educationally subnormal. Then I read some research that showed that most young boys have little or no contact with any generations other than their own. I read another piece of research that found that mathematical skills were considerably lower among boys than girls, in part because they have problems understanding and interpreting complex texts. I was speaking to a teacher who reckoned he was fairly in touch with contemporary language and was convinced we might be on the verge of total breakdown: a large part of his class did not understand the most basic words and concepts he used. And then I heard a spokesman for increased efficiency who was advocating cutting Icelandic teaching by a third. I wondered whether the language might be being emptied out from the inside, whether there might be some internal process going on within the language. Hollywood English provides us nothing to build on, and so all we'd be left with would be a kind of verbal dysphasia. I was listening to a youngster trying to describe a particular incident to his friends. He was groping around for words and came up empty handed, and just started flapping his arms about and spluttering. The language cycle is faster than it used to be. The language no longer spans ninety years, with the oldest teaching the youngest; nowadays the generations grow up more or less on their own. The egg is teaching the egg.

I remember listening to an old tape. A woman born in 1888 was reciting some verses she said she'd got from her grandmother who had been born in 1835, who had learned them from her grandmother who had been born in 1787, who had presumably learned them from her grandmother. The recording was made in 1969. The cycle spanned almost 250 years. Multiply that by four and you have the entire history of Iceland from the days of the first settlers. Four old women capable of spanning the thousand-year history of Icelandic in its entirety.

The Icelandic language is more than just old verses and sagas. Someone who knows Arabic or Swedish has obviously spent time mixing with and talking to Arabs or Swedes. Someone who knows the term 'adverse selection' has studied economics. Language is not a frilly extra, a question of right or wrong usage: language is first and foremost the means by which we communicate with each other, a channel for our memories, experiences and values; it is the tool we use to judge our surroundings and world we live in. Someone who does not understand the words and concepts the oldest generation uses has presumably been cut off from contact with that generation. If a word has fallen out of currency the chances are that knowledge, values, experience and memories have been lost along with it. If a teacher finds himself faced with a group of students who don't recognize words that used to be a part of everyday speech, there has plainly been a failure of contact and communication. What happens if a whole word, and consequently a whole meaning, disappears from the language? You get people waving their arms about with a look of bewilderment on their face. 'It's amazingly, you know, er, I mean, it's sort of... you know...'

People don't complain. This doesn't appear to have any effect on company performance, at least, not for the time being. I don't know if there's a word to describe the incremental decrease in literacy and articulacy as national income increases. As broadband connections shoot up past 8 Mb a second the brain is taking in fewer words through the optic nerve than the average brain did in 1970. Perhaps we need a word so that people can talk about this. We can always make one up. We Icelanders are good at that. Textual overload? Digilliteracy? Hyperdictability?

There's no way of knowing whether these new Icelandic words for diminishing marginal benefits or adverse selection are here to stay in the language. I had a friend once who was doing business studies and claimed to be suffering from chronic attacks of idioticum tremens. To meet international competition, business studies was taught in English. Not distinguished Oxford English, mind you, nor erudite Harvard English, nor even hard-bitten Texas English, but a kind of mongrel international English in which a teacher brought up in the outer suburbs of Reykjavík drip-fed the material into slavering young Icelanders with wet dreams of making it big on the international markets. All very efficient, but culturally stripped bare and utterly devoid of flavour and character.

Education is an investment. Man is a machine. The material is the soul.

--- --- ---

In George Orwell's *1984*, wherever you turned there were the slogans:

WAR IS PEACE
FREEDOM IS SLAVERY
IGNORANCE IS STRENGTH

A lot of people have seen 'War is peace' as a rather contrived and obvious contradiction in terms. During the Iraq War there was a big banner stretched over the president's head proclaiming 'War for Peace'. Words matter. The words make all the difference. You hear the words 'Icelandic Peace Corps' and it conjures up an image of a scout troop with guns. And indeed, it started off as a group of doctors and nurses working under the UN in troubled parts of the world. But then it all got more masculine and you got people exercising marching in step and doing target practice with pistols and machine guns, firing at cardboard cut-outs of human figures. You see films of them driving about in armoured Land Cruisers with guns cocked. It is probably only a matter of time before somebody gets killed in the name of the Icelandic Peace Corps. Doubtless in self-defence, but dead nonetheless. But the name makes all the difference: a peace corps is not an *army*. War is peace. The foreign media regularly refer to them as 'Icelandic troops'. The smallest army in the world. Something for us to be proud of. Newspeak from the top of the scale down to the bottom.

Words exist so we can break the world down into precise and manageable units and so understand it. But words can also be neglected and lost, leaving it impossible to be anything other than happy happy happy. Words distinguish tones and colours. Words distinguish sizes. Words distinguish the fundamental elements of our surroundings. But what happens when the words we have lose their power to make the distinctions we need? Is it ridiculous to imagine such a thing?

Andri Snær Magnason

Photograph:
The Icelandic Army.

A Self-Help Manual for a Frightened Nation

Suppose for the sake of argument that Icelandic had only one word for the concept 'feline animal', regardless of whether it was a domestic moggy, a Norwegian forest cat, a lion or a tiger. They were all just 'felines', with zoologists using a complicated system to tell one from another based on weight in grams against number of hairs on the body. A 50 g/h feline would then be a domestic house cat and a 70 g/h feline would be a lion. The difference would be largely incomprehensible to most people. In other respects we would be blind to felines and how far the categories extended, exactly as most of us can't tell whether a snake is a full-grown grass snake, a half-grown viper or a baby constrictor.

Let's imagine too that we had only the word 'rodent' and not rat, mouse and hamster. How then would ordinary people get by when faced with talking about a rodent problem and what to do about it?

I had a rodent problem that I dealt with by getting myself a 50 g/h feline. My neighbour is in the same boat, but he reckons it's best to get himself a rather more powerful variety, a 70 g/h feline. So I say to him, 'You're crazy! You can't bring a 70 g/h feline into your home!' To which he replies, 'You've got a nerve! Just dealt with your own rodent problem and you want to stop me dealing with mine.' So I say, 'You don't want a 70 g/h feline running around in your flat!' He comes home with a lion cub and later that summer gets eaten up down to the very last scrap. And his rodent problem remains unresolved: his dwarf hamster still has a cold.

Absurd example? In some of the biggest questions facing this country in the present day, language simply lacks the words to handle the issues involved and specify the dimensions. The technical terminology gets left entirely in the hands of experts.

Now let's suppose (again, purely for the sake of argument) that we had only one word for the entity 'hydroelectric power station', regardless of whether we were talking about the venerable plant on the Elliðaár river that runs down through Reykjavík, the Búrfellsvirkjun from the 1970s, or the Kárahnjúkavirkjun megaproject currently completing construction in the east of this country. To distinguish between them we were forced to rely on technical terms that were utterly opaque to the vast majority of us: 1 MW, 670

Andri Snær Magnason

MW or 4700 GWh/a. In general, a power station was just a power station. Now let's imagine we had only one word for reservoir: Elliðavatn, the pool of fresh water behind the Elliðaár dam that serves Reykjavík for much of its domestic water supply, would be a reservoir; and so, exactly the same, would be the valleyful of muddy filth building up at Kárahnjúkar, covering an expanse of highland vegetation bigger than the city of Reykjavík. Those with a special interest in the subject could look up the figures and try to memorize the sizes in square kilometres. To the rest of us, these reservoirs would be the same thing - reservoirs. Imagine too that the language also failed to designate according to purpose. So we would use the same term to refer to a power plant producing electricity for domestic supply on the one hand and a power plant for fuelling aluminium smelters on the other. Finally, imagine we had only one word for an aluminium plant, so that a plant producing 10,000 tons of aluminium a year would, to most of us, be the exactly thing the same as a plant producing 500,000 tons. In view of the paucity of the language at our disposal to describe and distinguish between these things – power station, reservoir and aluminium plant – how much sense would you expect to get from a discussion centred around these words? Wouldn't any discussion of the issues involved inevitably turn out to be incomparably vacuous and asinine?

Which means that even experts cannot talk about the subject. I ran into a discussion forum on University of Iceland website, where a professor of engineering was laying into a lecturer in philosophy who had posted a comment opposing the Kárahnjúkar scheme. 'Before anyone starts criticizing the Kárahnjúkar project and its reservoir, I recommend he go and take a look at the Elliðavatn reservoir here in Reykjavík, which we now consider an asset to the local environment and a popular place of recreation.'

In terms of our discussion of felines and rodent problems, this equates to something like this: 'Before anyone starts criticizing someone for keeping a feline (lion) in his home, he ought to come round and play with my little feline (domestic moggy); he's ever so sweet and cuddly.' Language fails to make the necessary distinctions, meaning that even professors of engineering can describe the massive Kárahnjúkar project in the east in terms of a power station six hundred times smaller.

Source:
From a discussion forum on the University of Iceland website. Responses from a professor of engineering to a philosopher's comments on the Kárahnjúkavirkjun HEP scheme.

This is like having just the word 'ship' and making no distinction between an open rowing boat like men used to fish from 150 years ago and an oil tanker. If the first aluminium plant to be built in Iceland, the one at Straumsvík that you pass on your way into Reykjavík from the airport, is seen as counting as one unit of aluminium plant, then what is currently going up at Reyðarfjörður on the east coast is eleven of the things. It will use almost six times as much electricity as all the homes in Iceland put together. A friend of mine was working out east. 'I never realized it was so big,' he said, and then lost for words like a tongue-tied teenager he spread his arms out wide: 'It's much bigger than Straumsvík. Much, much bigger. It's really, really enormous!'

Whether there is any solution to the rodent problem of the Eastfjords is another matter. Hopefully the dwarf hamster will recover from his sniffle and if we're lucky the lion brought in to deal with the problem will just rumble and purr a bit and keep his claws retracted.

If language gets coarsened and muddied, it becomes harder to think with any subtlety and precision, to make the fine distinctions. Our thoughts lose their tones of colour and in their place we get thinking in black and white, clumping and hamfisted. Polar opposites. For or against. If you can admire power schemes built on a small scale to supply a city with electricity, like the one on Elliðaár, or using geothermal energy, like at Krafla, you are being hypocritical if you balk at sacrificing the Thjórsárver wetlands and the pristine highlands of eastern Iceland in the interests of aluminium smelting. There is a Taliban requirement for a pure and absolute ideology: you are either for electricity or you are against it. You either want to wring every possible scrap of energy out of this country, or none at all. You are for all hydroelectric schemes or against them. Power plants are either beautiful or they are ugly. You are either in favour of aluminium smelting or you are against it. There is no room for shades of colour, not even for grey areas. Language forces people to think in sweeping generalizations and crude approximations, to descend into dogmatism and extremism. No allowance for diminishing marginal benefits here.

At the same time as all distinctions are wiped out in one area – equating a waterfall like Öxarárfoss with a hydroelectric dam like at Kárahnjúkar, a natural lake like Thingvallavatn with feeder reservoir like the one proposed at Thjórsárver – we see society becoming fragmentized into discrete groups and disconnected individuals tightly marshalled into separate camps: countrymen, conservatives, environmentalists, intellectuals, easterners – groups with a single, uniform aim and will, a single point of view, and a single interest. Anything but human beings. You see the effects. You read letters to the papers by 'Yours disgusted' complaining at the way people treat their environment, at the filth and squalor they leave behind them, as often as not signing off with the words '...and you don't hear the environmentalists going on about this'. Triumphant proof of the double standards of the environmentalists? Or just a demonstration of the absurdity of this kind of compartmentalization.

I worked six summers for the Reykjavík Electricity Company. Every day one summer we drove out to the geothermal plant at Nesjavellir, south of Lake Thingvallavatn. The road runs straight and flat with, running alongside it in dead straight lines, electricity pylons and a hot-water pipeline like an umbilical cord reaching out from the belly of the earth to feed the city. The clouds of steam that hang over the place give it an aura of mystery, of something powerful and majestic. It doesn't need publicity or advertising. I also worked at the hydro station on Elliðaár, the salmon stream that runs down through Reykjavík. It is a wonderful construction, like a cathedral to energy, worthy of preservation as one of the oldest and most elegant pieces of industrial architecture in the country. I lived beside the river; my mother was born there; my grandmother lived there and paddled in the waters that run down from the lake, where the surface was raised by a metre when the plant was built in 1921, flooding a few surrounding meadows. And I find it all indescribably beautiful. But does it mean I therefore have to give my unqualified support to every new power station anyone proposes to build? Can you say you are for or against houses? For or against felines? As a rule, I rather like cats.

Much of our thinking is done in metaphors. Language is saturated with old words and old senses that have been transferred for use in new areas: plummeting share prices; market turbulence; company collapse; corporate raiders; soft landing; buoyant sales. Metaphor is an indicator of cultural conditions and value judgements. What in English is called a 'windfall' in Icelandic is *hvalreki*, literally, a stranded whale washed up on the shore. Imagine it, in times of hunger and hardship, finding fifty tons of free meat out there on the beach! Picture the joy, the relief, the freedom from anxiety. Rather more spectacular than just a fallen apple lying on your lawn.

In the last few years another word has emerged from its specialist confines to rival the stranded whale: *stóriðja*, large-scale industry, heavy industry, used specifically in connection with the expansion of aluminium refining in Iceland and other energy-intensive and capital-intensive industries. Like the whale on the beach, 'heavy industry' has come to be viewed as the great hope, has acquired a popular connotation of the provider of great riches and the release from all concerns. The word has taken on a poetic, utopian, almost magical quality. To celebrate the 600th anniversary of the school at Hólar in the north of Iceland there was a programme on the radio in which we were told, 'Hólar school is the heavy industry of Skagafjörður.' According to the warden of the Skaftafell National Park – strange as it may sound to the ears of people from old industrialized nations – 'Skaftafell is our heavy industry.' I was listening to an interview with a woman from Grundarfjörður who said, 'The secondary high school is our heavy industry.' On the leftist web journal The Wall there was a headline: 'The University of Akureyri is the heavy industry of Eyjafjörður.'

So how come 'heavy industry' has acquired this value-laden new sense in the minds and language of the people of Iceland? Can it be that the word 'education' on its own is so light and inconsequential that it requires something a bit weightier as reinforcement – 'heavy industry'? The listener hears it and works it out from the context: 'OK, I get it. A university is an important and life-enhancing thing that affects a wide range of activities and creates a lot of jobs.' The metaphor becomes pretty mind-boggling if we remove the 'heavy industry' and substitute some other area of working life. Hólar school – the asphalt centre of Skagafjörður! The University of Akureyri – the cement factor of Eyjafjörður! We would start having serious doubts about the cultural level of the people of Massachusetts if they felt compelled to classify the value of Harvard to them with the words, 'Harvard is the heavy industry of Boston.' **War is Peace. A national park is a factory.**

So what precisely is this deeply symbolic heavy industry that has crept its way into our language? What is the prototype? There are not many Icelanders actually working in heavy industry: out of a total labour market of around 150,000, heavy industry in the Icelandic sense accounts for only about 800 jobs, that is, under 0.5 per cent of the workforce, and produces only around one per cent of GDP. Within allowable margins for error. So how did the word become so big? How did heavy industry become the stranded whale of contemporary Icelandic?

In all probability, this new quasi-mystical sense of 'heavy industry' has nothing to do with any real factories and real production, and much more to do with general conditions in Iceland at present and the heated debate over industrial expansion in the east. In all probability the new usage owes its origins to the vast Alcoa aluminium smelter currently under construction at Reyðarfjörður and the billion-dollar Kárahnjúkar hydroelectric scheme being built to serve it. The words 'heavy industry' are inextricably bound up with the hopes of people in the east of Iceland for a better future through massive capital investment. 'Heavy industry' has become the symbol for a final, definitive solution to their gnawing anxieties over unemployment through the sudden provision of a large-scale, regular source of work – reinforced by the razzmatazz of the signing ceremony, the fireworks, the rejoicing that followed, the 3-D models of the worksite, the bulldozers and the gold rush.

The prototype for the 'heavy industry' metaphor is thus nothing tangible, existing and productive. It owes its hold over Icelandic minds to the propaganda used to sell the idea to the nation – the talk of jobs that people 'will fight over', the politicians' promises of well-paid, permanent work, the dreams of a source of employment capable of attracting families of husbands and wives and three children to move out east and reverse the long-term depopulation of the area. The prototype lies in the newspaper headlines – 'Optimism', 'Regeneration' – in the millions that have been poured into public relations to load the word with a significance going far beyond the attention paid to ordinary job creation in Iceland. After all the blood, sweat and tears, the number of jobs actually created will be only 0.25 per cent of the Icelandic labour market. Heavy industry is all these things. Elsewhere in the country there are people building houses, going to the office or factory and making opportunities for themselves, and nobody notices. People ought to give thanks and celebrate each day that passes, sure, but there is surely something suspicious about a happiness that comes from above and outside and not from within.

Language reveals us for what we are; the significance of a word is not the work of any one person. If as an Icelander I talk about a 'stranded whale', it does not mean that I have found a real stranded whale outside my house, nor if I did I would regard it as an unexpected stroke of good fortune. The people who speak of 'heavy industry' for purposes of comparison are not necessarily preaching the gospel of heavy industry. To quicken others' minds to the possibility of some hope for society, we need a word that has a resonance people understand. All the talk about how vital heavy industry is for our future forces others to explain how they envisage life without heavy industry. The consequence is, *'This* is my heavy industry.' I read an article by someone from Akureyri arguing against the development of heavy industry in Iceland. The entire argument was based around how things might be balanced up through 'educational heavy industry'. I tried to explain the metaphor to some journalists from Belgium. They just stared at me open-mouthed: 'Educationalheavyindustry? You what!?'

Words mean something. It was a pure piece of heavy industry, me meeting my wife. Bringing up the kids is my heavy industry. It's a real heavy industry getting away to the weekend cottage. The new Harry Potter film – heavy industry for pre-teen movie-goers.

It suddenly occurs to me that integration is all about making things whole, fitting them into the overall picture. If we look at life and happiness as a graph, a line that moves above and below the x-axis, then at the end of our lives we can 'integrate happiness', add up all the hours of happiness and subtract the hours of unhappiness and so work out whether the balance is plus or minus. Someone who campaigned for an aluminium plant and achieved economic growth from above and outside if not from within is showing a massive plus if he integrates his happiness for the boom years 2002-6. Later he'll be faced with seeing the reservoir filled, the land sinking, and the magical greenish waters of Lake Lagarfljót fouled and turbid; he'll need to lay off building staff and take on factory staff, find something new for the bulldozers to do, pollute the fjord, rationalize the business, wake up, refine aluminium, sleep, haggle over wages and conditions, see the great tracts of mud uncovered at the bottom of the reservoir in spring, wake up, refine aluminium, sleep, wake up, refine aluminium, sleep. The University of Reyðarfjörður. How the integral of happiness with respect to x comes out at the end of his life, and whether in retrospect the years 2002-6 will be seen as lying above or below the x-axis, remains to be seen.

Education is heavy industry. The sun is a nuclear reactor. God is fish-meal processing.

Words matter. They direct our thoughts. Words that hardly anyone understands appear on the front pages of the papers and in the media and become a familiar part of our daily lives. I did an informal survey among my friends: 'Do you know what the term economic growth means?' Almost no one could give me an answer. Everyone agreed, however, that economic growth was something good, something positive. The economy, how much we own, growing, getting bigger. 'Economic growth is good. We need economic growth,' was a common response. Economic growth is a powerful example of a leading word, a word that directs people's responses. In current-affairs debates it is the person who offers the most economic growth that wins.

I was watching a programme on the television the other day. A politician and a naturalist were discussing the future of Thjórsárver. Thjórsárver is a world heritage site. The river Thjórsá flows from the glacier and runs through a dip in the highlands, creating a unique area of mountain wetlands, a sudden oasis of green in the bleak black desert of central Iceland. These wetlands are the most important nesting site in the world for the pink-footed goose. There were plans to build a dam and submerge a large part of the area to generate electricity for a new aluminium plant in Hvalfjörður.

The naturalist was saying how important this area was for Iceland, and for the world, and for the future of one of the world's most attractive species of geese. To which the politician countered with the 'need to ensure economic growth'. The naturalist tried to enter an objection: '…but do we absolutely need economic growth?' And with that his case was lost, and the politician smiled avuncularly. The politician was being 'realistic'; his views were founded on logic and broad perspective. The naturalist was being 'unrealistic', blinded by romanticism and the narrow self-interest of his particular field.

Both of them misunderstood the word. Economic growth is the annual increase in the production of an entire country. This increase takes in a whole range of factors, including rise in population, technological progress, and the increased value of knowledge as generations become better educated. A milking machine is economic growth. Education is economic growth.

Politicians, of course, are only too happy to appropriate the word for themselves and claim the credit for any increase in the whole country's production. 'This party has created economic growth,' we hear, and no one bats an eyelid. This is possible only because the word permits it. If we break down the word into its constituent parts, the inference becomes rather entertaining: 'If you don't vote for me, people will become lazier, computers will work slower, prosthetic limbs will turn into wooden legs, hotel bookings will be down and lawyers, doctors, policemen, economists, teachers and everyone else that keeps the systems afloat will do a sudden about-face and lay all to rack and ruin.' Anyone who said that would be considered insane. People would feel insulted. 'Did you design the filleting machine, you moron?' Economic growth involves a complex interplay of factors and does not stand or fall by one single company or one single possibility. But once the content has been wrapped up inside a technical term that no one understands, the result becomes something akin to religious mysticism.

Photograph:
Thjórsárver.
(Photographer:
Ragnar Axelsson.)

In 1995 one of our political parties issued a promise of 12,000 new jobs by the turn of the century. Based on economic growth of 3 per cent (increase in population, expansion of tourism, technological advance, educational improvements, improved efficiency, better utilization of unproductive investment, etc.) everything pointed to the jobs being created of their own accord, through natural processes. Nevertheless, the promise was made and the party 'paid out on its promise': 'We in the Progressive Party spoke of 12,000 new jobs by the end of the century. The outlook is that the figure will be at least 13,000...' You might as well put yourself up for election with promises that the grass will grow next summer and four thousand new Icelanders will come into the world. And then start calling yourself Almighty Father of Infants and Fertility. Leaders actually do matter. They can even affect the way we speak: Alcoa of Eyjafjörður – the University of Northern Iceland.

Economic growth measures only economic factors; it takes no account of consequences and long-term effects, the value of things or the quality they bring to our lives. Economic growth does not measure the time people spend with their children or families. A man who goes out and pays for a private dancer rather than stay at home for a jolly tumble with his missus has a positive impact on economic growth. Economic growth is blind to war or the plunder of natural resources or whether future generations are going to have to carry the burden of exorbitant loans and a polluted world. Wars, depletion of resources, natural disasters and the accumulation of debt can all stimulate economic growth. It is like setting a world record for the 100 metres and never taking a drugs test. Economic growth measures how fast the runner ran but not whether he will live to 40. Language lacks expressions along the lines of 'benign' or 'malignant economic growth'. We don't see front-page headlines like 'Fears of malignant economic growth next year'. Someone who stops working and goes off to university has a negative effect on economic growth, regardless of the fact that they are enhancing the possibilities of growth in both the long and the short term.

The term 'economic growth' has acquired a role that extends far beyond the areas it was originally designed to measure. It has become charged with such significance that merely saying it is enough to unman a naturalist on a current affairs programme. Economic growth is made up of a range of diverse and complex factors, and it is worth asking whether it has any genuine legitimacy as a covering term or an overall score for the state and well-being of society. The world could lose Thjórsárver for a 0.1 per cent rise in economic growth on one island in one year, and a letter of commendation would automatically come winging its way from some faceless bureaucratic at a computer in the small nations department at the OECD, to be splashed across the front page of the next day's Morning News: 'OECD commends increased economic growth in Iceland'. Looked at this way, the term can be seen as downright harmful, even dangerous. If we get rid of it and bring in ten new indexes to replace it, perhaps people could start talking about things without having to be for or against economic growth – separate formulas for education, technological progress, population growth, and a special index measuring the vocabulary of young people over the expansion of the Thjórsárver nature reserve squared.

Let me admit here and now that I do not understand the word. Anyone who could come up with a definitive explanation of what produces economic growth and what does not would be a shoe-in for the Nobel Prize for economics. It is fine measuring things, fun arranging the data into indices. But an index is there to serve people, not the other way round.

'Karl Örvarson, you total shit, are you telling me you've gone and blown a thousand dollars in some strip joint?'

'What's up with you then? Do you have something against economic growth?'

The metaphors are all around us, wherever we look. They influence and direct our thinking and perception of the world. The papers talk constantly about 'pillars' of the economy, the things that support us and keep us going. The image we get is of the defencelessness and dependence of the individual and the centrality of the 'pillar', the prop that everything else depends on. But the real pillar is nothing more than the people themselves.

Össur is one of the success stories of the high-tech industry in Iceland, a world leader in prosthetics and orthopaedics. Össur is a pillar of the economy and the pillar of Össur is amputees. It would make more sense to speak of people as the units that go together to form the houses and cities of the economy. If a building collapses, its component parts are freed up and can come together in some new way. The building is just the form the units create; the units are more important than the building itself and only reason for its existence. When the high-tech company OZ hit the wall, its skilled workforce simply went out and found new outlets for their talents. The reconstruction took longer than the collapse, and so no one noticed it. If the truth be told, society is not raised on pillars or foundations at all, and is hardly composed of units either; it is a complex web, a jungle. People live one off another, and who lives off whom is by no means obvious. In the economic jungle it is sometimes best to leave a sterile mammoth to die because then smaller animals can feed off its carcass.

When the Soviet Union collapsed, all the names got changed along with it. All of a sudden people didn't know what town they lived in, what street or country; at a stroke everything they had learned in school was obsolete, gone, utterly redundant. The old people couldn't find their city in the phone book and the young people just felt like partying. The few who mastered the language of the new age were able to get in and scoop up state companies, banks, factories and natural resources at knockdown prices while everyone else lacked the words to make sense of what was happening. I'm going to keep my mouth shut: someone might think I was against *freedom*. Now that's another word that could do with a bit of breaking down and sticking under the microscope.

This is all by the way. It's a very fine Icelandic my friends have taken to speaking, even if I can't say I fully understand it. So far as I can see, they've managed to integrate their happiness, but that's something only those who have learned to integrate can understand. Ignorance is strength. Enjoy the present while it's here.

TERROR ALERT

Terror Alert

It is not so long ago that Iceland was looked upon as one of the poorest countries in Europe; according to a recent UN standard of living chart, it now ranks as second richest. But strange as it may seem, this prosperity appears to have brought us precious little sense of security. If you listen to the way people talk, it is for all the world as if we are constantly teetering on the edge of an abyss.

In the United States the words TERROR ALERT HIGH flicker on the TV screen. People are filled with a sense of fear and insecurity. No one understands the danger. No one can see it with their own eyes or hear it with their own ears. We are all defenceless. Buy a gun? To shoot whom? TERROR ALERT HIGH. But it's pointless staying indoors. The children go to school, the sun shines, the birds are singing. Terror Alert High throughout the USA, reaching into the tiniest village and out to the farthest offshore island. But who can we turn to? Who can comprehend the full extent of the danger? The LEADER, and him alone. The only recourse is to put all power and responsibility in the hands of the leader and hope.

Here in Iceland the economic forecasts work like a TERROR ALERT. The Bank of Iceland foresees an upturn until the weekend and a difficult autumn ahead. The National Bank predicts a deep depression, then following winds and rising temperatures and sunshine later this summer. Analysts from KB Bank advise people to stay indoors until midday due to an unforeseen strengthening of the króna.

A pervasive sense of insecurity. What should I be doing? Should I be working harder? Should I be saving? Should I take a holiday? Should I be cutting back? Increasing consumption? Should I be boosting exports, producing more, cutting interest rates? Quitting school? What the hell am *I* supposed to do? Terror Alert High. I tried saving to help the balance of payments deficit but then the papers said, 'Consumption downturn imminent?' So I had a pang of conscience and bought myself a television. The Central Bank reacted swiftly and put up the base rate.

But LIFE does not change. Life continues in its customary way. The children cycle to school; hot and cold water gets pumped round the houses; the electric company powers the lights and the television, until you sit bolt upright in your chair: TERROR ALERT HIGH! Total meltdown is looming over us. Society is tottering. CAN'T YOU JUST FEEL SOCIETY TOTTERING?

Life continues in its customary way. One person gets a job, another gets laid off. One person gets divorced, another gets married. One is born and another dies. One falls in the sea and another one pulls him out. One gets the contract and another goes bust. One crashes his car, another finds happiness, a third goes off the rails, while for most of us it's just the continuing ups and downs of daily life – good day, bad day. But all this is all nothing in proportion to the ECONOMIC CRISIS LOOMING. There is a break in transmission. The finance minister appears on the screen. Sweat runs down his forehead. 'Economists detected hidden shoals beneath the surface but the ship of state has avoided the danger. It has been a close call.' Phew, you let out a sigh of relief. The pilot announces an economic soft landing: 'Unfasten your seat belts. Clear blue skies and warm summers ahead.' But THERE ARE DARK CLOUDS IN THE SKY! An economist at the Confederation of Labour is predicting a crash. 'Things could turn out to be as serious as at the turn of the century,' says the newsreader. The turn of the century! A chill runs down your spine; your mind calls up images of pack ice, tuberculosis and infant mortality. No, what he was actually talking about was 1999-2000. That was … yes, what was that? How could the calamities of the year 2000 have passed me by? Was it maybe something to do with the millennium bug?

But the feeling remains: there are dark clouds in the sky. There are always dark clouds in the sky. There is nothing solid underfoot. Society is raised on quicksand: how long before it all sinks to the bottom? Is that real reinforced concrete in those walls? How long can it all survive? Your eyes scan the horizon. Are those turf cottages I can see out there in the distance?

The past hovers like a ghost ship just offshore. One day the crew will come storming up the beach and grab our two cars and three TVs. Dress us up in sheepskin shoes, make us dance a ring dance, and then put a picture of us in the international media to give the world something to laugh at.

We fail to see the connection. Though this country has never been richer and the opportunities never greater, we can still be coerced into invidious choices. Economic growth or the highlands? It has never been so easy to put us up against the wall. 'What are we supposed to live on?' people ask. It is a powerful metaphor and deeply ingrained: a house needs a foundation to support it, and a society needs a base industry to support it. First we get something 'real', and then we can hang all the rest off it like decorations on a Christmas tree. But are our lives and living standards in proper proportion to the 'reality' we build them on?

It is as if our dominant world view is still founded on the circumscribed possibilities of a world that has long since passed away. Security resides in this 'reality' and this 'reality' alone, and everything else must be made to serve it.

It needs only 12,000 people to maintain basic production in Iceland. WORKSHOP ICELAND requires just 12,000 employees. You could run the country like a work camp and get in a Portuguese employment agency to provide the labour. Everyone else could happily get on with their unreality in America, Denmark or Australia. What is built on what? Can it be that this land is habitable for the simple reason that there are people living in it? In this country there is no tenth generation of goldsmiths, architects, furniture makers, merchants or tailors; throughout the land what we have is a first generation living in its first houses, in its first towns and first suburbs, and people have trouble believing it can really work.

It would of course be irresponsible blindness to ignore the reality and refuse to acknowledge those involved in it. In Iceland the fisheries employ something under 12,000 people. These 12,000 catch and process and render down around two million tons of fish a year. That is around 7000 kilos for each Icelander. Some 28 tons for each four-person family. About as much as three full-grown African elephants. At a very rough estimate, the nutritional value, the life mass, that the fishing fleet pulls in to land would be enough to sustain the lives of ten million people. That is on the assumption that they eat seafood and nothing else. TEN MILLION PEOPLE! The machines increase productivity and make people redundant. So they need to do something else.

Twelve thousand people on a little island can sustain the lives of ten million people out there in the world. No one eats fish for every meal, so the total number of customers is probably closer to 300 million. However un-scientifically arrived at, these are huge numbers. This is a big business with many diverse strands, and the fish from the cold seas of the north is tasty and nutritious. So what kind of image does this job have? To quote a phrase, 'Icelanders don't want to work in fish.' To judge by what you hear in the media, the self-image of just about all our fishing ports is pathetic. This is of course significant, and sad, because self-image is closely related to self-esteem, and people with low self-esteem are unhappy, and where people are unhappy they don't want to live. We will look at this more closely later.

What are the consequences of all this fishing? If they don't have to catch their own food, ten million people need to find something else to do. We can't all of us catch or eat 7000 kilos of fish. There is no way a four-person family could work its way through the equivalent of a humpback whale a year. So what are we to do with all this food? Sell it? In exchange for what? More fish? One man brings in sustenance for a thousand people. The other 999 need to do something different.

So the question arises, how come a village that catches 100,000 tons of seafood a year is dying on its feet? There are villages in Iceland that could feed a whole city on fish alone, and yet their population is falling. Is it because they are not allowed to catch more? Would the place do better if the people could fish enough to feed 1.1 million, or 1.2 million? Would that tip the balance? Is it because people have sometimes had their eyes so firmly glued on the real-ity that, sheltering behind their abundant natural resources, they have been able to allow themselves the luxury of overlooking other human talents and abilities? We hear a chorus of masculine voices emanating from our decaying fishing villages. 'We don't live by tapping away on computers. We don't live by selling stocks and shares. We can't all work in computers. You don't live off design' – instead of saying, 'People do design out there in the world, so why are there no designers here? People sell shares in the world, so why are there none of them here? There's a painter in New York who eats our fish. If he eats his fish *here* while he's working on his painting, wouldn't that be a perfect way to process fish?'

It is often said that alienation is predominantly a phenomenon of the city. But the definition of alienation is something along the lines that people have no overview over the context in which they live their lives, no perspective on the threads that hold their lives together. So isn't it rather curious to be living in a village that fills a million bellies and still be muttering pettishly, 'We don't live by selling stocks and shares'? The evidence shows that this refrain has its effect on people. Boys from outside Reykjavík do worse in school than girls. Is that perhaps in part because they see the 'reality' as their predetermined role in life? That achieving anything in school is a waste of time or a threat to their society, since those who do well go away and never return? Can it be that the greatest reality engenders the greatest alienation? That the broadest perspective becomes the narrowest perspective?

There is a rift, a schizophrenia that runs through Icelandic society. Few people in the world have shown such avidity in adopting technological innovations. People lap up the present with all the idiocy that goes with it. And yet it is as if they do not trust it. More than anything, people want to know that next year will be all right, and the year after. The paradox is that this craving for security might be one of the greatest dangers we have in front of us.

Beware of the future

Work needs to be found for 2000-4000 people a year. 2000 new people come onto the labour market, along with up to 2000 from sectors of industry that are becoming obsolete. They cannot all go and pick Iceland moss, or hardly into low-paid jobs in the tourist industry.

Guðmundur Ólafsson, economist, www.visir.is

The future is a terrifying prospect. In the next ten years 40,000 children will be born in this country. All around town there are people having unconsidered unprotected sex. In darkened bedrooms people are surrendering to basic urges and there is not a thing reason can do about it. Eggs are fertilized, bellies swell, and every day more children are born. Playschools spring up, and new ones are no sooner built than they are filled with infants. There are 40,000 children in the country's elementary schools! Every autumn the senior high schools spew out hordes of graduates, trampling over each other to get into university. In the next ten years the number will go up by 40,000. And what are all these people going to do? WHAT ARE WE SUPPOSED TO DO WITH 40,000 PEOPLE?

This is no laughing matter. This is a 40,000 problem. The most serious problem we have in front of us. How can people make a dispassionate decision about bringing a child into the world when no one knows what to do with all these people? When the balance of payments is as it is. Personal debt at an all-time high. Impending collapse of the stock market. Can anything be done to help?

'People die to balance things out,' someone might say. But what kind of people are they? Mostly old housewives and men too frail to compete with tough, hard-working women in China? WHAT ARE WE SUPPOSED TO DO WITH 40,000 PEOPLE IN THE NEXT 10 YEARS? They can't all become musicians. They can't all spend their time picking sheep sorrel and Icelandic moss and messing about with test tubes full of micro-organisms. So what are we to do? What do we do if the fish runs out? One aluminium plant employs 400 people. That doesn't cover 10 per cent of the jobs for one year! Come on, I want an answer. Now. Immediately! If you don't have a viable solution YOU ARE IRRESPONSIBLE! If you just say SOMETHING you're avoiding the issue. If you say EDUCATION you're a hippy idealist. If you say science, biotechnology, computers, economics, business studies, arts, tourism, you are INSANE. That's no answer. If you say variety, a mixed economy, this variety has to stands upon something, has to have something to SUPPORT it. If you say IT'LL ALL WORK OUT, you are consigning us to neglect and perdition. You've got to come up with a real solution! And the problem is actually far worse than that! This is an ongoing problem! Yes, in the last ten years these 40,000 children were born, and they will all be flooding onto the labour market at the same time as the next 40,000 are being born! It is a vicious circle. IS NO ONE GOING TO GET A GRIP ON THINGS? WHAT ARE ALL THESE PEOPLE SUPPOSED TO DO? WHO IS GOING TO DEAL WITH THE PROBLEM? IS NOBODY GOING TO TAKE RESPONSIBILITY? THE FUTURE NEEDS TO BE ORGANIZED!

Somebody might decide to deal with the 40,000 problem on their own initiative, out of a pure and dispassionate sense of responsibility. That could, for example, be a solid and benevolent leader. It maybe doesn't sound too bad at first sight, organizing the next ten years. It is only two five-year plans.

But anyone who tries to take on a problem of this magnitude can only throw up his hands in despair. 40,000 people! Most of us are number-blind. So to get an idea, it would take eleven hours to count up to 40,000. If you thought for a minute about each one as an individual, it would take 667 hours, or 83 working days. If you put in an hour planning the future of each of them, that would take 5000 working days, or nineteen whole years. By the time you were finished another 40,000 would have been added to the total! If the leader wanted to go into the problem in real depth and spend a whole day mapping out the potentials of each and every one, he'd be at it non-stop for 109 years!

Andri Snær Magnason

The leader could perhaps create fifty new jobs a month by getting able-bodied men to dig ditches and build tunnels. But that wouldn't be anything like enough. Every week a further seventy would flood onto the labour market. The leader would call in engineers and planners. But that wouldn't be enough either. He'd quickly find himself unable to sleep, his nerves shattered, until it became necessary to look at the world 'realistically' and come to some hard decisions:

1. Equality of the sexes has been a noble experiment, but unrestricted female participation in the workforce is not viable in times of uncertainty. If the women stay at home, that will save 20,000 jobs.
2. If 10,000 men work in the morning, then 10,000 can work after lunch.
3. We must agree long-term contracts with international manufacturing companies, plan their entry into the labour market, and calculate their human resources requirements. All prospective citizens shall be tested in their mothers' wombs to ascertain whether and to what extent they will meet the demands of the working economy.
4. The maternity ward of the National Hospital will be merged with the marketing agency of the ministry for industry.
5. On the signing of an energy sales contract, a directive shall be issued specifying the batch size of prospective citizenship that it is safe to allow out into the world.

The leader would be proud of his initiative, and if the nation was sufficiently conscious of the 40,000 problem and frightened enough of the future it would thank the leader and give him all due credit for having saved it in its hour of need. 'If he had not saved us, there would be 40,000 disaffected down-and-outs wandering the streets and social housing districts, fired up on crime, drugs and violence.' The leader would deliver impassioned speeches to the party conference:

> *Before any decision can be taken on the next round of births we have to assess projected future needs and make cuts in as many areas as possible. Is it necessary for cars to come in different colours?*

How many varieties of taste do we need? Does the future have any need for the oboe? In view of improvements in recording technology, is there perhaps room for cost cutting here? We need to assess viewing ratings for the Icelandic landscape, identify those with the lowest viewing appeal and utilize them for industry or mining enterprises. Mt Esja, as viewed from Reykjavík, is a facility of undisputed value. But what about the far side of the mountain? What kind of an audience does that get? Does it yield an adequate return?

The leader would understand that it required decisiveness, rigour and pertinacity to put the plans into operation. It would even need a level of uncompromising severity to ensure TOTAL UNITY OF PURPOSE and prevent CHAOS. Of course, many people might have different visions of the future. But dissent would not be tolerated. Those who subverted the future through presumptuous ideas or untimely and unauthorized reproduction, and who thus precipitated the nation into an uncertainty from which nothing could result but death itself, would be banished from the country and sent into exile.

'Whatever' is the only answer

OK, that was a bit over the top maybe. But what are we going to do after five years? What are we going to be living on ten years from now? It is as if people look on in terror at all the kids filling the senior high schools and colleges and think, 'What are we going to do with all these people?' We seem to live in constant fear of the great crash. Can we support so many trainee engineers and business studies graduates?

The future cannot be planned and organized, but it is possible to weigh things up and try to predict what we will be living on. If we have five hundred people studying biotechnology, that gives us the basis for a five-hundred-strong biotechnology company. This is how things work; a company cannot exist before the skills and education are in place to make it possible. Purely practical thinking, however, turns this on its head: 'What on earth are you studying biotechnology for? Where are you going to find a job?'

The answer to the question 'What are we going to do with all these people?' can never be more than a dour five-year plan. The question is inadmissible because it is too big. We don't need 'to do anything with all these people', because in the vast majority of cases they come fully equipped to take their own decisions and organize their own lives. The 'answer' would never be the outcome of the combined contributions of thousands of people, but singular and contingent. Even armed with a ruler, calculator and economic planning project technician, the leader would have to be some kind of superman if he tried to think and plan like 300,000 people. However deeply he went into things, he could never obtain a comprehensive overview of all the possibilities that reside in just one individual, let alone a whole nation. If you think the leader's head comes equipped with different equipment from the rest of us, you're in for a disappointment. He may stand at the top of the pyramid but that doesn't mean he has the best overview. The top is as often as not shrouded in mist. Nor does the leader necessarily have access to the best knowledge, advice and ideas. Kings have often enough brought their countries to rack and ruin with the loyal assistance of their advisors. Dante places royal counsellors in an even deeper pit of hell than the kings themselves. If we believe the leader is endowed with different equipment from other mere mortals, he might start believing himself that he is 'special' in some way, and even identify strange and mystical patterns in the world as if to confirm it. And then it is a racing certainty that we'd all be on the path to perdition.

Fear of the future and the unknown is as ridiculous as asking a kid who says he's going to be a songwriter, 'But what song are you going to write?' 'Whatever,' he replies. 'Whatever? *Whatever* is no answer!' It's like asking a youngster who wants to do business studies, 'You're going into business, are you? So what are you going to sell?' The aim is not to know *what* you are going to write or sell or invent, but to know *how* to write or sell or invent.

We may have an education system and talk a lot about it, but it is as if people aren't really interested in it. Middle-aged men get together to form pressure groups and draft resolutions about 'schemes capable of contributing to the national economy'. Cars clog the streets and bulldozers churn up the land. We catch two million tons of fish a year. But why don't we get whole classes of children coming home from school one day proudly clutching il-lustrated books with titles like *Everything You Wanted to Know About Fish and the Sea*, or *The Wonders of Science*, or *Space and the Universe*, or *Plants and Animals of Iceland*? All the kids in one year might suddenly become INTERESTED in fish. What use are books? Is usefulness measurable? A high-quality book of 300 pages, say like Guðmundur Páll Ólafsson's *Birds in the Icelandic Landscape,* costs less to produce than a couple of SUVs, and SUVs get imported by the shipful. How might the economy of Iceland be doing now if our current generation of rulers had been brought up on something that might have opened their minds and fired their imaginations. Instead, what we get is a dominant world-view that seems to have been formed on the dry-as-dust, black-and-white geography textbook that was used almost unaltered in Icelandic schools for getting on for forty years.

Poland sells coal, timber, rye, zinc, agricultural produce, etc.

Poland buys wool, cotton, machinery, industrial goods, etc.

Sheffield is sometimes called 'the steel city'.

Source: Guðjón Guðjónsson, *Geography*, Vol. 2, Icelandic Educational Publishing Co.: Reykjavík. No date of publication is given, but the book was taught and used in pretty much the same form from 1960 to 1990 and beyond in some Icelandic elementary schools.

Andri Snær Magnason

Maybe it's overstating the case to call this particular piece of writing intellectual genocide, but it's getting on that way.

For some reason it has been seen as perfectly acceptable for a significant section of our younger population to go through its schooling without finding any channel for its abilities in book learning, vocational skills, the arts or anything else. Sometimes it is as if people are stuck in some pre-industrial-age time warp – when all you needed was one doctor, one lawyer and one priest per thousand head of population, and society held itself together through sheer brawn. It was brawn that hauled in the fish and stacked the hay into the barn. So it is no matter for concern if boys from the rural parts of Iceland come out badly by international standards, since those who fail in school go into real work. They are the ones who are going to keep the rest of us going. And a negative attitude to education becomes even more understandable when you start looking at the charts in the elementary school *Geography*. 'Livestock in different countries. (Counted in thousands: figures from 1935).' The man who says he did not start learning until he went to sea is stating no more than the truth.

People talk about education but fail to see it as the foundation of the society we will live in because to them the foundation lies somewhere else. The front pages report the change in managing director at some company, but a new headteacher hardly gets a mention, let alone a whole page interview, despite the fact that he has a genuine influence over the lives and happiness of thousands of children. A new recruit to the internet banking arm of the Iceland Insurance Company is there in the business pages, but not a new teacher at our largest secondary school – somebody who will in all probability mean much more for business life in Iceland in the long term. The reason so many international banks have suddenly sprouted up here is, perhaps more than anything else, that we have so many people with educations in business studies. Disproportionately many. Design brings in nothing because we have too few people trained in woodwork, metalwork, machine tools, design and engineering:

> *Danish furniture exports performed exceptionally in 2004, according to new figures from the Danish Statistical Office. Danish producers sold furniture abroad to the value of **2.2 billion euros**, an*

Source:
www.danishfurniture.dk

increase of 5 per cent on the previous year. The leading markets are the Scandinavian countries but there is also significant growth in new markets.

In one year, 2.2 billion euros – 3.5 billion dollars – in designer furniture exports. That comes out at 260 billion Icelandic króna – as much as Iceland's total foreign earnings for the same year. As much as all the fish, all the aluminium, all the prosthetic limbs combined – THE LOT.

The future will be built on too many people learning too much for too long about too many things that nobody does in this country. This is the only way new jobs and new possibilities will come about. The future will be complicated and full of false starts and blind alleys, and the boundaries between reality and virtual reality will be obliterated. What constitutes a 'serious business', for example? Lots of people spend a couple of hours a day within an international community that has grown up around the internet game EVE Online. It takes a long time to work your way up in the game and get yourself a good vehicle. If someone decides to buy a virtual spaceship from someone else for five thousand dollars to improve their status and increase their travelling speed, isn't that just as 'real' business as upgrading your Toyota for a BMW? Virtual objects of this sort are already there to buy on eBay. Does it matter what material the vehicle is made of? Looked at this way, what kind of reality is an exorbitantly expensive motor car that gets driven for twenty minutes a day anyway? Whatever the case, the computer games industry is already bigger than the movies.

Society, the culture we live in and the educational system are capable of fostering and rewarding creative thought. But they can also kill it. Education can open doors but it can also act like an electric fence: you get a nasty jolt on first contact and keep away from it for ever after. By teaching kids a kind of fear-tinged awe for traditions and international borders you can create a situation where people fail to see things that should be obvious to everyone, and things that should present only minor problems appear as insurmountable barriers. 'No, that's not the way we do things here.' 'We don't think like that.' 'I'm not sure you're allowed to use that method.' This kind of thinking only serves to block the path to an easy fusion between different areas of life and

Andri Snær Magnason

the application of ideas from one area to another. Sometimes there is a duty to break the rules. If everyone says 'Poems shouldn't rhyme', it's probably about time to start thinking about rhyming. Excessive respect for received wisdom can stop people from taking the plunge for themselves.

My grandmother's brother ran a toy store when I was a child. Every year before Christmas they built an adventure land out of Lego. I dreamed of taking part but never dared to ask. My sister always worked there at Christmas. One night she came home late in a foul mood, having been given the stupid job of putting together a sodding steam train out of Lego to go in the window. I had let the idea that it was all too complicated get the better of me. I should have just taken the plunge and asked to do what I'd always wanted.

Films that cost tens of millions of dollars amazingly often turn out to be complete turkeys, with half the auditorium thinking to themselves, 'Anyone could have done that.' There's a lot in this. The people who actually do things are often those who by pure chance happened to take the plunge, but in other respects they don't really have anything most of the rest of us don't have as well. Anyone who thinks they can do better than the worst Hollywood movie they've seen lately has no reason not to go to Hollywood and try.

In recent years we have heard a lot about the function of education being to prepare young people for 'working life': the sooner kids get out into the world of work the better. We have heard a lot, too, about how little interest young people show in science and how few of them are opting to do scientific subjects. One reason for this could be that young people are never brought into contact with the idea that knowledge is worth seeking for its own sake, and are never introduced to the creative processes that lie behind scientific thought. People build up a thick layer of fact but cannot apply it to the real world. They never actually take the plunge. They forget that science is about huge, burning questions crying out to be answered, not answers that need to be learned. Science, philosophy and the arts were once branches of the same tree, not starkly demarcated opposites. 'There's no point re-inventing the wheel,' they say; perhaps the truth is more that the wheel has not been invented often enough.

Inventing the wheel

I once made a world-shattering mathematical discovery. The fact that it was discredited five minutes later is beside the point: the feeling while it lasted was breathtaking. I was in the middle of a maths class and I noticed a strange regularity in some of the sums. I realized I could save myself time by using a different, quicker method than the one we'd been taught, and it always came out with the correct result. I went to the teacher and showed him my new method. He looked at my sheet and then flicked through the book. 'Yes, very good, that comes up on this page,' he said dryly. I looked it up and saw, to my bitter disappointment, that my rule turned up in the next chapter. But despite the disappointment, I still remember the feeling. I felt a moment's intoxication, felt I had genuinely stumbled across something remarkable.

This is not to say I could ever have invented the whole of mathematics on my own, and the drudgery, repetition and self-discipline that goes into doing sums is doubtless an essential part of a scientific education. But even so, I think we were far too often shielded from any sense of discovery. The student's job was to learn by heart things that someone else had already discovered.

At senior high school I majored in physics. In astronomy lessons we learned how to calculate the co-ordinates of stars, the gravitational pull between planets and the orbiting speeds of artificial satellites – but not once did we look up at the heavens in order to understand why anyone should want to calculate these things. During this time there was an eclipse of the moon and the earth passed through a meteor belt with a consequent meteorite shower, but we just read about it in the paper the next day. I knew how to calculate the alternating current in logic circuits but not how to change a plug. I knew all sorts of things about electricity, had the rules off by heart, but I never really 'discovered' electricity. In the physics department there was an almost total separation between hand and mind; nowhere in the school system was the distance greater from the technical college and industrial skills, though the links between the two areas of study were patently obvious. I was haunted by the thought that, if I fell through a time warp and found myself back into the Middle Ages, I would not be able to move mankind forward so much as an inch. We sometimes got excited about the prospect of going on to do real engineering and designing a power station or electrical supply system, without knowing how to change a plug.

The arts have a habit of pussyfooting in a similar way. Like the sciences, the arts ought to be magnificent and inspiring but somehow fail to get through to people. What ought to be magnificent becomes dry; what ought to be progressive, revolutionary and mad comes across as old, lifeless, fossilized, odd and obsolete. In the worst case people can emerge from decades of schooling without ever really acquiring the taste.

Even so, in most of this country's higher schools we can find models that those with an interest in promoting learning could certainly learn from, by adapting successes in one area to their own field of study. Once we step outside the standard syllabus, we can find examples of kids and grown ups interacting in quite different ways from what goes on in the conventional classroom, each motivating the other and together creating a driving force that neither could produce on their own.

The drama societies in our higher schools are run entirely by the students themselves but with the financing to bring in professionals from outside to lead and direct. The students employ the teacher, and maybe there is a lesson for society in this alone. There are no doubt many who look on the school drama societies as bunches of hipsters and arty-farties or as a pretext for bunking off lessons and getting drunk. But a closer look turns up a rather different picture – as I got to see at first hand when I wrote a play for the drama club at Hamrahlíð School in Reykjavík. The society appointed a well-known professional actress, Harpa Arnardóttir, to direct, and proceedings got under way with a working trip into the country. Harpa said that no one was to take any alcohol. No one took any alcohol. This was a culture shock in itself.

These groups give school kids between the ages of 16 and 20 the opportunity, on their own initiative, to stage some of the most challenging works of world literature: Shakespeare, Brecht, the Greek tragedies. They go deeper into these works than is normally possible in literature lessons and so get closer to the meaning and purpose of the work and its creation. One might say that the wheel is being re-invented again and again, with every single year.

Activities of this kind are unlike, and more valuable than, any other kind of school-based teamwork because no one is compelled to take part. Rather than everything degenerating into anarchy, a structure takes shape organically, similar to what happens in a modern workplace, and people are driven by ambition, involuntarily, to take on the most difficult tasks. The boundaries are fluid and people's strengths and talents are automatically channelled to where they are likely to have the greatest effect. Everyone works together, musicians, set designers, costume makers, lighting crew and roadies, actors, choreographers, director and author, and finally programme designers and business managers – all leading up to a few weeks' run in a proper theatre.

The kids learn complex texts by heart until they become a part of their lives. The hardest parts are the most in demand. They learn how to express themselves, how to present themselves, self-confidence, body language, discipline and punctuality. The show starts on the stroke of 8. They learn how a performance is created, how a play is created, how a band is formed and how it all stacks up, how to rely on others, to work under pressure, to produce something within a set time, to work late into the night to 'maximize assets'. All without actually being aware that this is work and education. What on the surface appears to be a bit of light-hearted theatrical frivolity, as something that deflects time away from studies, in fact teaches the participants far more about working life and how things operate in the real world and the workplace than the chapter and group assignment on 'Founding a company' in their Business Studies 201 textbook.

In my case, I took the plunge and wrote my first ever piece for the stage, and came away convinced that I wasn't being unrealistic thinking about the National Theatre as the next step. The band Múm that came together as part of the play is still together and has built up a following around the world. All we are talking about is a fifty-strong group of drama enthusiasts from a single school. So it is worth wondering whether a similar approach might not pay off in other areas – if physics students, for instance, could get in a 'director' to help them invent the wheel. If drama kids can discover *Romeo and Juliet* year after year, why shouldn't it become part of the culture of physics teaching to appoint someone to help students harness the power of the local stream, again and again if need be, help them discover electricity, the light bulb, the machine, radio, the telephone, video games, the windmill and the computer, the rings of Saturn and the moons of Jupiter?

It is often said that people have the spirit of enterprise trained out of them, that education makes people averse to taking risks and reluctant to set up on their own and try to see their ideas into practice. This is probably nothing to do with the material itself; more that, despite all the educational grounding and the learning and the calculations and the ability to get the right answers in exams, people feel inhibited from taking the plunge by the institutionalized framework they have had inculcated into them in school. I had in fact done a course in dramatic writing at the university, but actual writing for the stage had always remained an equally implausible proposition; however creative the writing was supposed to be, taking the plunge was simply not on the syllabus. If someone like Harpa Arnardóttir had been in charge of a group of physics enthusiasts for the last fifteen years, who knows? there might by now be an Icelandic Space Institute up and running, with a full-time staff of 300 calculating the planetary co-ordinates and programming the broadcasting frequencies of the world's communications satellites.

The results of the play could not be measured in marks out of ten: there were no formal examiners and no grades were given. But the success was there for all to see. The unmeasurable seems to be an endangered species these days: education is an investment that has to yield a return; it should have a quantifiable and material utility, a direct practical value that manifests itself in measurable income and tangible results. Whatever cannot be expressed in numbers, hard-nosed functionality puts down as 'wastage'. Someone who has studied our ancient medieval poems – Völuspá and the like – and goes into business is like a dentist who has inadvertently invested in an air compressor. Economically, investment in Old Icelandic poetry counts as a non-recoverable loss against mean working life. Possibilities like those I encountered at the Hamrahlíð Drama Society are invisible to the eye of efficiency and we may wonder whether there is any future for them. But we may also ask, if they do disappear, whether along with them will be lost what for many is the most important school in life.

Andri Snær Magnason

Castles in the air? Too expensive? The total cost of the country's higher secondary school system is about 125 million dollars a year. The total teaching costs for all students at university level is a little over 75 million. An ambitious road-surfacing plan has recently been agreed for the next four years: 750 million dollars. Of course, we all love a bit of tarmac. But it's not a bad idea to consider where we're going before we wheel out the bulldozers and graders. The future is beyond our reckoning. But we can be sure of one thing: it will be built by those who are part of the 40,000 problem getting ideas from whoever knows where and turning them into reality.

Source:
www.rikiskassinn.is/
hvad-kostar

99.

Living in the best of all possible worlds

The world in which we live is a chance of fate [or, history], just one out of all possible worlds. But that is not the way we see it. The way things are presented to us, we are beguiled into thinking that this country is the result of a series of fortuitous coincidences; that the 300,000 tons of cod, the 300,000 tourists, the prosthetic limb company with its staff of 300, the 300,000 tons of aluminium and the 3000 people attached to the US airbase are a fluke of nature, a miraculous equilibrium of forces that somehow keeps us afloat and allows us to survive in this inhospitable land; that these 'pillars of the ecomony', this delicately poised balance of cod, tourists, soldiers and aluminium, are the only thing that lies between us and ruin. We fondly believe that all is for the best as it is and that it could be no other way. That this is the only one of all possibilities.

Instead of recognizing the existence of a myriad utopias in all directions, a thousand possible Icelands that might be or might have been, it is sometimes for all the world as if people perceive their society as the only possible outcome, that the country has stumbled upon its mysterious balance of forces by pure chance. We have achieved material prosperity, but it is as though people do not believe they have created it themselves or deserved it. We look over the city, all the houses, the cars and the shops, and we don't believe it can last, as if whoever it was gave it to us might come along at any moment and snatch it away from us again.

Strange as it may seem, despite all the affluence, all the success, all the investment, the education, the unexpected victories and the unforeseen heroes, even in the midst of unemploymentlessness, it is as if we cannot shake ourselves free from the crisis mentality. Even as the heroes stand everywhere before our eyes and we have come a mighty way from basic subsistence and into the excess fat, it is as if everyone is still gnawed by insecurity. We fish enough to feed ten million people, but it does nothing to fill us with a sense of 'perfect security'. It is as if deep down in us there is an ancient trauma that stops us thinking straight. Like a man who loses his jobs and for ever after works twice as hard just to be sure.

Source: Between 11 September 2001 and 2005, the US government spent $250 billion on anti-terrorism measures and the wars in Iraq and Afghanistan. Amy Belasco (2005), *CRS report to Congress: the cost of Iraq, Afghanistan and enhanced base security since 9/11*, Foreign Affairs, Defense, and Trade Division, Congressional Research Service: [no place of publication], www.fas.org/sgp/crs/natsec/RL33110.pdf.

It is easy to imagine other possible Icelands without resorting to worlds of extravagant fantasy. The US Congress recently agreed to increase funding for the war in Iraq by 5 billion dollars. This is the equivalent of forty Kárahnjúkar hydro schemes in a few short months. Seven times the GDP of Iceland in *increased spending*. Just a fraction of this sum would be enough to swamp the entire Icelandic economy. Iceland is so small that it can easily be overrun by a single company, a single possibility or a single idea. In 1945 the country stood before just such a possibility. And what we did then has lessons for us still today.

Andri Snær Magnason

Battleship Iceland

Last year the Americans asked us for Hvalfjörður, Skerjafjörður and Keflavík. They proposed a long-term lease, up to 100 years, in view of the large costs they intended to put in. These places were to become powerful military bases.

Ólafur Thors, prime minister,
speech before the Althingi, 1946

According to the terms of a defence agreement between the United States and Iceland during the Second World War, the Americans were supposed to leave Iceland once the war was over. But in 1945 Iceland had taken on a key position in the new world order. With the arrival of atomic weapons, the belief took hold that the next major war would be a nuclear war, conducted using long-range bombers. The department of defense in Washington saw a role for Iceland as the front line of defence for the USA in the case of an attack on, or from, the Soviet Union. From Keflavík it would be possible to launch strikes on targets anywhere in Europe and western Asia.

The US military presence became the bitterest and most fiercely contested political issue in Iceland throughout the second half of the twentieth century. The base at Keflavík divided the nation. Opponents organized protests marches between Reykjavík and Keflavík and there were repeated anti-NATO demonstrations. The splintered world-view of the cold war infected a whole generation of politicians, and even today all kinds of seemingly totally unrelated matters get lumped together in terms of bunkered cold war attitudes that still provide many of us with a kind of automatic classification system: if a leftist politician proposes putting up road signs saying WAIT, you can bet a rightist politician will want them to say STOP, and vice versa. The situation creates two clearly defined and entrenched poles, something for us to argue over at confirmation parties.

The 'base question' initially revolved around not one military base in Iceland but several. The Americans had ambitious plans for Iceland in the new world order. The battle lines at the start of the cold war were not always as simple and clear-cut as many think. Apart from bases at Hvalfjörður, Skerjafjörður (Reykjavík airport) and Keflavík, ideas were later floated for a military airfield for long-range bombers in the southern lowlands at Rangárvellir, near Hella.

Source:
Thór Whitehead (1976),
'Republic and military
bases 1941-46', Skírnir:
Journal of the Icelandic
Literary Society, Vol.
150, pp. 126-172.

The Icelanders favoured limiting the scope of the military in times of peace and preferred to see the army in terms of a purely defensive role. But the Americans were never in any doubt about the country's suitability as a launch pad for strikes on targets in the Soviet Union, especially if their military bases and airfields in Britain came under attack. The Icelanders were unhappy about their country being used for offensive purposes, but it is difficult to imagine how much say they would have had in the matter if push had come to shove. Not out of any ill-will, but for simple technical and strategic reasons.

So initially positions for and against the army were by no means as simple as they later became. In 1955 the US Research Information Office carried out a poll in Iceland. This revealed that 48 per cent of the population were against the defence agreement and only 28 per cent in support. A third of Independence Party supporters, i.e. Conservatives, later to become the Americans' staunchest allies, were against.

Source:
Valur Ingimundarson
(1996), In the firing line
of the cold war: US-
Icelandic relations, 1945-
1960, Vaka-Helgafell:
Reykjavík, p. 295.

The opposition was on various grounds: an insistence on neutrality, the nation's pride in its newly won independence in 1944, personal or ideological sympathies, bitter experience of foreign domination from the days as a Danish colony, and the fear of becoming sucked into war. In his Independence Day address to the nation, 17 June 1946, prime minister Ólafur Thors said, 'Icelanders do not wish to have military bases on their land in times of peace.' He is also said to have told the chief secretary at the US embassy that he was 'personally opposed to granting the USA military facilities' but had not come out publicly on the matter on account of his feelings of friendship towards the Americans. The insistence on neutrality lay at the very core of how the generation that had waged the struggle for Icelandic independence saw itself, and this applied to rightists and leftists alike. The penultimate article in the Danish-Icelandic Treaty of Union of 1918, granting Iceland full autonomy over internal affairs, could not be clearer:

Source
'Voice of the nation',
article in Morgunblaðið,
19 June 1946.

Source:
Valur Ingimundarson, In
the firing line of the cold
war, p. 61.

Andri Snær Magnason

Article 19

Denmark declares to foreign nations that, in accordance with the substance of this Treaty of Union, it recognizes Iceland as a sovereign state and declares moreover that Iceland affirms its permanent neutrality and that it will have no flag of war.

Article 20

This Treaty of Union takes effect on 1 December 1918.

In the aftermath of the obscenity of the First World War, it was the verdict of our best men that this country should affirm permanent neutrality and have no flag of war, no symbol of militarism. Even during the Second World War, when the Germans sank some Icelandic fishing boats and trading ships and in the grief and pain that followed, the insistence on neutrality remained so strong in Icelanders that they refused to join the newly formed United Nations on the grounds that membership would mean declaring war on Germany. The generation that was alive and in power at the time took the idea of war very seriously. Of all generations of Icelanders in the twentieth century, this was the one that had the greatest knowledge of war and its consequences.

But let's imagine what might have happened if war had not been such a contentious issue, if the US request for military bases had not come at a sensitive time for the newly independent nation but had rather been seen as a cause for celebration for the employment opportunities it offered. During the war years the standard of living in Iceland had improved out of all recognition and people had every reason to suppose that the end of the war would mean a speedy return to the years of depression.

I need only phone my grandparents to get a shot of the depression straight in the bloodstream. I rang my grandmother Herdís, who was born in 1925. 'I was so young, of course, when the depression hit us in the Eastfjords, but it was no life. There was never any milk except when our mother got a three-pint jug for doing some sewing for somebody. It was like being given gold, having milk in the house. I can remember we had to wear shoes sewn out of sheepskin. There weren't any boots. I remember it like yesterday, mother sewing those shoes for us.'

In 1945 no one could say for sure whether the depression was really a thing of the past and gone for good. The government could have looked on the US request for a powerful military presence as a *'stay of depression'*, an offer of *'full employment'*, a guaranteed standard of living and well-paid jobs, a promise of rich harvests and a natural continuation of the 'construction and progress of the war years'. Rather than haggling down and limiting the scope of military influence, the government might have encouraged the Americans to take things even further. Leaders, local dignitaries and work contractors could have accompanied generals and senators around the country, feeding them salmon, showing them what the land had to offer, and trying to smooth their arrival and help them expand their sphere of influence in every way.

Without any shadow of a doubt we'd have been in for the mother of all herring booms, a jamboree of gold-rush proportions. There'd have been people working night and day on building sites, money would have streamed into the country, houses gone up, consumer goods filled the shops and the age for driving trucks lowered to 15 to keep the machines rolling. When the army arrived in 1951, 350 Icelanders got work at the Keflavík airfield. By autumn 1953 this number was up to around 3000, about 4 per cent of the total Icelandic workforce. And that despite the government restricting the numbers involved. If there had been the same kinds of activity around the naval harbour in Hvalfjörður, at Reykjavík airport and at Rangárvellir in the south, it is perfectly conceivable that the US army would have had getting on for 20-30 per cent of the able-bodied men in Iceland on the payroll. In view of the country's position and the state of global politics, the military bases would have had enormous growth potential as one of the most important links in the defence systems of the cold war. And BICE – *Battleship Iceland* – would eventually have come into being.

Photograph: The B-36 'Peacemaker' was designed to drop nuclear bombs on distant targets. There were ideas to station thirty of these planes at Rangárvellir in southern Iceland, and the base would doubtless have become one of the central pillars of the Icelandic economy. (Photograph: Air Force Flight Test Center History Office.)

Rangárvellir might well have become one of the main centres of the US air force in the North Atlantic. In 1952 the US government had plans to set up a large-scale base there for thirty long-range B-36 nuclear bombers. The Keflavík airbase was seen as vulnerable to submarine attack, but from Rangárvellir it would be possible to defend Keflavík and launch strikes on targets in the Soviet Union. This Rangárvellir airfield would have been well placed to take over functions from bases on the east coast of the USA, Britain and Germany, or at Thule in northern Greenland.

With the advent of short-range nuclear missiles it would have been easier for the military authorities to reorganize their forces in Europe. Short-range tactical missiles from eastern Europe would have been able to wipe out the bases in Britain and West Germany within the first minutes of a war. The airfields at Rammstein, Hahn and elsewhere in Germany, getting on for 400,000 military personnel, the air fleet and tank squadrons, would have melted like chocolate in the sun. Because of Iceland's position and the existing facilities, the Americans would have decided to transfer here a still larger part of the forces originally intended for mainland Europe – even if no more than 10 per cent or 40,000 extra servicemen – bringing with them an attendant boom and further job opportunities.

Now let's imagine Iceland with a big naval base at Hvalfjörður, with anchorage for warships, docking for aircraft carriers and submarines, and weapons stores. At Reykjavík Airport there would be a fully operational base and the headquarters of the strategic air command. Smaller military facilities would have sprung up around the airfields at Ísafjörður and Akureyri in the north. At Reyðarfjörður in the east there would be a submarine dock, partly hollowed out of the mountain. Keflavík airport would be three times bigger. At Rangárvellir there would be a military airport and one of the main stationing points for B-36 and later B-52 bombers, with associated weapons arsenals, bomb silos and servicing equipment. There would probably be other military bases in the east at Egilsstaðir and in the north in Aðaldalur, and perhaps another on Melrakkaslétta in the far northeast. There would be some airfields up in the central highlands for military exercises. There would be a vastly expanded range of activities for the various radar stations dotted around the coast. There would be any number of no-entry zones both on land and within territorial waters, areas designated as being of 'military importance'.

Some of the wildest parts of the Icelandic highlands would have got the chance to live up to their spectacular names– the 'exploding sands' of Sprengisandur, the 'misdeed lavas' of Óðáðahraun – given a few years' target practice from fighter jets, exercises in carpet bombing from B-52s and tank manoeuvres in the imagined 'post-atomic' landscape of a nuclear winter. In 1960 the highlands were a largely unknown quantity to most people in Iceland, so no one would have complained too much. Farmers could have been compensated for loss of grazing lands and collateral damage to sheep. I'm not trying to paint an unduly bleak picture here: weapons have to be tested somewhere and it is perfectly natural to imagine them being tried out in the wide open spaces and barren wildernesses of central Iceland. An army needs to be prepared for anything; it needs to do exercises and to know how to use its equipment. The scientists would have employed the very best technology to ensure that contamination to groundwater was kept within internationally accepted limits.

I am not going to start imagining atomic tests in this country, a Nordic parallel to the Nevada desert, but prettier places than Iceland have been roasted in the name of nuclear weapons. Nuclear weapons generally have a negative resonance in people's minds, though tourism to Las Vegas actually increased after the tests in Nevada. People came flocking in to see the mushroom gliding up into the heavens. The bomb was turned into a spectacle, with a positive impact on tourism. That is the simple truth, and so reason not to be too pessimistic: nuclear testing here would probably have been a boon to the tourist industry.

Let's imagine the country had welcomed these employment opportunities. It would all have confirmed the dominant attitude, that people's ability to create opportunities for themselves was the exception rather than the rule. Above anything else, the people of Iceland wanted work, and this would have spared them the trouble of thinking about how to create it. You can picture the headlines:

5000 new jobs created in construction of Hvalfjörður naval base

Akureyri celebrates army expansion plans

Unions agree increased productivity deal

Eastfjords bullish over plans for new submarine dock

Húsavík: 66% in favour of new army base

Optimism in wake of US defence budget increase

Fisheries Bank analysis department forecasts 5.5% economic growth for next 7 years

Eastfjords still waiting for submarine dock

East-Húnavatn county restricts access to strategically important cabbage patch

What little individual could have outbid a great world power and said, 'I have an idea for a few jobs we could do instead'? People would just have laughed. Forty thousand people would have been in work directly as a result of the army's being here and everyone else would have seen their jobs in terms of the 'multiplier effect' or 'secondary industries' in areas like construction, services, cleaning, machine tools, contracting and workshops.

The Americans put a lot of pressure on the Icelanders in 1945. It was a hugely sensitive issue and the government found itself having to step very carefully. But despite it all, the country turned down the offer of thousands of well-paid jobs that would have been tailor-made for strong, hard-working Icelandic men, and along with them enormous benefits in terms of currency earnings and economic growth. Ólafur Thors had talked about powerful military bases and 99-year leases. If this had happened, Battleship Iceland would have become a genuine foundation for an improved standard of living in the country. Note the magic words: jobs, currency earnings, prosperity, economic growth, work, economic growth, work, work, work. It seems amazing that anyone should reject these glittering temptations dangled before their eyes when the alternative was little more than a hazy and uncertain future and pie-eyed idealism. But as it said in black and white in the Treaty of Union, something that for many Icelanders lay at the very core of what the country was: 'Iceland affirms its permanent neutrality and that it will have no flag of war.'

It was thanks to this I got a TV and microwave

And what would be our understanding of history now if Iceland had gone down the road of Battleship Iceland? The national myth would have been something along the lines that the army had come and saved us from sinking back into the squalor and destitution of the depression years. It was thanks to the army and the army alone that we were able to survive in this inhospitable land, that we had work and money and self-respect. It was thanks to this that we had crawled out of our turf cottages, won a victory over lice and infant mortality, acquired food mixers, washing machines, cars and televisions, heat and electricity. Without the army, rock music and the Beatles would never have made it to Iceland. My parents met while working for the army; that's why I'm here. We'll never forget the boom years when bomber command was extending the airfield at Rangárvellir, bringing in endless work and foreign currency. There hadn't been such a boom in this country since the Cuban missile crisis in 1962. It was thanks to this we were able to complete the final section of the ring road round the country in the time of the Ford administration. It was thanks to this we can all get medical treatment at the National Military Hospital. It was thanks to this it's so easy to go abroad: the army flies almost daily to the USA and sometimes to Europe. It all got a lot better in the Nixon years. It was thanks to this that the country was able to support a population of 200,000 at its peak in 1980. People can say what they like about the army, but they've got to remember where the money comes from. There may be the odd arty intellectual type with a gripe against the army being here. But they'd do well to remember you need money to buy their poems and paintings. And where does the money come from?

A single one-off possibility, an accident, a piece of pure chance in the unfolding of history always appears to be the only possibility of all possible worlds. Even if society was on its last legs people could still say, 'Things aren't nearly so bad as they were in 1935. We didn't have television then. It was the army that got us out of our turf cottages.'

The Icelanders would of course have feared war. But another, more terrible, word would have caused far greater consternation:

PEACE!
IMMINENT THREAT OF PEACE!
Fears for Icelandic economy in wake of peace summit

It is probably a gross oversimplification to put any cultural deterioration at the door of the American military. The USA is the most influential country in world culture and a leader in every field, and without doubt we would have had much to learn from them. Relations westwards would have been stronger than with Scandinavia and Europe and various influences would have arrived directly from the USA and quicker. Students would have gone to university and become genuine hippies and beatniks or Republicans rather than Icelandic-sweater Maoists and Swedish Trotskyites. We might even have had politicians who could express themselves decently in English. We would have got our first McDonald's in 1975 and shopping mall in 1980. We would not have sold herring to Russia and my grandfather would have had a Chevrolet pickup instead of a Russian Moskvich. We would perhaps have had our representatives in the Berkeley riots and a member of the Warhol set and a filmmaker in Hollywood, and maybe a handful of soldiers in Vietnam.

But unlike conventional business and commerce, unlike travel or study abroad, the culture the army feeds out to people and nations is not primarily that of the great cities and the creative centres of the world, is not at the leading edge of fertile thought. Army discipline and unquestioning obedience is actually in direct opposition to creative and critical thinking. In times of peace, the people who drive changes in how the world thinks do not go into the army. Soldiers in peacetime are as often as not from small towns and provincial backwaters. For security reasons, 'Baseland' could have become a rather inward-looking society, serving only to increase our isolation. The fisheries out on the open seas might perhaps have had to be curtailed as presenting an unacceptable risk of confusion and chaos in such a strategically sensitive area. Who knows what kind of atmosphere might have resulted from a culture of dependency and impotence – healthy opposition, youthful enthusiasm and solidarity; constructive co-operation; or spiritual lethargy and enervation, and a kind of 'indigenous race effect', inadequacy, alcoholism, social problems and a need for constant sympathy and support?

There is no way of knowing if the army would have been the equivalent of some kind of military rule. It could have turned out to be very popular and taken a responsible role in society. Whatever was peculiar to Iceland, how appropriate ideas and jobs might be to our own unique conditions, might have been left in the hands of the politicians. The army might even have puts its mind to the sustainability of Icelandic society. Who knows?

113.

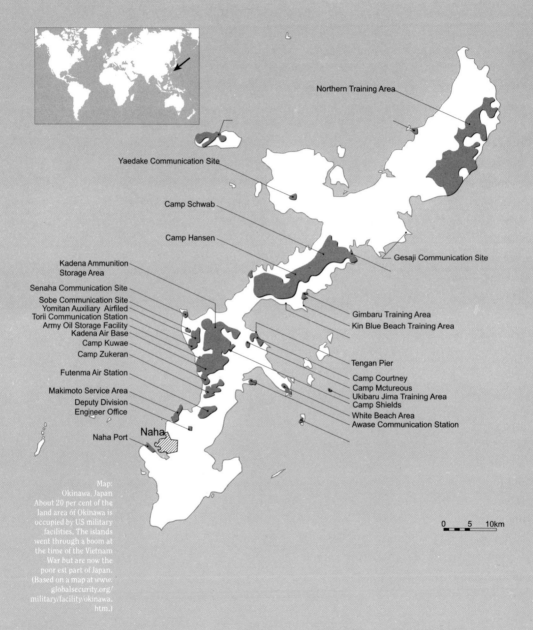

Northern Training Area

Yaedake Communication Site

Camp Schwab

Camp Hansen

Gesaji Communication Site

Kadena Ammunition
Storage Area

Senaha Communication Site
Sobe Communication Site
Yomitan Auxiliary Airfiled
Torii Communication Station
Army Oil Storage Facility
Kadena Air Base
Camp Kuwae
Camp Zukeran

Gimbaru Training Area
Kin Blue Beach Training Area

Futenma Air Station

Tengan Pier

Camp Courtney
Camp Mctureous
Ukibaru Jima Training Area
Camp Shields
White Beach Area
Awase Communication Station

Makimoto Service Area

Deputy Division
Engineer Office

Naha

Naha Port

Map:
Okinawa, Japan
About 20 per cent of the
land area of Okinawa is
occupied by US military
facilities. The islands
went through a boom at
the time of the Vietnam
War but are now the
poorest part of Japan.
(Based on a map at www.
globalsecurity.org/
military/facility/okinawa.
htm.)

0   5   10km

Okinawa, Japan

Okinawa gives us an insight into the reality that was on offer to the Icelanders in 1946. Okinawa is a group of islands to the south of Japan, with a population of about 1.4 million in an area only about a twentieth that of Iceland. The islands were occupied in 1945 and eleven military bases were set up there. Army and naval bases, airfields and training areas are scattered all over the islands, leaving the locals only limited access to their own land. Around 20 per cent of the land area is covered with military facilities and restricted zones. The military controls 40 per cent of Okinawa's airspace and about a third of its territorial waters. The army was and remains one of the main pillars of the economy and most of the islanders' income comes from the army and related services. At present there are around 30,000 US servicemen. At the peak in 1970 there were around 50,000 people working in connection with the bases. This number has now fallen to a little over 10,000.

Despite the massive military presence, Okinawa is the poorest part of Japan and the part with the highest unemployment. It is a beautiful place, with its own language, writing system and culture, related to but distinct from mainland Japan. It has the highest life expectancy of anywhere in the world. But tourism is underdeveloped and the islands suffer an image problem, largely bound up with the presence of the bases. For many people, Okinawa is nothing more than military facilities, a perception reinforced by the international coverage given to a number of serious crimes committed by US servicemen – crimes so brutal that describing them might sound like cheap propaganda intended to put the army in a bad light.

Source:
'Postwar legacy holds key to identity of Okinawans', interview with Matsusho Miyazato, Japan Times, 15 August 2002.

115.

Source:
Ota Masahide,
'Renegotiate with US
on Okinawa base issue',
International Herald
Tribune/Asahi, 5 June
2004.

The army is highly controversial in Okinawa. Many people are opposed to it. There have been big demonstrations and politicians have tried to envisage alternative ways for Okinawa to develop. In the Japan Times, the former deputy governor of Okinawa, Matsusho Miyazato, wrote an article considering what might have happened if there had not been any military bases: 'If we had not become dependent on the military, the economy of Okinawa would have flourished over the last fifty years.' Miyazato argued that, because of its location Okinawa, would have become a centre for trade between Japan, China and southeast Asia. Of the fifty-two towns and cities on Okinawa, average incomes are highest in those where there is no military presence.

So how come there is unemployment in the neighbourhood of an arsenal of this size? Shouldn't the *'multiplier effect'* be overwhelming? Is it possible that when a major section of the workforce is taken up servicing the demands of a single entity of this size it creates an imbalance? That this huge single force has a detrimental effect on the overall force? Can it be that, when people are cast in a mould that means that only one part of their powers is utilized, the 'security' destabilizes the equilibrium, the economy loses its energy, fluidity and resilience, and it becomes difficult to get talented people to take risks? Does it perhaps make it colder for those on the outside when so many are ensconced in the safe and warm? Can it be that a serious rift running through society acts like a tariff barrier and cripples people's natural interactions in some way?

Much has been written about the Okinawans' ambivalent attitude towards the army. There are indeed many who oppose it. But there are also strong indications that, if there was a vote on the issue, it would come out in favour of it staying. According to the webpage www.globalsecurity.org, 'There is no consensus among Okinawans on the bases. Since the employment of Okinawans on US bases is not inconsequential, there is even a sizeable though silent constituency in favor of the status quo.'

If Iceland had become Battleship Iceland with four big military bases, we would doubtless have done everything in our power to maintain the situation. There is no way we would ever have voted for changes that might have risked bringing collapse and unemployment down on our heads.

Andri Snær Magnason

In mankind there exists an incredible creative force and capacity to adapt, and at the same time a frighteningly powerful and tenacious desire to avoid change. The inhabitants of Battleship Iceland would doubtless have had the strength to transform their society, but in the situation they would also have been suckers for any leader who told them, 'Do not worry! We are in talks with people who are coming to save us.'

But as it was...

We got one base in Iceland, at the Keflavík airfield, a small thing to all the military facilities that might have gone up here. It is impossible to imagine how society might have developed without the army down in the southwest corner of our country. It is certainly the case that easy access to well-paid jobs had an adverse effect on educational levels in the Keflavík area. And that life has prospered on a non-militarized Snæfellsnes and in an Akureyri with no soldiers. But perhaps the case with Keflavík is not entirely comparable.

Going back to our real story, the army arrived here in 1951 and had a significant impact on national life – accounting at its high point in 1955 for 18 per cent of all Iceland's foreign earnings. Was this a good thing or a bad thing? Was this our destined path forward into the world we now inhabit, the only one of all possible ways into the modern age? Or did it hinder us from exploring other paths, grasping other opportunities and taking on greater challenges? The Marshall Plan for reconstruction after the Second World War provided much of the funding for the National Cement Works and the National Fertilizer Plant, for a pair of hydroelectric stations to meet the energy needs of an expanding Reykjavík, and for digging endless ditches to drain the sodden soils of the Icelandic countryside. But was it entirely the Marshall Plan and the benevolence of the US government that made this possible? Or would it have happened anyway? Or would, perhaps, society have developed in some completely different direction?

Was, for example, Marshall Plan aid an absolute prerequisite for the building of the two new power plants on the river Sogið in the years after 1950, when we had already built the one at Ljósifoss on the same river in 1937, just after the darkest days of the Great Depression? Had technology taken

Source:
Valur Ingimundarson, *In the firing line of the cold war*, p. 282.

a step backwards? Had the market for power fallen? Couldn't we have done it without the Americans? Or did the Marshall Plan maybe create a false basis, a distorted model and a skewing of natural selection in a society where a party membership card held more weight than professional qualifications, entrepreneurial skills, a cosmopolitan world-view and good, plain business sense? Did it give politicians more power than they warranted? Did we, through depending on others, fail to cultivate our own independence and creativity and choose instead to reward other things? Was it good that shipping companies were given monopolies for the transportation of certain goods, or that contractors with contacts in the right places cleared up on building projects on the Keflavík base, all with pretty certain guarantees of easy profits? Or did this blind people to the broader view, stop them from looking further afield, internationally for instance? At one time the US government considered buying up the entire catch of the entire Icelandic fishing fleet in order to prevent trade with the USSR. Is it likely that a closed deal of this kind would have led to better managed fisheries, better quality and higher profits, instead of having to compete on international markets?

So who was right, then? What would have happened if there had been someone other than Ólafur Thors at the helm, steering a delicate course between the demands of a great military power on one side and, on the other, national figures such as the bishop of Iceland, the writers Halldór Laxness and Thórbergur Thórðarson, the leader of his own coalition partners Hermann Jónasson, and a third of his own party members – in spite of the 'self-evident economic gains'? What would have happened if our leaders had taken the view that man's capacity to create his own opportunities for himself was the exception rather than the rule? If they had not had a different vision of the future, believed in other possibilities? Where would we be today?

Some might say, 'We would be the same Iceland, even if Battleship Iceland had become a reality. It would have been good at the time, too good an opportunity to miss, a sin to pass it up. With the end of the cold war we'd just have done something different.'

But if we really had become Battleship Iceland, we would almost certainly have been worse off in the long run. Icelanders would have been deprived of any influence over the growth and development of their national economy. People would have lived in a state of perpetual standby, straitjacketed by changes in US fiscal policy. All the country's wealth would have been concentrated within narrow channels, directly tied in with international affairs over which none of us had any control. On top of this, we would have placed enormous power in the hands of the military. An oversupply of secure work would have meant that fewer sought to get themselves educated. People maybe wouldn't have come to regard creativity and entrepreneurialism as central elements of economic life in this country, and many initiatives would probably have fallen by the wayside for want of qualified staff. In the long run, sudden wealth and rapid growth can undermine the foundations of a society and lock people into a system where some have it so easy that they no longer dare take risks.

Stokksnes

If anything deserves to be called the history of the generation of Icelanders now living it is probably the history of the cold war. However divided people's opinions may have been about the army, NATO, the peace movement or whatever else you want to call it, the fact remains that it happened and the cold war is *our* history every bit as much as the Soviet Union's and the United States'. Wherever you go in the world you can see memorials to ancient battles. But the cold war was primarily a condition, a state of being, not something so easily located on a map. The greatest battles took place inside our minds.

A little colony of islanders out in the north Atlantic had no say on the course of the cold war. Ten times more or less activity in this country presumably meant little on a global scale. A big build-up here would in fact only have called for a corresponding build-up somewhere else.

I was absolutely certain there would be a nuclear war before I reached my teens. I dreamed about it when I was 10, 11, 12. I read articles in *Morgunblaðið*, saw *The Day After* on the television, examined the instructions in the back of the phone book on how to protect oneself against radioactive fallout. I knew you should sleep under a supporting wall rather than an internal wall. I came to the conclusion that the store cupboard at home was probably the safest place to shelter and I had planned out in advance the route to the home of the girl I fancied at the time. Maybe I would need to save her life.

I don't know what effect it has if a whole generation grows up in the certain knowledge that the world is going to end, be poisoned and mutilated. What effect it has having no future to look forward to. I don't know whether there's actually been any research into this. When I asked my grandmother what it had been like being a child at the time of the Second World War she told me she had never been frightened. Unlike us, she had no pictures and films to feed her nightmares.

Like most of us, I have traipsed about the world and shuffled round ancient battlefields, palaces, monuments, pyramids and statues. Sometimes the places are interesting, sometimes not. Of all the historic sites I have ever visited, one of the most awe-inspiring experiences came as I roamed about the abandoned radar station at Stokksnes at the mouth of Hornafjörður, exposed to the elements on the bleak and windswept southern coast of our country. The place had the feel of some lost remains left behind by a world power, every bit as much as the Greek harbours of Sicily and the Roman columns you find throughout Europe.

Stokksnes was one of four radar stations in Iceland. It was built in 1954 and most of the buildings were abandoned in 1991. The station stands out on a headland not far from the national highway. It was like nothing else on earth, driving out along the neck of land on a heavy, grey December day and

Photographs:
The radar station at
Stokksnes. (Photograph:
Galdur/Sigurður Már
Halldórsson.)

seeing the mysterious antennas looming in the mist like something from a Star Wars film, with commanding mountain peaks to the right and the surf crashing on the rocks below where the tide rips through the channel between Hornafjörður and the open sea. The doors stood open and I was free to wander about the houses and control rooms and unearthly chambers as I wished. It was disconcerting to see this futuristic site crumbling into decay, like ruins from the future. There was little sign of wanton destruction at the hands of vandals; the ravages were down to the weather more likely. I climbed a flight

Andri Snær Magnason

of stairs and came out into the mushroom dome, one of the most stunning spaces I have ever been in. The material the dome was made of let through the light, making it bright inside, and the sound inside was like a hallucination of distorted echoes resonating from the walls straight back inside my head. In places there was an extraordinary amplification where two sound waves came together and interacted, turning a whisper into an ear-splitting wail; in others the sounds seemed to cancel each other out, so I stood in muffled silence however loud I shouted.

Stokksnes is the site of a history that never actually happened, a place of battles without bloodshed. The station was part of a situation that affected the lives of every single person in the northern hemisphere, the place where all the threads came together. One could picture the chain of events where some unidentified object on the screen at Stokksnes led to a command on the red

telephone in the White House. Thinking of the terrors of the cold war, the imminent apocalypse the world lived with, and then seeing the area abandoned and derelict, produced a feeling of vertigo. You became aware how everything can change in an instant. The station was built as a defence against a world power that no longer exists. But at the time, imagining the Soviet Union falling to pieces was as ludicrous as imagining the United States breaking up into ten separate little countries.

Countless possibilities for this place sprang to mind. The radar station and its surroundings would have made an amazing set for a film, advertisements or fashion photographs. It would have offered a perfect opportunity to put people into an unfamiliar environment, to educate them about the dangers on the oceans during the cold war, to hang up pictures of Russian submarines lurking underneath Icelandic fishing vessels, listening in to Icelandic radio with the noses of their warheads pointed on Keflavík and Reykjavík. They could have played interviews with old American and Russian servicemen. What it was like spending two years in a submarine? They could have had some retired soldiers come over for the summer and tell their stories. There could have been information on the science and technology, the weapons of mass destruction, and perhaps the importance of peace.

For almost forty years there were most of the time around 200 men stationed at Stokksnes, on the edge of the world, keeping track of submarines, aeroplanes, missiles and the movement of ships. The station formed part of a network that stretched right around the northern hemisphere. The antennas at Stokksnes maintained contact with other antennas in Greenland and the Azores. The resonating chamber, the antennas, the surf and the buildings. I found it extraordinary, and beautiful in its way, and I know my children would have thought the same, and my friends, and American soldiers. It would have made a fitting memorial to the 'battles' and the sacrifices involved in spending years of one's life in this place. I am convinced that people who once campaigned against the military bases, or for them, NATO men and supporters of non-alignment, government ministers and tourists would have got something worthwhile out of being able to see what this place was like.

There were forms and architectural styles unlike anything else that has been or ever will be built in this country. Their architectural history is just as much a part of Iceland as the timber-frame houses imported from Norway at the end of the nineteenth century that grace the streets of our towns and villages and attract visitors to our folk museums. The structures were powerfully built – you see it even in their decay – designed to withstand the worst the Icelandic climate could throw at them.

The Stokksnes radar station was demolished in spring 2003 at huge expense. The antennas, the vast white 'golf ball' spheres, everything was ground into dust. It had been an impressive piece of human engineering while it stood, but for some reason people seemed blind to the value inherent in the place and unwilling to use their money for reconstruction rather than demolition.

It seemed somehow emblematic of our cultural myopia that, at the same time as Stokksnes was being torn to pieces, people should want to build a permanent memorial the set of the third-rate James Bond movie *Die Another Day* being filmed nearby among the glacial debris of Jökulsárlón.

Perhaps one shouldn't interfere. But that doesn't mean lining up nuclear weapons and terrifying the wits out of a whole generation, and then acting as if nothing happened. By always pulling down the old instead of finding a new and constructive role for it is cutting the links that connect man to the physical world he lives in. The demolition cost millions. The bulldozer drivers were busy for a month. We all like a bit of digging. Great to shovel stuff around.

At Keflavík the possibilities are still there – even though the government has just recently set aside 1.3 million dollars for the demolition of the radar station at Rockville. The job will probably be finished by the time this book comes out. We live in the golden age of the digger. History gets shovelled over and the threads get broken, and with them we lose opportunities for the future and our chances of understanding the past.

Blessed war

One good thing about having lots of soldiers here in this country is that then they can't be out creating havoc somewhere else in the world. Our contribution to world peace. It wasn't the intention to launch into a diatribe against the army; what I wanted first and foremost was to use the army as an example of a comprehensive system that would have seen us all for work and so saved us from poverty. We got one military base, which maybe saved us from incorporation within the Soviet bloc at the time of the occupation of Czechoslovakia. There were Russian fishing boats lurking just outside our territorial waters, so perhaps the fear of invasion was not ungrounded. Iceland was a strategically important area. If the Americans were so crazy about being here, presumably the Russians would be too. The defence force made us an obvious target. Militarily, an attack on Iceland would have been the perfect scenario for trying out a nuclear weapon without plunging the world into all-out war, a perfect way to show you were serious and it was time to sit down at the negotiating table. We would have been targeted in exactly the same way as a puppet of the Soviet Union. All rather complicated. Maybe the best protection lay in the third utopia apparently on offer to us in the 1950´s, as headquarters of the United Nations. But that's another story. If the Marshall Plan had not enabled the country to build the State Fertilizer Plant, the government might even have been tempted to cosy up to the Soviet Union so as to be able to build the State Fertilizer Plant.

The controversy over the army in Iceland perhaps explains why the world cannot be a better place. We are facing the imminent threat of peace. The Americans want to reduce their military presence, even to pull out entirely. The world's leading defence experts consider the Keflavík air base surplus to requirements; we are no longer under any threat of attack. That must be regarded as a good thing. If because of the costs and our strategic unimportance the Americans don't want to be here, the Russians will doubtless want it still less. Long-range aircraft and guided missiles can take out targets anywhere in the world, from anywhere – from the US Midwest, from the middle of the Pacific Ocean. The spectre of peace looms not only over the northern hemisphere, it reigns supreme. This isn't just good, isn't just extraordinary, it's totally insane. In the last few years I've been to Tallinn in Estonia and to Lithuania, to Croatia and St Petersburg and East Germany and Poland, and I've met and made friends with people in countries that were previously locked away in isolation behind the Iron Curtain. In New York I met a man about the same age as me who had grown up in Moscow and drunk Icelandic cod liver oil sent there in exchange for granddad's Moskvich, as part of a trade deal set up in 1969. He said to me, 'When I was small I thought you were going to blow me to kingdom come.' To which I answered, 'Ditto.' Ha ha. Cod liver oil, Moskvich cars and nuclear warheads. There's nothing like shared memories. We should be making the most of the peace, having a good time, holding peace parties in the house in Reykjavík where Reagan met Gorbachov, inviting all the Russians we know, and all the Americans and the Germans and the Jews and the Muslims, and nurturing the peace with trade and relations and marriages, speed dating, dinner parties and holidays.

Peace is the best thing anyone can ask for. If people disarm on both sides of all borders we'll all feel better for it and we'll be able to get on with normal relations and down to business. Weapons demand to be used. My neighbour feels safe because I don't have a gun. Iceland will not split up into warring clans like in the Middle Ages – the Sturlungs and the Ásbirnings and the rest – while the men of the country haven't been trained in carrying weapons. Arms make it easier for leaders to issue threats that they are then forced to carry out if they don't want their 'credibility' to be blown.

It's a complicated business. Clearly. Understandably, people who work for the army don't want to lose their jobs. But the military presence is being cut year by year. This is a major part of the economy, a big typewriter factory faced by the terrifying advance of the computer revolution. I met a woman who works on the base. She said the atmosphere there was dreadful – this man and that given his notice, everyone keeping their heads down, no one daring to say a word, no one knowing who would be next. The warning signs were there, writ large. Lots of people are feeling bad. A sensitive matter. The army is a pillar of the economy. One journalist said it was the equivalent of an aluminium plant. According to information from the defence force, there were 910 Icelanders working on the base in 2002. By 1 January 2005 the number was down to 674. Disbursements to Icelandic companies were reckoned to be around 150 million dollars in 2003, representing about 4 per cent of our foreign earnings, 1.5 per cent of GNP – well down on 1970, when the army accounted for 2.6 per cent of GNP. The whole amount is not in fact directly due to the army: the figures take in people working at the airport, which is to remain, so not all the jobs are at risk. By way of comparison, currency earnings from tourism in 2004 were around 500 million dollars.

But there is imminent danger of peace. People are losing their jobs. They feel bad, they fear the future and the unknown. Union leaders are getting anxious, politicians too. They don't want to be seen as being impotent. But the burden is too great. A politician cannot just magic up all these jobs. All he can do is attempt to find a suitable factory to replace them all. 'Be patient, discussions are under way.' But no guarantees anything will turn up. The future hangs in the air and the only solution is to hold on to what we've got. The entire *raison d'être* for the work is evaporating. No one is buying the typewriters, but what can we do? Keep churning them out and hope? Perpetuate a system that was built on a fractured world-view? Or confront reality face to face? Is it really such a terrifying prospect?

What happens if the army goes? It will leave behind in total rather over four million square feet of living space. The equivalent of seven decent-sized shopping malls. Enough for a cocktail party to which the entire Icelandic nation could be invited. Offices, shopping space, restaurants, canteens, bars, hospitals, schools, nurseries, baseball pitches, football pitches, a skating rink, bowling alleys, sports halls, aircraft hangars, garages. A whole small town ready for handing over, turfed and tarmacked. Nine hundred flats built to Icelandic standards, with roads, pavements and playgrounds. The army will leave behind an area that does not exist in the minds of most Icelanders. We see the houses, and yet don't see them an imaginary world, a whole town outside our borders, another planet, the realm of the hidden people. The district is

131.

Map:
If the army leaves, an entire small town with associated amenities will become available: flats, schools, offices, industrial workspace, sports facilities and more. The numbers on the map indicate the following:
1. Bank.
2. Icelandic bank.
3. Filling station.
4. Car wash.
5. Library.
6. Air force hangar.
7. Football pitch.
8. Elementary school.
9. Softball field.
10. Gymnasium.
11. Chapel. 12. Cinema.
13. Pre-school nursery.
14. University of Maryland and Webster.
15. High school.
16. Hairdresser's (Icelandic).
17. Hospital.
18. Skating rink.
19. Fire station.
20. Swimming pool.
21. Youth centre.
22. Kids club.
(Based on a map published by the US Army Command in Iceland.)

cut off from Keflavík by a Berlin Wall, but there would be no problem bringing the two together. In four million square feet there must be some opportunities. Parts of it are run down but there is lots that isn't. The houses lie half an hour from a booming, expanding capital city and a stone's throw from an international airport, slap-bang on the route between Europe and America. And yet somehow people find it hard to see the possibilities that are staring them in the face.

Talking is easy. None of this is my responsibility. But the main point is this: is it the army that sustains the people, or is it the other way round? If the people were not there, who would keep the army going? Doesn't keeping it going require certain skills and talents? The metaphor that we all live *on* something means that people fail to appreciate their own contributions and capabilities and see themselves as the product of a process rather than the driving force behind the process itself.

All these facilities are there to be sold. Builders and fitters can get work converting them. People can move into the houses and shop in the shops. People can find jobs selling things in the shops. People could work in Reykjavík, Keflavík, at the airport, at the nearby Blue Lagoon spa, in new companies or in old companies that relocate. The children can go to school. Teachers can teach them to read, teach them sports and music. The children will grow and get married and have kids of their own who will go to the school. A second cycle gets under way. History can be brought in to give the place value and identity. We can preserve such military remains as are worth preserving, create a museum of the cold war and breathe new life into all the rest. Worth keeping the US/Icelandic street names? Consciously conserve the American influences and play with them? Allow old aircraft to remain in place for the sake of decoration?

Is there a company out there that's been hounded from pillar to post for premises that might finally find a suitable home in these big, unusual spaces? Car workshops and warehousemen? Any chance of stopping turning the lavafields around Hafnarfjörður into a tip and moving some of the businesses out to Keflavík? Maybe SOMETHING might come of this that no one can foresee because we don't know what song is going to be written next. Who knows? No guarantees, and there might be many slips and false starts on the way. Yes, OK, I'm organizing the world again. But this is blank space, free for anyone to think into. Just musings. And of course, the future is a terrifying prospect.

I met a man who said, 'If the army goes, the Keflavík area's finished, and the whole place'll be down the pan.' I met another who had worked for years for contractors on the base; he was despondent about the future. 'It'll be terrible,' he said. 'We'll maybe get some work pulling down all the buildings and things. After that, nothing I can see.' 'Pulling down the buildings?' I asked. 'Yes, it's all got to be demolished. According to the defence agreement they're supposed to leave the land in the state they found it.' 'Isn't there some way to use these buildings?' I asked. 'No, because then property prices in the area would collapse,' he said. 'The buildings have got to be demolished. The army's supposed to put the area back in its original condition. Aren't you an environmentalist? Isn't it their job to clean up after themselves?'

These fears are not entirely unfounded. Property prices could collapse. The region could experience a sudden mass exodus. But for simple reasons of geography it is unlikely that everything will go bottom up: the place is too close to Reykjavík, too close to the airport; too much space is going to become free, and there are too many people who can, will, and know how to build it up. There are simply too many who will have something to gain from the opportunities. Still, it would be showing a culpable lack of sensitivity to act as if watching people losing their jobs is a wonderful opportunity. You wouldn't get elected to parliament on the platform: 'Recession is opportunity. Recession is constructive. No transformation without recession.'

There was an interview on the news with a woman who worked in a store on the base. 'I mean, I only know how to serve in dollars,' she said. Which of course elicited sighs of sympathy from the listeners. Instead of people seeing this as a patent example of someone who seemed utterly unaware of her own capabilities, I was half expecting someone to step forward on her behalf and claim to be acting as spokesman for women who only know how to sell things in dollars.

Despite the problem – and the run-down – having been evident for ages, no kind of constructive debate on the subject yet appears to have surfaced. The problem has never been subjected to public scrutiny and analysis. No one has put forward models of how things might be handled – not unless the demolition counts as constructive debate in the eyes of the demolition company. Maybe this is something they could take up with their political representatives, something even that people might fight for 'in Keflavík's interests'. The demolition was to be financed by the US army, so I suppose it could be marked down as 'currency earnings'. The fear of economic collapse is a cousin to the fear of technological advance and other changes – the spreadsheet, the foreigner, the tractor and the filleting machine.

If the change is inevitable, which is better, a swift mercy killing or a painful and lingering death? The system is locked and cannot grow organically. The number employed will not go up naturally in line with capabilities and human resources. A workforce of 700 will not become 730 or 750 or 1200 after five years; just the odd hand-picked recruit here or there. Someone who under normal circumstances has the talent, energy and expertise to create or manage a workforce of twenty counts himself lucky not to get his own papers. Is it better for the army to shrivel away over ten years or for it all to go in one fell swoop? When things get really bad, something generally turns up to take their place – people's strength in numbers is unleashed, existing hierarchies break down, and the old pecking order changes. A real crisis or a total collapse can be necessary for a reshuffling of the pack and a transformation of society. The slow approach might actually lock those with the greatest powers to transform society into the dying system. The hand-picking might leave too many people in some way broken or twisted by their experiences rather than emerging stronger as a whole.

This is a complicated matter, of course, and a genuinely sensitive and painful business to many people. When someone's self-esteem is shattered it can be difficult to build it up again. So it is important that no one takes it personally if the cold war is over and done with: it was not because somebody wasn't doing their job properly.

Iceland's slice of a trillion dollars

Warfare is a science: people try to know their opponent, find out how he thinks and what forces he has and the weapons at his command; they try to achieve maximum preparedness at minimum expense, look for focused and cost-effective solutions rather than just setting up defences at random. If Iceland needs defence, the first thing to do is to identify and define the enemy, consider why he is the enemy, what danger he represents, how he might attack us, with what weapons and how such an attack might be repelled. We need to consider ways of countering the enemy, or, failing that, of improving relations with him. It can hardly be so complicated.

For whatever reason, the defence debate in Iceland has centred primarily on employment, money, foreign earnings, GNP, pillars of the economy and yesterday's politics. The Americans tell us to specify our defence needs, but so far no one in the media nor any of the experts has made any serious attempt to do so. Would we need tanks? A helicopter gunship? Torpedoes? Who is the enemy? What kind of preparation do we need to be able to respond to him? The only thing we hear is the refrain, 'We must have four fighter jets as a symbol of intent.' The cheapest thing would be to fit them out from Britain. If neither the politicians nor the people can see the enemy, is it possible he simply doesn't exist? Do we lack the enemies to justify the defences?

Headline in *Morgunblaðið*, 17 March 2004
**'Could have a positive effect on discussions
over future of base.'**
Solveig Pétursdóttir, Chair of the Parliamentary Foreign Affairs Committee,
on the Re-assessment of Priorities in the Wake of the Atrocities in Madrid.

Anyone can fall into that trap, though few of us would ever openly admit to thinking that way. This is not a malicious glorying in catastrophe but a human reaction. Protecting the interests of an entire country places politicians under a heavy burden. Those who work for the defence forces are racked with uncertainty, a perfectly understandable uncertainty: fear of unemployment and perhaps poverty, recession, unhappiness and despair. This all lies on the shoulders of the politician who has to bear this responsibility, and so the mind is apt to seek a cold appra : Blessed war – the atrocities were appalling, but they 'could have a positive effect'. If we look at the army as any other business, service or line of work, then it is perfectly consistent to regard atrocities as a 'new market' or a 'business opportunity' now that the Russian enemy has evaporated into thin air.

Looking out to the broader context, Iceland's problem helps us to understand why the world cannot become a better place. If, for economic reasons, and in spite of the great prosperity and the opportunities it currently enjoys, a country which has no enemies is unwilling to reduce the scale of its military, we get a vivid insight into why most countries in the world find it hard to reduce their militaries – even though the majority of their citizens might want them to and the revenue and creative effort that goes into the military is astronomically, criminally high when set against the hunger and poverty in the world. The amount of knowledge in the world ought to be enough to alleviate the suffering of millions. Thirty thousand children die of hunger and curable diseases every day. Millions are dying of aids. What the world needs more than military training is basic education in healthcare and medicine. Young boys are being taught to kill before they have learned to live.

Source:
SIPRI (Stockholm
International Peace
Research Institute)
(2005), 'Military
expenditure',
*SIPRI Yearbook
2005: armaments,
disarmament and
international security*,
SIPRI: [Stockholm].
Details available on
http://yearbook2005.
sipri.org/ch8/ch8.

Total spending on defence around the world in 2005 amounted to almost 1000 billion dollars. This was the sixth consecutive year the figure had increased. The most significant factor in this was the American government's 'war on terror', with the USA responsible for around half of all military spending in the world. After the USA the biggest spenders on defence are Britain, France, China and Japan. However, military spending is down by about 6 per cent from at the height of the cold war in the years 1987-8.

Most of us have doubtless allowed ourselves to imagine how the world would be if all this time, energy, thought and resources were channelled into

138.

something better – not far short of one trillion dollars. $1,000,000,000,000. You would hardly notice it if some of the noughts disappeared. But everywhere there are military bases and weapons factories you get the Keflavík problem, you get military interests sustaining jobs and communities, schools and welfare systems. In many cases it is the army itself that provides the principal source of employment for a town, a state or a country. Working in the factories you will find good, honest folk – labourers, technicians, specialists, cleaners and managers, people who want to live and bring up their children and pay off their loans and, above all else, not lose their jobs. This makes it easier to understand why childhood dreams of disarmament are not going to come true. Of course no one wants war. Of course no one wants nuclear bombs. But the fact is that this man makes his living from designing the bomb, and that woman pays her bills by screwing it together, and if the factory closes down WHAT ARE THEY GOING TO DO THEN?

The Keflavík case maybe gives us a terrifying picture of what might happen if peace were one day to spread across the planet like some sort of a virus. How could we fail to be moved by the headlines in the world's press?

WORLD PEACE THREATENS LOCAL ECONOMY

RIOTS IN DETROIT BLAMED ON WORLD PEACE

WORLD PEACE – THE TRAGEDY OF MY LIFE

People's fears and sense of impotence are open to manipulation, consciously or unconsciously. The owner of a weapons factory can hold up the powerlessness of his staff and use it for his own ends. Picture the little town of Jättebra in Sweden. The pillar of the town's economy is the arms manufacturer Bofors. Cutbacks in the Swedish army left the town facing redundancies – until the trades union put pressure on the local council and the local council put pressure on the politicians and the politicians got the army to buy more weapons to keep the factory going, thereby 'supporting' the local economy. And so the politician thereby saved his job, and the local councillor his, and the union leader his, and the people of the town theirs: and there were celebrations all around for all concerned. (Jättebra is an alias for another town whose name I am withholding to protect the good name of its citizens.)

Thus a vicious circle of impotence can sustain a system that no sane person would ever have set out deliberately to create. The people of Jättebra could even provide an indirect pretext for the unilateral contravention of arms embargoes: 'If you forbid me from selling to that army general out in Africa, I might be forced to lay off a number of family breadwinners. But of course it's entirely up to you if you don't want economic growth and export earnings and the French company gets the contract and our former employees turn to drink and drugs and start beating their wives and their children go the dogs...'

If we look at how the people of Iceland reacted to the imminent closure of the Keflavík base, we can better understand President Eisenhower's prescient warnings in his farewell address to the American nation in 1961:

> *This conjunction of an immense military establishment and a large arms industry is new in the American experience. The total influence – economic, political, even spiritual – is felt in every city, every state house, every office of the Federal government. We recognize the imperative need for this development. Yet we must not fail to comprehend its grave implications. Our toil, resources and livelihood are all involved; so is the very structure of our society.*

In the councils of government, we must guard against the acquisition of unwarranted influence, whether sought or unsought, by the military-industrial complex. The potential for the disastrous rise of misplaced power exists and will persist.

We must never let the weight of this combination endanger our liberties or democratic processes. We should take nothing for granted. Only an alert and knowledgeable citizenry can compel the proper meshing of the huge industrial and military machinery of defense with our peaceful methods and goals, so that security and liberty may prosper together.

The world is full of working people, good people, industrious people, fine and honest people, people with industrial skills, highly educated people and people with no education at all and everything in between, most of them united by a desire not to stop doing what they are doing at present. And for this reason it is impossible to turn our resources to something more intelligent, like healthcare and education. If the people themselves see no way out of their predicament and have no wish to change their society, that just makes it all the less likely that the leader will be able to do so! And so he keeps the system as it is, because there is nothing more difficult than organizing the future of a whole nation and bearing the responsibility for its possible collapse. And so weapons are churned out for a thousand billions dollars, just waiting for some idiot to come along and use them. For decades on end the people in charge may be sane and moderate, but sooner or later, wherever you are, some disreputable wannabe will come crawling out of the woodwork, his fingers just itching to get hold of those weapons and his mind on the lookout for a reason to use them.

Throughout the world there are societies built around the manufacture of tanks, bombs, missiles, nuclear weapons and assault rifles specifically designed for killing people and of no earthly use at all for shooting rabbits. There are thousands of communities and factories whose whole existence depends on the industry. Never in the history of mankind have so many people shown so much ingenuity in the construction of these devices. Many of them are works of the purest genius, created with incredible expertise, imagination and skill to fulfil the most intricate and demanding technical requirements. How do you get a bomb to go round a corner? Every bomb used in the Iraq war cost more than each house that was blown up.

But despite the hordes of highly educated people and the craftsmen and businessmen who pour their talents into the most complex projects every day of their working lives, the fear of the unknown remains. Peace prevails, maybe, and war is over, and the threat is as inconceivable as Germany invading France. The object is not to have built weapons and to have fought wars; the object is to be continually developing and building new weapons. The weapons pile up and create new problems.

What are we going to do with all these weapons? They need either to be sold or put into storage. If bombs are stored for too long they corrode and become unstable and liable to self-detonate. They are full of poisons, heavy metals, radioactive materials like depleted uranium used to harden warheads for piercing armoured tanks. All this stuff is difficult and expensive to dispose of in your own country. Dismantling weapons is a tricky business. In which case, there might be a temptation to *use* them. What are the chances that the next international dispute to come along might provide just too tempting an opportunity to flush away the excess stock out of airborne B-52 garbage trucks? If that bomber was never used, what was the point in having it in the first place? Isn't there something in the nature of things that calls for their being used? Doesn't a bomber ask to be used? Doesn't its pilot want to use it? Does the general who ordered it want it to look as if he made a mistake?

It is hardly pure coincidence that in each and every air war of recent years the quantity of bombs dropped has exceeded by some distance the total quantity dropped in the whole of the Second World War. Is the bombing solely for military purposes, or is the war being used as a pretext to clear out excess stock? A B-52 bomber can fly all the way from the USA to Afghanistan and back again without landing, so the method is neither expensive nor dangerous. The pilot can set off at midnight and be home in time for dinner. Is there any connection between carpet bombing a desert and the fact that a congressman saved the jobs of the people of a small town in Missouri and so *staved off* unemployment? Of course we don't want more wars, but there's no avoiding the fact that it has a positive effect on shopping and services.

The headlines appear in the local paper: 'Unrest in the Middle East raises hopes of better times.' 'Property prices up in Nebraska suburbs after reprisal attacks in Palestine.' 'Saudi government expresses interest in new missile system.' The companies have owners and shareholders, and the owners and shareholders make their profits, often very nice profits, out of highly reliable and solvent customers like governments, or maybe some dictator who has pocketed the wealth of his subjects to feed his personal ambitions. A lot of people do very well out of war. There are fortunes to be made out of fear and instability. One man's death is another man's microwave. There are two sides to every dispute, so if you arm one side you might as well arm the other – with double the profit for yourself. That is business. You need to create a market. Insecurity breeds the need for increased security. Just as burglar-alarm salesmen play up the dangers of burglary, so national leaders play up dangers of international unrest in direct proportion to the power and money available.

There is, for example, a nagging suspicion here in Iceland that this country's support for the Iraq War was motivated partly by economic considerations. If this is true of us, we can just imagine how the directors of arms companies in the USA would have viewed the matters, especially given their easy access to the political leaders making the decisions. Where would they have seen their interests better served, by going down the path of war or through a summit of world leaders, say, on a neutral rock in the North Atlantic? I met a politician who whispered in my ear, 'Would you put several hundred jobs at risk for a signature that means nothing?'

Our particular situation allows us to look with clearer eyes into the wider context. Here we have one of the richest countries in the world, a country with no natural enemies bar the polar bear and the humpback whale, and with a vast store of unexploited international opportunities. And yet even so we cannot approach the question of the army base in an open and imaginative manner. If you look at things this way, you can understand why so many systems are so determined to keep things as they are. Why the people of Jättebra in Sweden do not want to stop building bombs. Why cutting production at the Tomahawk guided missile factory in Colorado is not an option. Why experts at Lockheed in Nebraska want to develop ever bigger and more powerful long-range missiles. All societies want to grow. And because of this, the trillion, the thousand billion, is inevitably going to grow in line with international economic growth. And it is also, inevitably, going to grow even faster if there is any sign of recession, since this is the one sure method open to politicians in many countries to create jobs, to protect jobs, to get the wheels of the economy moving, to shore up the foundations of society.

Of course we ought to be in NATO, taking an active part and having our voice heard. Doing something useful. Membership of NATO puts us in an unrivalled position to put forward points of view that other countries have filtered out on their way up the military hierarchy. The world, for example, has a considerably greater need for rescue helicopters than for jet fighters. Machines call to be used, and what an amazing sight it would be, a thousand helicopters on the tarmac, prepared for take-off, in readiness for the next major flood, earthquake or hurricane! We have seamen here who can tell you what it is like, seeing the light appear in the sky and the winchman coming down like God from heaven.

A Self-Help Manual for a Frightened Nation

A leader rules and yet not. In the struggle for narrow self-interests, people are liable to forget history, what the experience of war taught previous generations. The crowning point of the Icelanders' struggle for independence occurred in 1918, and was sealed in words that were not just empty blather. A war had just ended that had cost twenty million lives:

Denmark declares to foreign nations that, in accordance with the substance of this Treaty of Union, it recognizes Iceland as a sovereign state and declares moreover that Iceland affirms its permanent neutrality and that it will have no flag of war.

PERMANENT. Words mean something. The people who drafted the Treaty of Union presumably did not envisage the remotest possibility of any generation yet to come ever being better equipped to take an informed decision on war. No subsequent generation would ever know more about the horrors and suffering and their consequences. And so they used the word PERMANENT, because any other conclusion was unthinkable. In 1945 people still took this seriously. Why? Probably this is something that only those who have looked on twice as Europe burned to the ground can understand. It is the militarism that turns ideals into monsters.

It is a very serious matter when people lose sight of the basic values human life is built on, when the danger signs are disregarded and the unthinkable floats up to the surface. Nightmare examples offer themselves from all quarters – phoney wars, deception, propaganda and torture:

Source:
'Against torture', leading
article, Morgunblaðið, 8
October 2005.

It is extraordinary to think that at the start of the 21st century the US Congress should need to agree a ban on American soldiers torturing and degrading prisoners. Even more amazing is the idea that it is thought that George W. Bush, the US President, may use his veto against the resolution.

At times like these it is good to be a sovereign nation, to have learned from the experience of the generations that experienced war, to have a voice and to use it to have a constructive influence on the unfolding of world events.

Andri Snær Magnason

144.

But this provides no guarantee against people ignoring the fundamental principles and getting wrapped up in the interests of the woman who only knows
how to serve in dollars. For a taste of the authentic voice of Iceland, see the
seven-minute dramatic interlude that follows, taken from the White House
webpage, www.whitehouse.gov.

This country is host to a world power that is looking to reduce its
spending on war. If it succeeds in this without society going down the drain,
we will perhaps have gained something important in the way of knowledge
and experience that we can export to other parts of the world – a change in
attitude maybe, a lesson in how to shut down military bases and weapons factories elsewhere. The army is probably going to go whatever happens. There
would be a certain glory in having pre-empted the cuts through a conscious
decision rather than waiting to be driven into it by compulsion. Perhaps the
options are not everywhere as clear as they are in Keflavík. But wherever an
army shuts down, housing and propriety be freed up and people with a wide
range of talents, enough even to maintain an entire army division, will be able
to move on and pursue other careers.

And it is by such means that mankind might be able to edge its way
towards the main goal: a better world.

President Bush Welcomes Iceland Prime Minister to White House
Remarks by President Bush and Prime Minister Oddsson of Iceland
in a Photo Opportunity

The Oval Office

10:59 A.M. EDT

PRESIDENT BUSH: It's my honor to welcome the Prime Minister of Iceland to the Oval Office. [...] Mr. Prime Minister, thank you for coming.

PRIME MINISTER ODDSSON: Thank you very much, Mr. President. I'm very happy to be here, not least on the President's birthday. It's a privilege.

PRESIDENT BUSH: Thank you for remembering.
[...]
Q: Mr. Prime Minister, did you reach an agreement on the defense treaty with Iceland?

PRIME MINISTER ODDSSON: That was never -- the meeting -- was to have an agreement. Now, today I had the opportunity to explain my view of the issue to the President, and he is looking into my position and the Iceland position, but he had an open mind.

PRESIDENT BUSH: Yes. Let me comment on this, about -- this is an issue related to the F-15s. For the American press, we've got four F15 fighters stationed there. The Prime Minister pressed very hard for us to keep the fighters there. He was very eloquent, very determined that the United States keep the troops there. [...] I told the Prime Minister I'm -- I appreciate our alliance, I appreciate his friendship. I fully understand the arguments he's made and we will work together to solve the issue. Holland, where are you?

Q: Here, sir. Thank you. There's a story today that the CIA held back information from you that Iraq had abandoned its WMD [Weapons of Mass Destruction] programs. Is that true? [...]

PRESIDENT BUSH: [...] This is information from the report of the United States Senate [...]. I will look at the whole report. I will tell you, however, that I know that Saddam Hussein was a threat. He was a threat to the neighborhood; he was a threat to the people of Iraq. He harbored terrorists. Mr. Zarqawi, who continues to kill and maim inside of Iraq, was in the country prior to our arrival. Saddam Hussein had the intent, he had the capability, and the world is better off without Saddam Hussein in power. And the world will be more peaceful when this Iraqi government, under Prime Minister Allawi, emerges and there are elections. And that's what we're seeing. We're seeing a transformation in a part of the world that needs liberty and freedom. And so I look forward to the full report, and I'll react to it when I see it. Anybody else?

PRIME MINISTER ODDSSON: Well, I just -- on this, I must say I agree with the President about Iraq. The future of Iraq is -- the future of the world is much better because of the undertaking that the United States, United Kingdom and their alliances took there. And without that done, the situation in that area of the world would be much more dangerous than it is now. There's hope now. There was no hope before.

PRESIDENT BUSH: Thank you, Mr. Prime Minister.

(Everyone sings "Happy Birthday" to the President.)

PRESIDENT BUSH: Thanks. You actually call that singing? (Laughter.) It was beautiful.

END 11:06 A.M. EDT

Source:
'President Bush welcomes Iceland prime minister to White House,' transcript of conversation between the US president and the prime minister of Iceland, 6 July 2004. www.whitehouse. gov/news/ releases/ 2004/07/20040706-2. html.

It is not possible to build one pyramid

Man has a tendency to preserve established systems whether they make sense or not. A longing for security and fear of change and uncertainty make people hold fast to the existence they know, however unreasonable it may be. A look at the Egyptian pyramids with this in mind gives cause for some interesting conjectures, without our actually needing to know anything much about the history of Egypt itself. We can assume that all the pyramids were built during a continuous period of production, rather than at intervals of say two hundred or a thousand years, we can express one conjecture as follows: it is not possible to build one pyramid. If people are going to build pyramids at all, then there will be at least three of them, and they will have to get progressively bigger. The third one must be the biggest of all.

The pyramids were built as the burial sites for dictators, so we can also assume a building time of not more than thirty or forty years: dictators trust no one, least of all their successors. For God it is maybe possible to raise a church that takes five hundred years to finish, but dictators are generally of a type: they may set themselves on a divine pedestal, but they are mortal men that want things to happen while they are still alive to see the results.

The fertility of the Nile valley was such that tens of thousands of men found themselves in a position to spend their time doing more than just sowing and reaping to fill their bellies. They had already managed to build themselves houses, set up schools and invent letters to preserve their laws and stories. Life was doubtless very good in the cradle of civilization. The pharaoh was filled with a sense of his smallness, even loneliness, seeing all those people filling their storehouses with food, having fun, lying in the sun, swimming in the Nile, and even doubting his power and superior intelligence. And he thought to himself, 'Just look at all that strength and vitality going to waste! What couldn't we achieve if it all was channelled into one mighty stream?' And it hit him that everything would be better if he himself controlled the harvest and put it to use for something more worthwhile.

Pharaoh calls in this chief engineer and gets him to work out what it would be possible to do if he himself cornered the whole harvest and portioned it out in exchange for work. The engineer sketches out the simplest form there is – a pyramid. The genius lies in this involving an extremely simple idea and at the same time a very large amount of work. The job makes only moderate demands of people's expertise and experience and leaves the labourers too physically tired to threaten the pharaoh's power.

Pharaoh announces to the masses that a gigantic pyramid will now be built, a tomb for himself, and rounds up the harvest. The engineer unveils the big plan. Many are outraged, there is some grumbling, but he doesn't let that get at him. Whether he allows the people to talk and just ignores them or throws them to the crocodiles of the Nile is no big issue. To save on costs Pharaoh decides not to use slaves but wage slaves – slaves need watching over, feeding, clothing and driving forward; they may be physically bound, but spiritually they are free and look to escape at the first opportunity. Wage slaves turn up to work voluntarily and can work for wages way below subsistence levels. What they fear above all else is freedom, which they call unemployment.

The project gets under way and before you know it there is a splendid 30,000 man conveyor belt with a chief engineer, foremen and wage slaves. Never before in the history of the world has such a huge group of men worked in such united fashion on such a stupendous project. It is a MAGNIFICENT SIGHT, no denying it, looking across the desert and seeing the army of workers bowed to a single will. The gigantic conception is in reality incredibly tiny: a pyramid is just as much a pyramid if it is one metre tall or a hundred. The difference lies in the time and work involved. A big pyramid is no more use than a little one. A dead man in a little pyramid is just as dead as a dead man in a big pyramid.

And so the building of the pyramid comes to an end. The pharaoh dies and is laid in his crypt with pomp and circumstance and is succeeded by his son, Pharaoh II. He is of a different cast of mind to his father and has his own ideas, but he inherits the pharaoh's chief engineer and right-hand man, and

Andri Snær Magnason

the first day Pharaoh II turns up to work the chief engineer lays before his feet a design for an even bigger pyramid. Pharaoh II is not quite sure, but a resolution arrives on his desk from the AEWS (Association of Egyptian Wage Slaves): 'The general council of the AEWS resolves that, in so far as Pharaoh II surpasses his father in all respects, he deserves an EVEN MORE MAGNIFICENT PYRAMID.'

The pharaoh looks across the sands and sees the danger: thirty thousand wage slaves who have finished a magnificent edifice, thirty thousand strong men who are experts in building precisely this kind of edifice, banging their pickaxes and shovels and shouting, MORE WORK! But Pharaoh II decides to take the risk. He calls a referendum: What do you want to do? Though thousands have sacrificed their lives in building this thing, the majority still votes for the plan the engineer puts before them: a NEW AND EVEN BIGGER PYRAMID! And so everything goes round again. A new period of progress ensues and the sons of the men who built the first pyramid join in with the work and everything proceeds as before for the next twenty or thirty years. Pharaoh II dies without anything having changed. His son takes over and unsolicited another resolution comes in from the AEWS to the effect that he shall be built the biggest pyramid in history. Nobody questions what the point is: the need for a new pyramid is self-evident. The third and last pyramid rises from the sands and no one remembers any longer how life was before all this madness got going.

The third pyramid is a monster, and everyone gawks at the three pyramids that stand in a row shining in the desert. Then, suddenly, it is as if somebody sobers up. One man scratches his head, then another. What now? Are we supposed to build a fourth pyramid, then a fifth, sixth, seventh and all the way forward to the end of time? Can this work in the long run? The rumour gets round that over in the barren land of Greece there are men who are not hellbent on death but on life. There are people there building theatres where you can go and sit at the weekend with a glass of wine and a basket of bread and watch tragedies. The people there are not all slaves – at most only one in every two. Down south along the Nile three generations have squandered their lives for three dead men.

So what happened after the third pyramid? Hard to say. Maybe pharaoh sent the wage slaves off to war to conquer the neighbouring kingdom and got shot of the Association of Wage Slaves that way. Maybe there was a timely rebellion. Maybe the harvest failed, which solved the matter of its own accord by decimating the workforce. Maybe he threw them all to the crocodiles. Maybe there was a period of uncertainty for a couple of years while society readjusted. But the conclusion is this: It is not possible to build one pyramid. Given reasonable stability, there must be at least three, whether the leader likes it or not. Once an idea or possibility has come into the picture, it has a tendency to spread and fill the whole frame available.

If this parable is set against the findings of archaeological research, it seems there may be something in the conjecture. The pyramids were built over a period of around 110 years about 4500 years ago, between about 2575 and 2465 BC. This was a very brief moment in human history, a bizarre interval, but those who were stuck in the middle of it seem to have been blind to the possibility of any different arrangement or way of living. Dragging rocks is necessary. It is work. For that I get food. For that I exist.

It is not possible to build just one pyramid. And maybe it is not possible to win one war. You have to go on, constantly winning wars, to keep the cogs of the machine turning, to sustain the employment, the consumption, the economic growth. And so it is here in Iceland: it seems not to be possible to build one dam and one aluminium refinery. We are currently completing the largest construction project in Icelandic history. And in doing so we have also created the need for more. The infrastructure is now in place, a machine whose goal is to turn Iceland into one of the biggest aluminium producers in the world. This machine is blind to the fact that many of our greatest treasures and our most beautiful places are at stake.

Illustration: Cross-section of the Kárahnjúkar dam. (Diagram: Landsvirkjun).

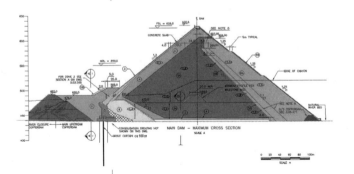

Andri Snær Magnason

152.

Energy prices are low. The people have been primed. Whatever the reputation of the companies involved, whatever the other possibilities this country might discover within itself, everything is dwarfed by the temptation of the billion-dollar investment, the economic boom, freedom from anxiety in the short term.

It probably makes no difference who is in charge over the coming years. A machine has been set in motion that is set on creating ever bigger aluminium plants and building ever bigger dams across ever more rivers. More energy means more aluminium. More aluminium needs more energy. That is the reality. We can ask ourselves how far it is possible to take this. On and on, more of one, more of the other. Until finally we run up against natural limits. And what happens then? Then people will scratch their heads and have a look round and see what has been going on in other countries meanwhile. How did we get to here? How the hell do the Danes get by? Five million of them, lots of designer furniture, and not so much as one gram of aluminium smelting. The raw materials are the cheapest part of what they make and sell. It is the thought that people are paying for.

Did we really have no alternatives?

Napoleon behind the desk

Icelanders may be well-off nowadays, but it is as if a particular myth is fixed in the mind of the nation, the myth that we are a poor little country that needs something to save us. The war saved us from the Depression, and then came the Marshall Plan once the war was over; then it was the herring that saved us, and when that disappeared we had the aluminium plant and the Búrfell hydro scheme to save us. And that's the way the country has kept its head above water since the Great Depression in 1933. This is a pattern, a myth, a metaphor our thinking has become hooked on. One single big possibility needs to come along and save us, and the politicians have got their spotlights out to find it. What they are looking for is an idea that will become a new 'base industry', something that will hold up all the rest. We are frightened of the present, it is complicated and incomprehensible. We do not trust the dislocation, the unintelligible intricacies of the division of labour in a post-industrial world. We have to live off something. We are well educated: we learned all about the world and how it operates when we were ten in school. Countries live by producing and exporting something tangible and real. In Sheffield they make iron and steel and knives and forks. In Holland they grow tulips.

Somewhere in the ministry for agriculture someone comes across some figures for world market prices in animal furs and everything becomes clear: we could save the country's farmers by having them trade in their scrawny sheep for mink. The idea spreads like a disease. In the office next door sits a man with a calculator: if we turn over the southern lowlands to tree farming, by the year 2080 we'll have a new base industry in timber, with exports to Finland and Canada a real feasibility. Somewhere else in town there is another man who has created a genetically modified pharmaceutical barley, and having grown a square metre of the stuff he sees that square metre expanding to cover the whole of the south of Iceland.

The vision of the future is announced on the news, ending with the comment that this idea is set to become the foundation of the Icelandic economy, the 'heavy industry' of tomorrow. The ideas may be fine and many, and high aims and ambition are of course a good thing, but what is really worth looking at is the myth. It is a myth the entrepreneurs of Iceland are happy to subscribe to and have their part in promoting. The idea is not for one successful company of medium size, one possibility out of a hundred, a chance for a bit of personal profit, a part of a variegated flora. No. It is an idea that will bring about a revolution, will become our leading export, the foundation and pillar of life in this country. The heavy industry of tomorrow. It is the next stage in the natural cycle of revolutions: to start with we were all farmers; then came the army and changed all that; then we were all in fish. Then everything went a bit unclear for a while, until I had *my big idea*, with a place in it for everyone.

The American Dream is an example of a myth the mind can comprehend. The Icelandic National Myth is perhaps best embodied in the figure of our poet of progress, Einar Benediktsson (1864-1940). His most recent biography gives a good picture of the kind of man he was and the impulses that motivated his actions:

Source:
Guðjón Friðriksson
(1999), *Einar
Benediktsson: a
biography*, Vol. 2, Iðunn:
Reykjavík, pp. 6-7.

> *What drives Einar Benediktsson on to undertake this long journey [...] is his unshakeable belief in his own abilities to be of use to his impoverished fatherland in countries abroad. His dream is to furnish the money that will transform Iceland into a modern country with towns, factories, railways, roads, harbours and large-scale farms. He carries nothing with him except his belief in himself...*

Einar Benediktsson had great dreams for the future of Iceland, replete with hydroelectric dams, factories and railways. While his generation on both sides of the Atlantic saw their dreams become a reality, and sometimes a nightmare, Einar was to be disappointed in all his great hopes and ambitions. Henry Ford was born a year before Benediktsson, and Sam Eyde, the founder of Norsk Hydro in Norway, was born three years after him. But Iceland failed

Andri Snær Magnason

to industrialize in the way Einar envisaged. Whether Iceland was fortunate or unfortunate to have missed out on the Industrial Revolution is something we can argue over. But the failure of Einar's dreams left an unfilled space in the Icelandic soul. Iceland's wealth came from fishing, but Einar's ideas still hovered in the air, leaving a sense of a task left unfulfilled – the unfinished Icelandic dream. The Americans could move on from Ford to Gates. The Icelanders had still had no Ford.

Though no one says it in so many words, we are still stuck in this pattern of thinking: This is a land that needs dragging from its turf huts. Whatever we say, it is as if Iceland remains the same Iceland as Einar Ben tried to but could not save; as if people are still just as susceptible to anyone who says, I can make you rich, I will save you, I will turn you into a modern country, a nation among nations.

Iceland's lurch into the present age did not come organically from inside, not from the entrepreneurial spirit of Einar Benediktsson and participation in the international world of commerce and finance; rather, the country was occupied by the present in the Second World War. The people were never given the space to create their own present – they were taken by caesarean section and they are still suffering the trauma. And many of us believe that this is the way it will always be, that this is the only way forward: someone will come from outside with something big to save us. It will always be one great answer, one single possibility out of many, that will rescue us from poverty and keep us afloat.

Instead of feeling insecure that the risks are spread so thinly, it seems the very size gives us a sense of security. That is how we knew the world: we lived on one particular something and that worked. A basis, a mainstay, a foundation. A central pillar sustaining the whole economy. We lack the courage to face a future that is a complex web of 100,000 units, all of equal importance and each relying on others, in which when one thing withers another expands to occupy the space. We want something big, something tangible, something with room for as many as possible.

The world continues in its customary way. People live their lives, drive to work, fly off to foreign countries, and go into hospital and get cut up. And then one day something clicks into gear. A single possibility lights up. There is maybe even money in it. No sooner out and round the corner than an epidemic breaks loose. In the idea a politician finds the foothold he was searching for. An ordinary person who blundered into parliament after serving time as secretary to the transport committee of the regional association of the progressive federation finally gets the chance to show his worth. The doors of the national coffers are flung open wide and an unremarkable office bureaucrat has become a general, a Napoleon. He is Einar Benediktsson. He is economic growth. He is the rain and the sun.

At this very moment, a single idea, a single possibility, is in full swing saving the east of Iceland. A billion-dollar Alcoa smelting plant is going up, powered by the billion-dollar Kárahnjúkar megaproject. With three new smelters on the horizon.

At the signing of the contract with Alcoa in 2002, one of our ministers waxed lyrical: 'Finally the dreams of Einar Benediktsson are becoming a reality.' He recited one of Einar's poems that begins 'Oh nation of poverty and despair ...', which perhaps sounded a little strange in a land that at the time, according to the United Nations, ranked second in the world for standard of living. After the Alcoa smelter in the east, the next Alcoa smelter is scheduled for the north, close to Husavík. It has been proposed that it should bear the name the Einar Benediktsson Aluminium Plant. When it is built it will destroy the farm where Einar grew up.

Where before there was pessimism and torpor in Iceland's rural areas, now there is boom and a sense of expectancy. A lot of people got together and saw one type of engineering, one metal on the world markets, and one contract with one company as the basis for the future. But is the future genuinely bound up with this single possibility? Or is it rather that a mixed and varied view, a broad faith in the future, might constitute a threat to how these people view the world?

Is the biggest piece of civil engineering in Iceland's history really a 'foundation', a 'basis', something deep and solid and essential to support the rest. Is it really an essential part of our existence, like fish and potatoes, water, cod liver oil, light and heat and the electricity for the fridge? Or is it something that lies closer to the surface, somewhere in the excess fat? A bit of light relief, a Mickey Mouse or a Britney Spears? Nothing more than a pyramid, a memorial to dead men? Are our ideas on reality based on a misconception?

Let us consider another possible Iceland.

TERAWATTS TO KINGDOM COME

War against the land,
and the Iceland of Jakob Björnsson

At Christmas 1970, Iceland's Nobel Prize-winning novelist, Halldór Kiljan Laxness, wrote one of his most famous articles, 'War against the land'. In this article Laxness discusses the immense damage Icelanders have wrought on their country and their cavalier disregard for its proper care and upkeep. He speaks of the destruction of woodlands and overgrazing, how the authorities have rewarded people for draining the marshes, 'the lungs and respiratory system of the country', more often than not to the benefit of nobody. He asks whether it would not make sense to pay to have the ditches filled in again. He talks about the ravages perpetrated on Mývatn, one of Europe's most important lakes, with its rich bird life and amazing volcanic scenery. He speaks of Laxá, Iceland's most celebrated salmon river, that flows out of Mývatn and whose valley was set to be flooded by a dam that would drown local farms and destroy much of the wildlife. He speaks of the factory set up for extracting diatomite from the bed of Mývatn and the government-subsidized sales of electricity to the new aluminium plant at Straumsvík. A particular target for his invective was what he called the 'apparatchiks of the National Energy Authority':

Source:
Halldór Laxness (1971), 'War against the land', reprinted in *Yfirskyggðir Staðir: Ýmsar Athuganir* ('Overshadowed Places: Various Observations'), Helgafell: Reykjavík, p. 131.

The problem is the unquestioning faith of the people at the National Energy Authority in filling this country with endless metal smelters. For it presents a grave danger to the land and its community when a group of men in suits, at the say-so of their slide rules, sets out to obliterate as many of the places we hold sacred as they can in as short a time as possible, drowning familiar settlements in water (twelve kilometres of the Laxá valley are to set to be submerged, ac-

cording to their plans), and, given the chance, declaring war upon everything that lives and draws breath in Iceland.

As well as the assault on Mývatn, Laxness turned particular attention on the Thjórsárver wetlands in the highlands:

Source:
Halldór Laxness (1971),
pp. 138-140.

Naturalists from every corner of the earth, singly and in groups, have pleaded with the Icelandic government, the parliament and finally the people of Iceland themselves to spare Thjórsárver from destruction... Last September a meeting of international conservation associations was held in London and declared itself ready to put up the funds for biological research into this Icelandic paradise, where ten thousand pairs of pink-footed geese act as representatives of the vast infinitude in a northern tundra enclosed in desert. The delegates expressed their wish to the Icelandic nation that the country might preserve this treasure of theirs unspoilt in perpetuity...

At this international gathering of conservationists in London only one person came forward as an adversary of Iceland, a man sent there by the National Energy Authority in Reykjavík. In his speech he stressed that 'Icelanders were most certainly not prepared to abandon operations at Thjórsárver' (as quoted in [the newspaper] Morgunblaðið, 24 September 1970).

The message behind this churlish reply on the part of the Icelander is clear: the National Energy Authority accepts no responsibility for life in this country. The power inherent in the vast infinitude is of no value whatsoever so far as the Energy Authority is concerned. We Icelanders are blind to reason, and once we have started believing some absurdity we hold on to it fast till the crack of doom. We have the right to treat our country howsoever we desire.

So far as the general public in Iceland is concerned, what this response implies is clear: now we've spent the money we've had from you the taxpayers getting these schemes going, you're going to have to carry on stumping up to keep them going – because if you don't you'll lose the lot!

164.

Andri Snær Magnason

I imagine we have some word for this kind of reasoning in Icelandic; in English it is known as blackmail. What must those people from around the world have thought of the Icelandic representative when he stood up in London and announced that, even if the whole world stood shoulder to shoulder with his country, he himself would act against it?

Source:
Jakob Björnsson (1970),
'On nature conservation,
with particular reference
to hydroelectric
development in Iceland',
Samvinnan ('Co-
operative Enterprise'),
vol. 2, 1970, pp. 23-27.

Laxness does not mince his words. He speaks of 'war against the land', 'war upon everything that lives and draws breath in Iceland'. His article can only be understood when viewed in the light of the ideology and general official policy it was written to oppose. It can be seen as a direct riposte to another article, by Jakob Björnsson, at the time a member of staff at the National Energy Authority, published in 1970 in the journal Samvinnan ('Co-operative Enterprise'). This Jakob Björnsson was in fact the selfsame man as spoke on behalf of the National Energy Authority at the international conference on the protection of Thjórsárver, and whom Halldór calls 'an adversary of Iceland', of whom he says that 'even if the whole world stood beside his country, he himself would go against it'.

Laxness's comments doubtless stung. Jakob Björnsson's article in Samvinnan makes powerful reading and deserves a place among the classic works of 20th-century Icelandic ideology. It presents a vision of an Iceland that came close to becoming reality. The article is called 'On nature conservation, with particular reference to hydroelectric development in Iceland'. It was not written out of the blue: at the time, as Björnsson himself says, the nation stood at a crossroads in its history:

Man has as yet done so little to modify his environment here in Iceland that many people do not notice it ... even eminent and intelligent men appear to imagine that things can go on like this indefinitely. In their dreams and visions of the future, it seems that Iceland should remain forever 'the untouched land'.

What Björnsson presents is a kind of ideological manifesto, a technocrat's policy statement on the role of nature conservation in a future that will inescapably encompass a total transformation of the face and appearance of Iceland, its hydrology, and the working conditions and the self-perception of the people themselves. In 1970 the nation had only exploited a small fragment of the country's potential HEP reserves, and change was inevitable:

> *If we are to exploit a significant part of this hydropower in the future, we need to bring in power-intensive industries such as, aluminium smelting. In the face of increasing competition from nuclear power, we must assume that, if we are to benefit from our resources, we will need to make use of just about all our water power before the end of this century. After this time it is very likely that equally cheap, or cheaper, energy will be obtainable from radioactive materials. The exploitation of our water power is thus a matter of the utmost urgency.*

Björnsson clearly foresees the potential for direct conflicts of interests, particularly where the interests of pisciculture come up against those of power development. This is the case specifically with the salmon river Laxá that runs out of Lake Mývatn and with the proposed channelling of the glacial river Blanda down into the Vatnsdalur valley. He therefore sets out a kind of 'compromise solution' aimed at satisfying both sides:

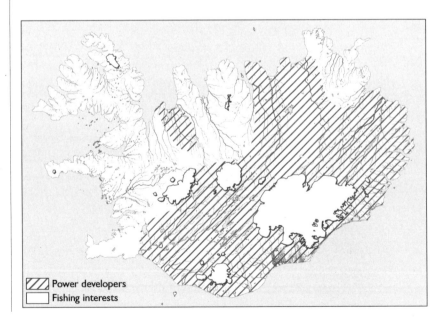

Map:
Jakob Björnsson's proposal for the division of Iceland between the 'fishing interests' and the 'power developers'. Map drawn up by the author.

Power developers
Fishing interests

Andri Snær Magnason

In other respects, it seems to me that the electricity developers and the fishing interests can, as it were, 'divide the country between themselves', and then each leave the other to their own devices.

In broad detail, Björnsson's plan was that the fishing interests should 'get' the area from Hellisheiði/Mosfellsheiði (the Reykjavík area) west and north up to and including the river Fnjóská, just east of Akureyri and Eyjafjörður, i.e. most of the west and northwest of Iceland, since 'this area appears to offer little in the way of worthwhile hydropower'. Within this area, as mentioned, he excepts the river Vatnsdalsá, which, once combined with the waters flowing north from the Hofsjökull glacier, is too valuable an asset not to be dammed and harnessed. For similar reasons, the 'fishing interests' would be allowed to hold on to the rivers in the northeast, from Öxarfjörður up to and including Vopnafjörður.

The power development interests, on the other hand, would 'get' the rivers Jökulsá á Fjöllum, Jökulsá á Brú and Jökulsá á Dal [i.e. the Fljótsdalur valley], and the rivers flowing into the Eastfjords in general, as well as Hverfisfljót, Skaftá, Markarfljót and the Thjórsá/Hvítá basin [i.e. the rivers flowing to the south coast].

The subject of Björnsson's paper is, one might say, the 'total development' and 'maximal exploitation' of Iceland – not whether, but how full use can be got from the land – and the role of nature conservation in this process. Björnsson makes a number of telling observations on nature conservation: that for it to succeed there must be a coherent overall strategy; that it needs to be conducted as a continuous process rather than stop-start and with empty sloganeering; that it must take account of the total picture rather than the odd crater here and there; and that it needs to be based on achieving a balance of nature, so far as the concept applies. But in general he has reservations about the usefulness of conservation: 'There is no point trying to hold us technologists back, for our way is the way to the future. But we are open to guidance.' He lays down principles for what he calls 'positive conservation':

Positive nature conservation takes as its starting point man's fundamental need to shape his environment. It takes cognizance of the fact that man is a creative being. To create is to change. So it does not ask whether, but how.

He points out that the origin of environmental problems lies in systems becoming unstable, leading to erosion and pollution. But under positive conservation naturalists and technologists can work together to create a new balance and design for the environment:

> *Negative nature conservation puts the emphasis on the question whether. Whether there should be any change at all. In its eyes, the best solution is always the status quo. Everything new is shrouded in uncertainty. Should we abandon the known and venture out into the unknown? That could be a mistake. 'Radical change must be resisted.' This is the perspective of stagnation. And stagnation is death.*

The article is written in moderate and reasoned language, without resort to hyperbole or hysteria. Björnsson complains about the conservationists' fondness for bans and vetoes, about their argumentation based on emotional appeal and unfounded inference, about their references to 'power development mania' among engineers. He foresees potential clashes with purely conservational viewpoints, particularly in three instances: (1) the waterfall Gullfoss, (2) the Thjórsárver wetlands, and (3) Lake Mývatn and the river Laxá. Of Gullfoss, the crown jewel of Iceland, he says: 'A common misconception has become prevalent, that under no circumstance may Gullfoss be developed.' He points out that it would be possible to harness the falls for hydroelectric generation but allow water over them in summer for the tourists without any pipes, electricity lines or human constructions being visible from the falls themselves.

He next turns to the Thjórsárver wetlands:

> *Thjórsárver contains the biggest breeding grounds of pink-footed geese in Iceland. These grounds are so important that experts believe their destruction with nothing to replace them would have an adverse effect on world stocks of the species. Thjórsárver is also scientifically remarkable from its flora. It is therefore of great value to the natural sciences.*
> *At Thjórsárver there are good conditions for creating by far the biggest energy reserves in Iceland in the form of a large permanent*

*head of water. This reservoir would in time prove valuable to all the
hydroelectric schemes on the river Thjórsá.*

Björnsson weighs up the alternatives, calculates the economic gains and,
based on the cost-effectiveness of the reservoir, arrives at his conclusion:

> *There is a clash between something of great economic value and of
> great natural value.*
>
> *The issue of Thjórsárver cannot be resolved along comparable
> lines to the development of Gullfoss. If the water supply scheme is in-
> troduced at all, the present goose nesting grounds will be destroyed.*
>
> *In my judgement, any way of saving the natural riches here under
> discussion would come at an unacceptable cost to the nation...*

He imagines ways might be found to move the goose nests, but beyond
this he sees the flooding of Thjórsárver as inevitable. The proposal on the
drawing board at the time was for a supply reservoir of about 75 square miles
that would have drowned all the most valuable parts of the wetlands right up
to the base of the Hofsjökull glacier. Since domestic and normal industrial
demand for electricity in Iceland was already fully catered for, the energy produced would have had to go for aluminium smelting, which would have neces-
sitated a new aluminium plant.

Jakob Björnsson concludes his case with a piece of criticism aimed at
the Nature Conservation Agency:

> *Last year the Nature Conservation Agency petitioned the depart-
> ment for education and culture to have Thjórsárver declared a con-
> servation area. According to the Agency's submission, it is impor-
> tant that Thjórsárver be left entirely undisturbed. I.e. status quo.
> Veto, veto. Fortunately, the department for education did not ac-
> cede to the agency's proposal...*

Finally, Björnsson turns to Mývatn. With regard to the natural resources of the Mývatn area, Björnsson says that:

169.

...it is bordering on childishness to imagine that the present environment of the region can be kept in an unaltered state. This of course does not mean to say that individual places, such as craters, volcanos, islands, etc., cannot be preserved within a rational master plan.

One of the suggestions being mooted at the time was to divert the river Skjálfandafljót into Lake Mývatn, filling it up with glacial water. Both Skjálfandafljót and Laxá would then be siphoned out of the lake by a single channel and collected behind a 220 foot dam lower down, drowning most of the Laxárdalur valley and destroying one of Iceland's prime salmon rivers.

The mapping out of potential schemes is an obvious essential prerequisite for assessing the options. But Björnsson goes considerably further than this:

If the Icelandic nation has ambitions of living in a country with comparable material standards of living to the best found elsewhere in the world, it needs to make maximum use of the country's resources, which in return entails, as it were, a total reformation of the country itself. These two things are inseparable.

Björnsson goes on the present what he sees as compelling reasons why his article represents not just one possible path to economic prosperity, but the *only* path: so far as he is concerned, it is this or nothing.

Björnsson sets out his argument in a clear and organized fashion, logically and consistently. He looks forward to the next thirty years, weighing up and assessing the hard choices that have to be faced, and arrives at his conclusion. It is, to be sure, a grim conclusion, but this needs to be tempered by the fact that it is grounded on a pure sense of responsibility. A single man takes upon himself the noble task of planning the industry and economy, and thus the culture and day-to-day life, of an entire nation, apportioning its natural resources in the light of his own analysis of what is necessary, and redesigning the hydrology of the whole island along the way.

Andri Snær Magnason

Björnsson represents the 'total development' of Iceland's resources as an ineluctable fact, an inevitable conclusion grounded on science and technology, and it was doubtless difficult for ordinary people at the time to dispute such an appeal to scientific reason. In 1970 Björnsson belonged to a comparatively small group of technocrats in Iceland. He presents himself as the incarnation of technological reason, cool-headedness and dispassionate truth. He stresses repeatedly that we have no choice. In discussing the 'cost-effective development options' it is the technocrats and they alone who will be the judge of how this cost-effectiveness is constituted. The conservationists are dismissed as romantics, their arguments a hodgepodge of emotion, quotations from the national poets, pseudo-religious perceptions of sanctity and the power of the vast infinitude, and even appeals to the creed that money is not everything. Whatever people say, whatever people may wish or argue, there is one, and only one, route to quality of life. Björnsson lays out the alternatives starkly in black and white:

> ...there may be some that take the view that economic progress on a par with other countries is not necessarily a goal worth aiming for. Against such a view there is nothing to say. But is it something the majority of the nation will go along with?

Björnsson's ideas are arguably some of the most profound and radical to have been put forward at any time in Iceland by a single individual, involving as they do not only politics and ideology but permanent changes to the appearance and ecology of the land. By far the greatest source of energy lies in the rivers rising from the glaciers, so this water needs to be collected in reservoirs to regulate the flow over the course of the year. Since the most suitable sites for reservoirs are also the main pockets of vegetation in the highlands, what is at stake is several hundred square miles of the most sensitive flora in Iceland. The waterfalls, rapids and canyons formed by the rivers as they descend from the highlands constitute much of Iceland's most impressive landscape, and thus Björnsson's ideas would have involved huge sacrifices of landscape and beauty.

The full-scale development of Mývatn would have resulted in the destruction of the highly sensitive biosystem in one of Europe's most important

Source:
The Thjórsárlón reservoir will be half silted up in 30 years, Vesturlón in about 50-60 years. A report produced for Landsvirkjun (The National Power Company of Iceland) in June 2001 estimated the lifetime of Sultartangalón at about 80 years. In November the same year, a report was published showing that sediment discharge in Sultartangalón had been significantly underestimated, i.e. around 1.5 million tonnes a year as opposed to 1.1 million tonnes. This reduces the expected lifetime of the reservoir accordingly. 1.5 million tonnes of mud equates to 150,000 truckloads a year, or seventeen truckloads an hour, every hour of the day, every day of the year. According to the report: 'In view of the comparatively short lifetime of Sultartangalón, particularly if the Norðlingaalda Diversion scheme does not go ahead, it is important to monitor sedimentation in the reservoir carefully.'
VST and Almenna Consulting Engineers (2001), *Fluvial sediment transport and sedimentation on upper Thjórsá*, Landsvirkjun: Reykjavík.
VST and Almenna Consulting Engineers (2001), *Sediment build-up in the Sultartangi reservoir*, Landsvirkjun: Reykjavík.

lakes. One of the loveliest valleys in all of Iceland would have been submerged, together with one of its finest salmon rivers, with its luxuriant islands and its bird and fish life. Several farms would have been lost to the waters and the magnificent waterfall at Goðafoss would probably have disappeared. It is difficult to see how the Aðaldalur valley could have accommodated the additional waters of Skjálfandafljót other than with extensive drainage ditches and protective walls. A diatomite plant was established at Mývatn in the 1960s using sediment dredged from the bottom of the lake. The present generation has inherited water in which the natural balance has already been disturbed. Trout stocks in the lake have plummeted. The diatomite plant was demolished in August 2005.

The reservoir at Thjórsárver would have been very shallow, with an area about three times that of Iceland's largest natural lake, Thingvallavatn. Every spring, fluctuations in the surface level would have laid bare enormous open expanses of sand, mud and rotting vegetation. Reservoirs and hydroelectric schemes based on glacial waters are not perpetual motion machines like the power plants on Elliðaár and Sogið, that a thousand generations can build and remove at will. The effective lifetime of a glacier-fed reservoir can be very short – it would perhaps be truer to call them mines rather than reservoirs. In many cases such a reservoir will last no more than a human lifetime. Glacial rivers can only be held back by dams for a limited period: they bring corrosion, they dig away at or fill up everything that gets in their way. The end is already in sight for some of the existing reservoirs along Thjórsá, mostly dating from the 1970s: according to reports, Vesturlón and Thjórsárlón have only a few decades to go, and the one at Sultartangi is silting up much quicker than was originally anticipated.

The pink-footed goose is totally dependent on Iceland and the Thjórsárver wetlands are far and away its most important breeding grounds. The proposed works would perhaps have consigned it to the glass cabinet alongside the great auk – it was a close run thing. The geese will move, some say, but in Björnsson's master plan any new habitat they might have moved to would also have been flooded.

It is a good thing to think, to look into things, to set out the options and to pool one's collective knowledge. But to present the total development of Iceland as the Icelanders' only possible route to economic prosperity is to

Andri Snær Magnason

see the world in highly simplistic terms. One might say that Björnsson uses his position as an expert with a privileged specialist command of the subject to put people up against the wall. He plays off two powerful basic instincts one against the other and presents them as being mutually incompatible. Any ordinary person that might be inclined to object to this future that has been worked out for him would have been written off as insane, a fantasist, an *un-realist*. He would have been seen as a threat to the future, our children and their education. He would have been marked down as 'someone who puts the interests of nature above the economic progress of mankind'.

Many people doubtless believed that the country really needed all this energy. But to power all the homes, schools, offices and ordinary factories in Iceland required, and still requires today, only a fraction of the energy Björnsson says the country cannot survive without exploiting. The new Alcoa plant at Reyðarfjörður on the east coast, for example, will use six times as much electricity as all the homes in Iceland put together. A factory providing work for less than 500 people will devour almost twice the electricity needed to power a community of 300,000, with all their homes and household equipment, lamps and streetlights, schools, fish factories and freezing plants, hospitals, shopping malls, cinemas, shipyards, print works, power drills and Coke factories. Its CO_2 emissions will be equivalent to 170,000 cars, more than the entire family car fleet of Iceland.

You cannot have a modern society without electricity. But this does not mean you cannot have job creation and standards of living without a massive build-up of heavy industry. The country does not need all this power. The 'total development' of Iceland only serves as an excuse for a small group of men to carry on setting up more and more power schemes. It is no coincidence that the arguments put forward by the power developers, and the whole debate within society, centres on aluminium and has done so for the last forty years. The aim is not to create valuable and rewarding jobs, or to profit from our expertise, talents and special strengths, but first and foremost to attract to this country foreign companies with the highest possible energy requirements. The nation has been turned into an accessory in the problem facing a tiny number of engineers, men who might have built up powerful companies of their own if their minds had not been so obsessed with such a limited area of global production.

In order to 'utilise' all this power by the end of the 20th century, a large part of our human resources would have needed to be directed into heavy industry – or, more correctly, into a narrow area within the most energy-intensive of all heavy industries. Aluminium smelting is by far the most energy-intensive industry in the world – as kids might say, way, way, way ahead of anything else. When the aluminium refinery at Straumsvík first opened, it was producing around 30,000 tonnes a year. To use the amount of energy Jakob was talking about, we would have needed the equivalent of around fifty such plants. The power of heavy industry and the economic interests of the power companies would have dwarfed that of all other parts of the Icelandic economy. Not only would they have had enormous power within Iceland, their influence would have stretched well beyond its borders.

'There is no point trying to hold us technologists back, for our way is the way to the future.' The claim might appear logical, since no one can predict the unpredictable – even if it provides much of the driving force for many of the world's most successful societies. The technocrat presents himself to the nation and tailors a whole society as closely as possible to the pattern of his own area of expertise. He adopts the role of sole arbiter of progress and science, alone qualified to define the interests of 'mankind'. Those who disagree with him and cavil at particular plans, ideas or possibilities, such as the 'fundamental redesign' of Thjórsárver and Mývatn, are objecting to electricity itself; they are showing ingratitude to technology for the gifts it has bestowed on us and a failure to understand the interests of 'mankind'. They face questions like, 'Where would we be without electricity?' A negative attitude is classed as acquiescence to poverty, the status quo, a willingness to accept misery and squalor. Protection must yield to 'positive nature conservation' – not whether, but how.

Source:
www.alcan.is

Despite presenting the appearance of total reasonableness, of having thought everything through, Björnsson says nothing about how big a 'base industry' needs to be to sustain the society around it. No explanation is offered for the extraordinary coincidence that the sum total of exploitable water power on this little island happens to equate precisely to the only possible route by which a small nation may attain quality of life. We are given no reasoned analysis of just how much energy a society needs to grow and flourish, no graph giving the optimum energy levels required per person. We find nothing about how many jobs there need to be in raw materials processing as a per-

174.

centage of total workforce in the countries we wish to emulate; nothing about job numbers in heavy industry based on a country's size and educational level, or about standards of living in countries that are totally reliant on heavy industry. No explanation of why the country's future and potential for economic growth are inextricably bound to this one possibility, i.e. of drowning the land and turning off waterfalls to refine aluminium and produce raw materials – as opposed to, say, designing, developing, inventing and selling the goods ourselves. Nothing about health, culture, self-esteem, life expectancy and pollution in the industrial and mining areas of America, Britain, Europe and the Soviet Union. As Halldór Laxness allows himself to ask in his riposte, 'It would be nice if someone could tell us where in the world there is a heavy-industrial working class that lives under better economic conditions than people do in Akureyri without any heavy industry.'

Source:
Halldór Laxness (1971),
'War against the land',
p. 135.

Within this technocentric ideology there seems to be not a single thing in Iceland that possesses a uniqueness or beauty that is worth preserving. Such beauty as might survive might be called a residue, vestiges, something left behind *despite* the people living there rather than *because of* them. Someone who protects the land also shapes the land, because he has taken a conscious decision not to destroy it. To Jakob Björnsson 'exploitation is a matter of the utmost urgency', an aim in itself. People do not go out of their way to conserve; rather they are willing to go to great lengths not to conserve. Thjórsárver must be sacrificed, because in thirty years it may not be worth sacrificing it. It is perhaps no wonder Halldór Laxness talked about 'war upon everything that lives and draws breath in Iceland' – not least because what Björnsson is proposing are not dreams and utopian visions but a realistic technical possibility and a single-minded determination to act, based on a coherent ideology and world view.

This technological mindset cuts all the deeper because, by embracing such a narrow system of values, we are creating our own poverty. Wealth is not to be measured in money but in whether people have the ability to endow their lives, their environment and culture with meaning and value. Our aesthetic sensibilities, biodiversity and non-material riches are closely related to literacy and our appreciation of history, heritage, language, the arts and even human life. A nation that cannot appreciate things like Mývatn and Thjórsárver and is blind to their riches is like an Italian who sees the Colosseum as just a handy pile of rubble for patching up walls. Seeing the Colosseum solely in terms of its mass as potential building material and overlooking its significance as a place is to strip our lives of meaning and value. Depreciating the value of Thjórsárver and seeing it merely as a prime site for hydroelectric development is depreciating the value and significance of Iceland.

Iceland's energy policy has always been wreathed in a mythic glow going back to Einar Benediktsson and his aspirations for a society and political system that rejected him. Our whole thinking about energy has become associated with 'magnificent ideals', grand plans and the struggles of men of vision. But what is so magnificent about this Iceland that Björnsson laid out for us to admire in 1970? Are these really great ideals that we can 'finally turn into reality'? In all truth, there are fatal flaws in the Iceland of Einar Benediktsson. In the name of progress, Iceland's apostle of modernization sold all the water rights on the river Jökulsá á Fjöllum to Nitrogen Products and Carbide in Norway, a company that went on to manufacture enormous quantities of explosives for use in the First World War: Dettifoss, the mightiest of Icelandic waterfalls, would have powered the deaths of thousands of men and made Iceland into a prime strategic target during the Second World War.

It is not within the compass of one man to comprehend all the opportunities that lie open to an entire country. But there are times when a single, obvious technological possibility, a single easily garnered natural resource, seems so big that a whole nation falls under its spell. A limited area of knowledge that fulfils a conventional ancillary role in most countries in one becomes a dominant force.

It is probably only thanks to chance that Jakob Björnsson's millennial vision failed to become a reality, a chance related to flatness on the world's aluminium markets in the last decades of the 20th century and fluctuations in energy prices. A million, a million and a half, tonnes of aluminium production would have eaten deep into the fastnesses of Iceland. So why bring up now an article written thirty-five years ago? What is it to us today who our Nobel laureate dubbed 'an adversary of Iceland'? Except, perhaps it does matter, a great deal. Jakob Björnsson was appointed director general of the National Energy Authority in 1973 and held the post for the next twenty-three years, up until 1996.

Andri Snær Magnason

An old horror movie

If you go looking, you can always dig up all kinds of horror movies from the past, unearth ancient bits of writing and then use them against the writers. Björnsson did not spend hours of work compiling his manifesto out of any sense of ill-will; on the contrary, it expresses an ideal, based on strong conviction and a belief in planning, reason and technology.

Probably Björnsson's contemporaries had, and have, no idea of how far the power sector was prepared to go. Doubtless most of them confused the need for domestic electricity with the 'total development' of Iceland's energy potential. Doubtless, too, they confused words like development and resources with words like profit and living standards. There is no way of knowing how history and the world at large would have judged a nation that sank Thjórsárver, and sent the waters of Jökulsá á Fjöllum gushing eastward into Lake Lagarfljót, and rooted up much of the highlands for power lines, flood walls, dams and reservoirs. Most likely we would never have been able to imagine the possibility of any other possibility: this was how we managed to survive; it was for this that we made the 'necessary sacrifices'.

The aim is not to create some kind of bogeyman out of the power development interests by dragging up an old article that envisaged turning Gullfoss and Dettifoss over for electricity generation. Björnsson's article is fundamental reading for an understanding of contemporary Iceland, its context and its immediate future. While Icelanders and the world around were discovering Iceland, learning to appreciate its delicate hardness and incorporating its barren and isolated beauty into this image, a sleeping giant suddenly awoke and things lurched forward on a new tack. Before us stands a brave new world:

Source:
Valgerður Sverrisdóttir
(2005), Address by the
minister for industry
and commerce to the
Industry Conference
of the Federation of
Icelandic Industries,
18 March 2005, www.
idnadarraduneyti.is/
radherra/raedur-og-
greinar/nr/1597.

Extensive marketing efforts over the past decade aimed at attracting the attention of foreign investors to the qualities of this country as a location for energy-intensive industry have paid off in spectacular fashion, with the result that Iceland is now spoken of among aluminium producers as Europe's best kept secret, a sure sign of how highly they regard conditions in this country for operations of this kind.

At present, this country's two refineries produce a total of 268,000 tonnes of aluminium a year. By the end of this decade, with the completion of the Fjarðarál plant and the recently agreed expansion of Norðurál, aluminium production of this country will have almost tripled, to around 760,000 tonnes a year. This is a big leap in a short time and needs to be viewed in the light of the framework set down in the 1950s and a policy objective of all governments since. It has taken a full fifty years to achieve this result, a result perhaps most clearly reflected in the fact that six world-famous aluminium companies have already expressed an interest in investing in new aluminium plants in Iceland in the coming years.

In order to understand the world at the time the heavy-industry ideology became established fifty years ago, it is worth having another look at the semi-official geography textbook used in elementary schools at the time. The postwar years appear before us in living detail:

Source:
Guðjón Guðjónssón (no
date given), *Geography*,
Vol. 2, Icelandic
Educational Publishing
Co.: Reykjavík, p. 35-37.

More than a million men a year work in England's coal mines... Belgium is a land of heavy industry. There are large coal mines along the River Maas. The belching factory smokestacks tower high over the rooftops like a black petrified forest and everything is submerged in smoke and soot... In Luxembourg there are big iron mines and steelworks.

When we look to the future, we need to bear in mind that the policy that is being put into practice now was originally laid down in the 1950s. It has taken a full fifty years to achieve this 'result'. So what was this policy of the 1950s, and what was the prevailing ideology of the times? What were the attitudes of those who championed it, and what other possibilities for job creation

Andri Snær Magnason

were they aware of? And what did they know about the world we live in today? Was it the aim to create the Iceland of Jakob Björnsson? What kind of government department follows a policy that was established before the computer age, the internet age, the leisure age, the jet age, the image age, the service age, and the age where everything is 'Made in China'? What kind of policy is it that was formulated before 90 percent of the jobs that people do in Iceland nowadays existed, before most of the people in the country were even born? Before a single man working in Iceland today was old enough to vote?

Presenting his image of the future of Iceland in 1970 as the only alternative to stagnation and death, Jakob Björnsson asked, 'Is it possible to answer this in any other way? I do not think so.' Thirty-five years on, the minister for industry and commerce categorized Iceland's options for the future to the 2005 conference of the Federation of Icelandic Industries as follows:

*It seems fairly clear that, when heavy-industrial output reaches the equivalent of a million tonnes of aluminium a year, it will for various reasons be proper to call a halt to further development. **We will then have achieved best use of the economic and social benefits we could not have provided ourselves with through any other means.***

We will also have created for ourselves a secure foundation from which to make a concerted advance into new fields of knowledge, skills and work development. After this point economic development should be sustainable through advanced technology and other knowledge-based industries.

'WE WILL THEN HAVE ACHIEVED BEST USE OF THE ECONOMIC AND SOCIAL BENEFITS WE COULD NOT HAVE PROVIDED OURSELVES WITH THROUGH ANY OTHER MEANS.' Read these words a hundred times. The meaning is crystal clear. There is no alternative. It is this, or nothing.

Put aside all the nature conservation, the waterfalls, the mountains and streams, the flowers and the grasses, and pause for a moment over these words. Is this the recipe for our dreamland? Does this country really want to go down this path? Or is it frightened of the unknown, the unseen power of

A Self-Help Manual for a Frightened Nation

(Something strange happened here. The minister's speech to the Industry Conference was originally published in full on the ministry website, www.idnadarraduneyti. is. I copied the speech off the web immediately for use in this book because I felt it provided an excellent example of how politicians see the future and how they limit our perspectives and downplay our options in order to steer us in the direction they want us to go. On 3 September 2005, however, an article submitted by the same minister appeared in Morgunblaðið under the headline 'Benefits of heavy industry to the national economy'. In this article she wrote, 'I have never maintained that the aluminium industry is the only means by which we Icelanders can create high standards of living.' This struck me as curious as it appeared to directly contradict what she had said at the Industry Conference. So I went back to the ministry website: the speech was still there, but the paragraph I quote from here had disappeared from the text, together with some words to the effect that, once production reached a million tonnes, that would probably be enough. I had to dig a bit deeper to verify the source and found only a shortened summary of the speech in *Icelandic Industry: Journal of the Federation of Icelandic Industries*, March/April 2005. Here it says: 'At the conclusion of her speech, Valgerður said that the country now stood at a turning point in the development of energy-intensive industry. When heavy-industrial output reached the equivalent of a million tonnes of aluminium a year, it would for various reasons be proper to call a halt to further development. After this point economic development should be sustainable through advanced technology and other knowledge-based industries.' This indicates that a part of what disappeared from the speech on the web was indeed said at the Conference.

creativity that promises nothing but never fails those who put their trust in it. Is this country afraid of the future? How does the herd react when the shepherd claps his hands. TERROR ALERT! Bunch up and hold together! Evening News, Channel 2, 24 May 2005:

Source:
'Possibly no downturn',
Evening News, Channel
2, 24 May 2005.

> *There will be no economic downturn as previously predicted, or at least it will be put off for some years. This, according to the minister for finance, could be the outcome of the large interest shown in further heavy-industrial operations.*

Sometimes we can only wonder what has become of this affluent, enterprising, hard-working nation, a nation that likes to think it has an Einar Benediktsson for every sphere of life, believing the impossible. The politicians could hardly have stated it clearer: more and more heavy industry, or recession. The brain is a wonderfully sophisticated device, but when it comes to fundamental issues it can be extraordinarily primitive. What we crave, above anything else, is certainty, security. We cannot say what song will be written next. Perhaps the last song has already been sung, the last idea already thought. We cower beneath the threat of lasting recession. Perhaps there will be no economic growth. Perhaps Iceland will go out of fashion. Perhaps no one will do better next year. Perhaps all the computers and filleting machines will break down and stop working. Terror alert! Your land or your life! And all at once, all around the country, the bulldozers grunt and roar into action, ready to drown valleys and dry up waterfalls. And that is the big question: Is this the magnificent future we want for ourselves? Or is this a Stalinist fifty-year plan that has slipped in between us and Einar Benediktsson while no one was watching? Is this our free choice?

Source:
'What are we supposed
to live on?' Leader in
Morgunblaðið, 19 August
2001.

> *In the debate around the Fljótsdalur hydroelectric scheme, it emerged that the younger generation was as keen as anyone to leave the wildernesses of the country untouched. This younger generation is now experiencing redundancies and economic difficulties for the first time. It remains to be seen how far it will be prepared to go in sacrificing future material benefits in order to protect the natural world of Iceland.*

Andri Snær Magnason

What kinds of material benefits was Ólafur Thors ready to sacrifice when he rejected the American requests for military bases at Hvalfjörður and Reykjavík airport? And how much in the way of jobs and income did our refusal to sanction a bomber airfield at Rangárvellir cost this country? What improvements in standards did we lose out on by not seeing the Iceland of Jakob Björnsson become a reality before the year 2000? How much poorer are we because our mountains are not made of gold?

Picture: Coat of arms of North Korea.

The world turns on choices, not ultimatums. All possibilities cannot be used at once. Can it be, even in the crudest economic terms, in SUVs per head of population for instance, that we are richer precisely because we missed out on or turned down opportunities that appeared self-evident and were forced to stand on our own two feet?

PEOPLE'S REPUBLIC OF ICELAND

181.

The great leap forward

A million tonnes is a lot of aluminium, about five per cent of total world production. A hell of a lot for a community of 300,000 people. The intention seems to be to turn the land our children will inherit into one of the biggest aluminium smelting nations on earth, without any clear idea of what we are letting ourselves in for. The minister seems to think it will be possible to stop at a million tonnes a year. But if the country has the know-how, to say nothing of the 'underexploited energy resources', why stop at a million? Is that some kind of magic figure where everything balances out? Why stop then rather than now?

It is not possible to build one pyramid. When there are enough good, honest family fathers tied into the system, will they accept things running idle when they see obvious opportunities for expansion staring them in the face? The energy and heavy-industry system will have proportionally greater combined power than of any other area of working life. If the only thing standing in the way of systemic growth is some kind of democratic will, isn't is just as likely that the system will try to alter this will?

Within half a year of the million tonne target being announced, the figure had gone up to 1.5 million. To achieve this target, the entire hydrology of the east of Iceland is being redesigned, from the roots of the ice cap, down into Lake Lagarfljót and out to the sea in the bay of Héraðsflói. Many of the most sensitive geothermal areas in the country will have to be disrupted and every drop of potential energy squeezed out the river Thjórsá. Other rivers are under direct threat: Skjálfandafljót and the great glacial torrents that flow north from the Hofsjökull glacier to Skagafjörður. Langisjór, the brooding ribbon lake under the Vatnajökull ice cap, is set to be filled with sludge. There are many who feel a sense of revulsion: these are some of the loveliest gems of Icelandic nature. But maybe, they think, once we reach the million tonne mark we can sit back and relax and admire our place in the new world order:

> Iceland sells fish, aluminium and timber.
> Iceland buys SUVs, reality TV and Cocoa Puffs.

So what options for development will that leave still untapped? Don't we have infinite reserves of water power? Now, that is a question. And the answer may come as a surprise to many people. The intention here is not to get drawn into some kind of political slanging match but to look at the overall picture and the ideology behind it. There is no point laying into the minister personally; it is much closer to the mark to regard her as a *host*, a shell around a policy going back fifty years. The host animal delivers the text at the Industry Conference, but neither writes nor thinks the words itself. What the minister says is the product of an objective and a system that has lived an independent life within the corridors of the ministry for industry for decades. The attitudes of the 'power developers' have marked out the direction, identified the options, prioritized the development alternatives and 'informed' the politicians. While life has been going on in its customary manner outside the flowchart-clad walls of their offices, unremarkable civil servants have had a whole land and the fate of a nation laid out on their drawing boards.

'Extensive marketing efforts over the past decade aimed at attracting the attention of foreign investors to the qualities of this country as a location for energy-intensive industry have paid off in spectacular fashion,' announced the minister at the 2005 Industry Conference. So what kind of *annus mirabilis* was this year, 1995, in the life and natural history of this land and its people? This was the year that saw the inception of the formal clearance sale of Iceland's energy resources. The policy manifests itself in concrete form in a brochure issued by the Icelandic Energy Marketing Agency (MÍL), an initiative set up jointly by the National Power Company (Landsvirkjun) and the ministry for industry, under the title: *LOWEST ENERGY PRICES!!*

184.

In parts the booklet reads like a tourist brochure: 'Iceland is nature at its purest. The freshest air you will ever breath [*sic.*] and the purest water in the world are goals worth striving to maintain.' There are eulogies to the health service, the education system, the theatres, and general welfare. Icelandic society is presented as a paradise upon earth:

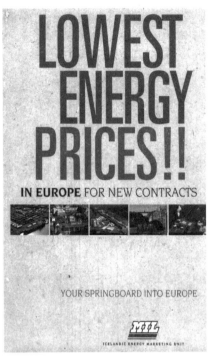

The brochure *Lowest Energy Prices!!* was published in 1995. It promises prospective purchasers low wage bills and 30 terawatt-hours of clean water power at rock-bottom prices.

Source:
Icelandic Energy Marketing Agency (MÍL), (1995), *Lowest Energy Prices!! in Europe for new contracts: your springboard into Europe*, Icelandic Energy Marketing Agency (MÍL), Landsvirkjun and the Ministry for Industry and Commerce: Reykjavík.

> *Iceland is pure and beautiful. Because of the relatively small population, nature is remarkably undisturbed... Longevity is among the highest in the world, which may be explained by the nation's fit population, clean air and unpolluted water, above-average nourishment and one of the world's best health care systems.*

I just love the bit about 'above-average nourishment'. The brochure goes on to offer the cheapest labour costs in the western world and a workforce that takes very few days off sick. The high life-expectancy is down to the pure air – 'The freshest air you will ever breath[e]' – perhaps making our fresh air the central element in Iceland's healthcare system. We live on air, partly. But there is a kind of schizophrenia about the brochure, since its aim appears to be an all-out air attack on the very qualities of life it celebrates: 'The operating licence is usually granted with a minimum of environmental red tape.'

It is an impressive achievement that only ten years after this brochure came out the results are all but with us. In September 2004, Oddur Benediktsson, professor at the University of Iceland, one of Iceland's first computer scientists and incidentally a grandson of Einar Benediktsson, wrote an open letter to the minister for the environment:

A Self-Help Manual for a Frightened Nation

Source:
Oddur Benediktsson,
professor of the
University of Iceland
(2004), 'Open letter to
the minister for the
environment regarding
operating licences for
an anode factory at
Katanes in Hvalfjörður',
Reykjavík, 28 September
2004.

During the calm weather last summer it was reported on the radio that air pollution in Reykjavík was reaching danger levels. Sulphurous air pollution in the area from Grundartangi [Hvalfjörður] to Straumsvík [Hafnarfjörður] is set to almost double in the near future. This will be due to the expansion of the Century Aluminum Norðurál smelter, the already agreed expansion of the Alcan plant, and the proposed anode factory at Katanes in Hvalfjörður. Air pollution may be expected to rise to danger levels throughout this area. For this reason I urge against the granting of an operating licence for an anode factory at Katanes.

In his letter Oddur points out that permitted emissions of SO_2 (sulphur dioxide) in the Reykjavík region will be close to half the total emissions for Norway or Denmark. Among other things, SO_2 gives rise to acid rain, since $SO_2 + H_2O = H_2SO_3$, sulphurous acid. The Icelandic Environment Association (Landvernd) issued a statement about the proposed anode factory and its likely effects on pollution, including the following:

Source:
'Challenge to anode
factory ruling',
statement issued by
the executive of the
Icelandic Environment
Association (Landvernd)
following the outcome
of the environmental
assessment of the
proposed anode plant at
Katanes in Hvalfjörður,
1 October 2004, www.
landvernd.is/page3.
asp?ID=1372.

Polycyclic aromatic hydrocarbons (PAHs) are believed to constitute a serious risk to the environment and are in many cases carcinogenic. The proposed factory would probably become the largest single emitter of PAHs in Iceland. The report makes no attempt to hide the fact that PAHs can be harmful to human and animal life.

The factory at Katanes in Hvalfjörður is set to pump out into the environment around 680 kilograms of carcinogenic PAHs a year. If you listened to some people, you would think it was only the most hardline environmentalists that objected to the allowing emissions of cancerous PAHs in Hvalfjörður. The factory, of course, got the go-ahead. Construction has not started but already Hvalfjörður has a decidedly unappetizing appearance on calm days, and the way things are heading the entire capital region will soon be one of the most polluted areas in the whole of Scandinavia.

Source:
Ruling of the Ministry
for the Environment,
dated 7 September 2005,
for the granting of an
operating licence for
the Kapla anode works
at Katanes, Hvalfjörður,
Case no. 05060050, 4
October 2005, www.
rettarheimild.is/
Umhverfis/UrskurdirRa
duneytisins/2005/10/04/
nr/2036.

Iceland's total SO_2 emissions are expected to pass 20,000 tonnes a year. According to the Norwegian environmental monitoring website www.miljostatus.no, Norway, with a population fifteen times that of Iceland, is aiming to limit its SO_2 emissions to 22,000 tonnes by the year 2010.

The glossy brochure produced by Landsvirkjun and the ministry for industry promises more. Much, much more. It provides prospective buyers with details of Iceland's economically viable reserves of water power. There is a bar chart, according to which the country has the potential to harness 30 TERAWATT-HOURS of hydropower cost-effectively and, in the words of the brochure, 'with relatively little environmental impact'.

I beg your indulgence for a piece of technical language: TERAWATT-HOURS A YEAR. We need to translate this into human terms. To most people's ears, a TERAWATT sounds like a zillion, something incredible big, the distance to the moon, something infinite. Which is exactly the way we have been led to regard this country's hydropower reserves and how we have always talked about them. But this is where the reader needs to step back for a moment, because it is precisely at places like these, precisely where the TERA word begins, that ordinary people are likely to switch off. You think: Terawatt? Terawhat? Isn't it best to leave this up to the boss of the Energy Authority to make sense of? That's just it! The whole matter *has* been left up to the boss of the Energy Authority. So let's ask one stupid question: What exactly is the connection between these 30 TERAWATT-HOURS of water power and the reality in which we live our lives?

Thirty is an innocent enough looking number on the surface. But what is it, what does it involve? How was it arrived at? As a number, it simply denotes what is reckoned to be the total quantity of potentially harnessable water power in Iceland. Converted into terms of life and experience, what this 30 TERAWATTS is made up of is RIVERS and WATERFALLS, VALLEYS and CANYONS, VEGETATION and ANIMAL LIFE.

If we go back at Jakob Björnsson's article in 1970, in it he estimates the technically exploitable hydropower potential of the whole country at around 35 terawatt-hours a year, abbreviated to 35 TWh/y. Of this, perhaps 25-30 terawatt-hours a year are potentially profitable. A lot of water has presumably flowed under the bridge since then. In 2003, the ministry for industry and the National Energy Authority put out a booklet entitled *Iceland's energy: an information factsheet on energy issues*. In it it says: 'Discussions on practicable

Source:
Árni Ragnarsson and Thorkell Helgason (2003), *Iceland's energy: an information factsheet on energy issues*, National Energy Authority of Iceland and the Ministry for Industry and Commerce: Reykjavík, pp. 15-16.

187.

hydropower have generally been based on a working figure of 30 TWh a year...
This figure has then been reduced by deduction of the amount that it is supposed cannot be developed for environmental reasons.' Note this well.

Map:
By 2002 Iceland had
developed 7 TWh/y of
hydropower, of which
60 per cent was used
in heavy industry. Blue
indicates power schemes
serving the general
market; black indicates
schemes serving heavy
industry. Small-scale
and local plants are not
shown.

So the question arises: How is this much vaunted thirty terawatt-hours
a year made up? Decades of work has gone into investigating Iceland's main
rivers and their hydroelectric potential. By adding up the figures we can get an
idea of exactly what it is that is being offered for sale in the glossy brochures
and at business conferences abroad. The mathematics is not complicated:
a child of ten could do it.

By 2002, Iceland had already harnessed **7 terawatt-hours** a year. Of this,
around 4 terawatt-hours went to heavy industry.

So all we need to do is to count up the rest. This is easy as the figures
are public and freely available from the National Energy Authority. By far the
biggest part of Iceland's water power lies in the rivers flowing out from the
glaciers, so we can start there and look into exactly how great the country's
supposedly inexhaustible supplies of hydropower really are. The following table brings together the main glacial rivers of the Icelandic highlands, going

Andri Snær Magnason

clockwise round the country, along with the names by which their potential power development schemes would likely be known.

	TWh/y
NORTH FLOWING	
Skagafjörður region (Héraðsvötn)	1.2
Skatastaðir	1.0
Villinganes	0.2
Skjálfandafljót (upper section)	1,0
Fljótshnjúkur	0.4
Hrafnabjörg	0.6
Jökulsá á Fjöllum	4.0
EAST FLOWING	
Jökulsá á Dal and Jökulsá á Fljótsdal	
(Kárahnjúkar)	4.7
SOUTH FLOWING	
Skaftafell region	
Skaftá hydro scheme	0.9
Hólmsá	0.4
Skaftá diversion (Lake Langisjór)	0.5
Markarfljót	0.8
Thjórsá	
(4 schemes, including Thjórsárver)	3.2
Total	16.6 TWh/y

Source:
Project management group for the creation of a master plan for the exploitation of hydroelectric and geothermal energy resources (2003), *Findings of 1st stage of the master plan*, Ministry for Industry and Commerce: Reykjavík. The project names are based on the names of the probable sites for power stations. Figures for TWh/y are rounded to one decimal place.

A Self-Help Manual for a Frightened Nation

So, adding them all together, the main rivers in Iceland as yet undeveloped come to only about 16.6 terawatt-hours a year. This figure includes the Kárahnjúkar scheme currently about to come on stream.

If we add to these 16.6 terawatt-hours the 7 generated by existing plants, it only gets us up to about 23.6 terawatt-hours a year. Which still leaves us seven short of the famous thirty the National Energy Authority keeps touting as being available and up for sale.

The list above includes all the main mountain rivers in Iceland and thus the majority of the most 'cost-effective' development options. But very few, I suspect, would feel that harnessing all their energy would involve 'relatively little environmental impact'. Even hardline advocates of power development would probably be a bit chary of sticking a dam across Jökulsá á Fjöllum and thereby destroying Dettifoss, Europe's most spectacular waterfall. They too have families and friends. A hydro scheme on Markarfljót would deface a large part of one of the most popular hiking trails in Iceland with power lines, ditches, tips, track making and a reservoir at Álftavatn (Swan Lake). The Icelandic Touring Association describes the Laugavegur trail as 'offering a great variety of landscapes with mountains in almost every colour of the rainbow, immense glaciers, roaring hot springs, and spectacular rivers and lakes'. Which would doubtless be much enhanced by a few pylons and power lines.

The Kárahnjúkar project is there on the list, and to say that that has been controversial would be something of an understatement. So is Skjálfandafljót, and that means the waterfall at Aldeyjafoss with its basalt columns and the spectacular ravine at Kiðagil. There would be storms of protest at any scheme to divert the waters of Skaftá through Langisjór and so dump tons of mud and sand into one of Iceland's loveliest lakes. Disrupting the balance of Thjórsárver to serve the interests of an aluminium company hardly strikes one as evidence of good taste and refinement on the part of a wealthy nation, although the wetlands have been under constant threat for decades. The idea of erecting a series of power stations on the lower reaches of Thjórsá is highly unpopular with the residents of the area. The Skagafjörður hydro schemes would shatter a vital link in the ecology of the region and destroy some of the best white-water and river rafting locations in Europe. Selling them off cheap would be like slaughtering a prize stallion to make horsemeat sausages to feed to a man who has already eaten his fill. In addition, the expected lifetime of a power plant at Villinganes would be at the extreme bottom end of the scale, only thirty to forty years. And despite everything, this energy is supposedly clean, green and renewable. It is simply not true.

The vast majority of these options are, to put it mildly, highly controversial. But even so, this only gets us up to 23 TWh a year! Were all of these places really up for sale at *LOWEST ENERGY PRICES!!* to the heavy-industry interests?

Now, some people might think that this list of beautiful places supposedly under threat is a cheap bit of propaganda on my part aimed at discrediting my opponents, that I am deliberately overlooking some patently obvious energy-rich and easily harnessable sources. Hardly anyone, I suspect, will believe that the National Energy Authority had ALL these rivers in mind when it came up with its figure of 30 terawatt-hours in 2003. Was it really these places the ministry was thinking about as the reason why 'six world-famous aluminium companies' had already expressed an interest in setting up in Iceland? To operate efficiently, a modern aluminium smelter needs ready supplies of at least 4-5 TWh/y of electricity. Setting up a 'small-scale smelter' is at best an illusion. Markarfljót would do for a quarter of an aluminium plant. Thjórsárver for a sixth. Langisjór for an eighth.

Whatever the case, the list still leaves us seven terawatt-hours a year short. The power developers must have some trump card hidden up their sleeve? The list given above comes from the first stage of the 'Master plan for the harnessing of hydro and geothermal energy resources in Iceland'. Other assets (or liabilities) are considered in the second stage. This time we are talking bits and pieces, drops in the ocean. The new list includes many of our best salmon rivers like Stóra-Laxá, Selá in Vopnafjörður, Grímsá, Vatnsdalsá and Eystri-Rangá, and spring- as opposed to glacier-fed tributaries like Tungufljót, Norðlingafljót and Brúará. Are these places really up for sale at *LOWEST ENERGY PRICES*? It needs more than ten salmon rivers to muster up one TWh/y. But where there is a will you can put together a nice little bundle of rivers such as these and squeeze out a further two to three TWh/y. Some of these schemes would be incredibly messy, involving corralling together all the small streams over an entire catchment area with cuttings and trenches and embankments and diverting them into a single channel or reservoir. Of the final possibilities, the larger ones would presumably be:

	TWh/y
Skjálfandafljót, lower reaches	0.8
Gláma (Vatnsfjörður)	0.5
Djúpá (Skaftafell)	0.5
Jökulfall 0.4	
Hvítá in Borgarfjörður	0.3
Hvalá in Ófeigsfjörður	0.3
Total:	**2.8 TWh/y**

Even if we put all the options together, it still only gets us up to 28 TWh/y. So while the pudding's there in front of us, we'll just put in our thumb and pull out the plum...

...Hvítá in Árnessýsla! Gullfoss! The 'Golden Falls'.
The crown jewel itself. 2 TWh!
Oh what fun! 28+2=30! 30 TWh a year.
We've made it!

EVERYTHING MUST GO.
HALLELUJAH!

The energy potential of Gullfoss itself amounts to only about 0.6 TWh a year. If you're looking to present a nice public image of reasonableness and restraint, it is easy enough to say, 'There's no way we would ever develop Gullfoss.' But the truth is that Gullfoss is a much better option for electricity generation than a lot of the places listed above. Many of these other rivers have waterfalls every bit as majestic as Gullfoss, only not as famous and accessible: the awesome Dynkur (Búðarhálsfoss) on Thjórsá, the stunning series of rapids on Kringilsá in the east, lost already under the Kárahnjúkar reservoir, and the line of golden falls where Jökulsá á Fljótsdal plunges two thousand feet from the highlands in the space of a few miles – almost twice the height of the Empire State Building – set to run dry in the summer of 2008 when the water is diverted to drive the turbines of the Kárahnjúkar project. Our loss is Alcoa's gain. Where it is heavy industry that is calling the tune, it is simply not worth rounding up lots of little streams and salmon rivers to power a single aluminium smelter. All the water power that really matters is on the first list.

Andri Snær Magnason

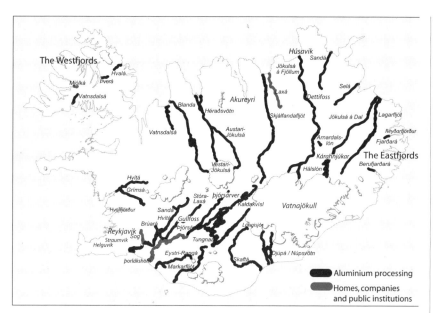

Map:
The energy authorities claim that Iceland has a total realisable hydroelectric capacity of 30 TWh a year, this figure supposedly taking account of environmental factors. The map shows the rivers that would need to be used to get up to 30 TWh a year. Blue indicates rivers used for domestic supply; black indicates rivers that would be used exclusively to serve heavy industry.

In view of the beauty of these places, and how close they are to Icelanders' hearts, and to the hearts of most of those who visit Iceland, we are fully justified in making very high demands of anything that goes beyond the country's immediate energy needs. The gains must be really worth the losses. The damage to the environment must be as little as possible. Were people really aware that the list included all the rivers listed above when Landsvirkjun and the ministry for industry advertised this country as having thirty terawatt-hours of hydropower for sale at *LOWEST ENERGY PRICES*? Hardly. The trouble is, this is it: there simply are not any other rivers that come into question.

Small-scale generating plants like the old city power station on the river Elliðár above Reykjavík are not included. Technically, about two hundred schemes of this type, or 7000 mountain streams, could power an aluminium smelter the size of the one currently being built on the shores of Reyðarfjörður. But that simply does not work economically. I have no idea whether the lovely Skógar foss under the Eyjafjallajökull ice cap is useable. But we could maybe run a generator from the water flowing down the gutters in the steeper parts of town or off the roofs of some of our taller tower blocks. Only the operating costs would never get down to *LOWEST ENERGY PRICES* levels. Or perhaps these are the options the Energy Authority rejected on environmental grounds.

The electricity used in all the homes, schools, street lights, hospitals, offices, factories and other institutions in Iceland – everything outside heavy industry – comes to less than three terawatt-hours a year. This is the real need, the genuine basis for a modern society. T here is no dispute about this, and it is a need that has already been met. This is the power that drives the life-support systems, streetlights, computer screens and nightlife. Initially, the idea behind heavy industry in Iceland was as something to serve the general public – at least, that is how it was presented. One large-scale purchaser would be able to share development costs with ordinary consumers, it was said, and this would create economies of scale. The power from one plant could be split between homes and heavy industry. This was the idea behind the Búrfell scheme in the late 1960s, for instance. It is not a question of being 'for' or 'against' electricity. If this country ever made the move to a hydrogen or electrical transport economy, it would take around four terawatt-hours a year to power all the ships and road vehicles in Iceland. This electricity could easily be generated through geothermal power, without inconvenience to God or man. A change like this would take several decades to go through, allowing us plenty of time to consider the consequences and explore the feasibility of deep-hole drilling. The nation itself has no call for more schemes. It does not need more electricity. It is chock-a-block, full to the gills, quits. So everything on the lists above is intended for aluminium smelting or for heavy industry in some guise. It must be obvious to anyone who looks at the lists above carefully that the policy has been pushed to its ultimate limit and that the final figure of thirty terawatt-hours of ecofriendly, cost-effective water power is a very big exaggeration. The objective, however, is clear:

Source:
Ingi G. Ingason, ed.
(2004), *Doing business
in Iceland*, 3rd ed.,
Ministry for Industry and
Commerce: Reykjavík,
p. 18.

Even after a build up in power-intensive industry towards the end of the 1990s, only 23% of Iceland's 30 TWh of technically, ecologically and economically feasible hydropower potential has been harnessed...

We live in a society that is supposed to be founded on information and transparency. Those who have been entrusted with the care of the highlands of Iceland appear to be happy to sleepwalk their way into the most important decisions of the present time. In 2004 Landsvirkjun put out a booklet called

Andri Snær Magnason

The environment in our hands. No concessions here. The 30 TERAWATTS puts in its customary appearance, with claims of only marginal effects on the environment: 'Harnessing the main glacial rivers and geothermal sites in Iceland would result in less than 2% of the country's land area being taken up by power installations.'

Source: Landsvirkjun (2004), *The environment in our hands*, Landsvirkjun: Reykjavík, p. 12

Two per cent is even more innocent looking than 30 TERAWATTS. A percentage is not, I fear, a legitimate unit of measure. Consider this sentence: 'A kitten was crushed under the wheels of a truck and 0.5 per cent of the world's population was drowned.' Do our brains register that the second half of the sentence entails the deaths of thirty million people? Did the second part have thirty million times more impact on us than the squashed kitten? Percentages and statistics are irrelevant in this context; the 'only two per cent' argument is presumably there to show how extreme the environmentalists are being. And it works. 'Are you against electricity?'

In Landsvirkjun's propaganda campaigns there is a direct line of connection running back to the ideology informing Jakob Björnsson's article. The company's interests are the interests of 'mankind'. 'Mankind' is 'a part of nature', and so the changes it brings about are completely analogous to those brought about by nature with its weathering, volcanic eruptions and the meteorite collisions. Those who oppose turning over all of Iceland's hydropower potential to the service of heavy industry are in some way 'unnatural'. They are failing to serve the interests of 'mankind'. The company puts out pictures of waterfalls spouting from the overflow of newly-filled reservoirs and describes them as 'works of man'. Landsvirkjun is *man*, it is *humanity*. There are no pictures of the places under threat if Landsvirkjun sees its 30 TERAWATT-HOUR dreams come true.

No self-respecting power developer is going to include small beer like Selá and Stóra-Laxá in a sales brochure for sending out to foreign companies. Nor for that matter Dettifoss, Thjórsárver, Langisjór and Skjálfandi. Not at least without asking permission. If we translate that 30 TWh/y into human language, it comes out something like this: 'Stóra-Laxá, Selá and Grímsá are full of salmon but that doesn't matter because they have considerable potential for aluminium smelting.' Once you start really looking into these things, the conclusion becomes inescapable:

A Self-Help Manual for a Frightened Nation

THE SALEABLE HYDROPOWER RESERVES
OF ICELAND HAVE BEEN
VASTLY OVERSTATED.

Source:
Thorkell Helgason and
Hákon Aðalsteinsson
(2002), 'Energy policy
considerations for the
people of southern
Iceland', lecture by
the director general
and project manager
of the National Energy
Authority at the general
meeting of SASS
(Association of Local
Authorities in Southern
Iceland), 30 August 2002,
www.sudurland.is/sass/
Hugleiding.pdf.

It is not overstating the case to say that Iceland's greatest natural treasures have been on clearance sale for the last thirty years, without the nation ever having had it explained to them what was on sale and what the power was going to be used for. Bearing in mind that the lifetime of many of these schemes will be less than that of a single human being, you can hardly avoid concluding that the people who run the country have, alas, lost all touch with reality. Is this Iceland? Or is it the cloud-cuckoo-land of the present director general of the National Energy Authority, describing our power reserves in 2002: '30 TWh/y. There to be harnessed: cost-effective and environmentally friendly.'

Let's turn back for a moment to Jakob Björnsson's proposal from 1970 for a compromise solution between the power developers and the 'fishing interests':

Source:
Jakob Björnsson (1970),
'On nature conservation,
with particular reference
to hydroelectric
development in Iceland',
p. 25.

> *The power development interests, on the other hand, would 'get' the rivers Jökulsá á Fjöllum, Jökulsá á Brú and Jökulsá á Dal, and the rivers flowing into the Eastfjords in general, as well as Hverfisfljót, Skaftá, Markarfljót and the Thjórsá/Hvítá basin.*

That is, what Björnsson was proposing was that the entire northeast, east and south of Iceland should be turned over to the 'power developers', to treat as they saw fit.

Björnsson's proposal is fairly moderate inasmuch as it does at least take account of interests beyond those of the power developers. After years of stasis, the great objective – the 'total development' of Iceland's rivers in the service of aluminium smelting – has bubbled back up to the surface. The policy is now viewed as so sacrosanct that it appears without any semblance of apology: 'Now to tame the waterfalls of Iceland' proclaims the macho headline on the front cover of *Living Science* in autumn 2004, introducing an article apparently co-written by Landsvirkjun, with a subheading designed to conjure up visions of a golden age – 'The Kuwait of the North' (sadly, not the Norway

Andri Snær Magnason

of the North). 'Even when the enormous power scheme at Kárahnjúkar comes on stream, it is reckoned we will be STILL WELL SHORT of having harnessed even a half of the rivers that it might be profitable to develop.' [My capitals]

Source:
'Now to tame the
waterfalls of Iceland',
article in *Living Science*,
vol. 8, 2004, pp. 50-55.

Sure. We have not yet had any use out of Thjórsárver for aluminium refining, nor from Skjálfandafljót, nor Langisjór, nor Jökulsá á Fjöllum, Hvítá, Stóra-Laxá or Selá. The Kuwait of the North! So, our model, what we aspire to become, is a dictatorship based on finite energy resources, where only ten per cent of the people have the vote, where women are not allowed to drive cars, where the ruling class surrounds itself with meretricious luxury and illiteracy runs at about twenty per cent.

It is considered a good thing to have ambitions and aspirations, to take on a task and see it as far as it will go. But what would we make of a cardiologist who thought along these lines? 'Hmm, only two per cent of the nation have been fitted with pacemakers so far.' Would we see it as a justified aim, a right and proper aim, to get the entire nation on the operating table? 'Lovesick teenagers need treating with cardiac catheterization...' The biggest project in medical history? Are dairy scientists supposed to start tut-tutting about underutilization of resources when they calculate that the technical milk production of 70,000 women of childbearing age could amount to 7 million litres a year? 'Based on an average price of 6 dollars a litre, society is losing out to the tune of something like 45 million dollars a year, or X million in projected national income at current price levels. It must be clear to all concerned that a failure to raise utilization rates by some means would constitute a culpable waste of natural resources.' Are meat exporters supposed to announce a glut of red meat while failing to mention that thirty per cent of this meats in fact consists of dogs, cats and *Homo sapiens*? 'We have still only exploited thirty per cent of the rainforests.' It reminds me of an interview I read with the marketing director of Coca Cola: 'Human beings need to take in two litres of fluids a day. My objective is to satisfy this fluid requirement with Coke.'

So what is it that causes an officeful of ordinary Icelandic family fathers to do a volte-face when they get to their drawing boards? What is it that compels them to set themselves the ludicrous aim of stripping their nation of its most sacred places and turning their country into a polluted wasteland of heavy industry? What is it that obliterates from their minds all considerations of public health, other possibilities, social cohesion or the value that the unharnessed TERAWATTS in the vast infinitude have for the self-esteem, image, culture and therefore the wealth and economy of Iceland? A nation with a shattered self-image will never be rich.

Born into paradise, a tiny group of men have painted themselves into a corner by putting all their talents unconditionally at the service of a single, narrow possibility that can only be realized by dragging the whole nation with them into a future that stands in direct opposition to the alternatives that lay before it in 1995. Even if there were a million of us here in Iceland, we could still keep Jökulsá á Fjöllum, Hvítá, Langisjór, Thjórsárver, Skjálfandafljót, the rivers of Skagafjörður and the east, all of them in pristine condition, without any risk of running short of 'clean energy'.

We can only wonder if those who go flying off to international energy conferences to wave their magic 30 TERAWATT-HOURS in the faces of prospective buyers have ever bothered to consult their lifelong friends, their brothers, sisters, fathers, mothers or children, to ask them if what they are doing is OK. It is for all the world as if these people have built up a picture in their minds of hordes of imaginary adversaries, dangerous mobs of 'environmental extremists'. You can only sympathize with how ordinary people who work for these institutions must feel – biologists, geologists and others who are not hell-bent on the power-development mania, people even with some appreciation of the riches that are being squandered.

The debate reaches the level of absurdity when we hear people talking about granting Jökulsá á Fjöllum protected status as if this were a fantastic victory for the conservationists. As if any affluent nation in a fully functioning democracy would dream of destroying the most majestic waterfall in Europe to power a single factory instead. As if people do not want to preserve the river simply for itself, for their own community, for their children and grandchildren, and seek every means possible to do so.

I have said almost nothing about geothermal sources. There has been talk about a further twenty terawatt-hours a year of electricity available here, but there is considerably more uncertainty about the size and potential of these resources, and new deep drilling techniques may change the picture radically. A geothermal power station can tap into an invisible force and bring it to the surface; it can create an awesome environment, even produce health spas and tourist attractions like the Blue Lagoon and the mudbaths at Lake Mývatn. A geothermal power station itself can be invisible. But the geothermal sites of Iceland are, many of them, in extraordinary places and highly sensitive – untouched and remote places of vivid colour, like Brennisteinsalda, Reykjadalir, and the hot springs of Landmannalaugar and Laugavegur under the ice of Torfajökull; places like Grændalur, Brennisteinsfjöll, Hveravellir, Kerlingafjöll, Askja and Kverkfjöll. We need to mind our words here. An 'exploration licence' sounds innocent enough, but this is exploration that involves bulldozers and tracks for heavy vehicles, drilling platforms, water pipes and overflow. Even as I write, there is a steady stream of people applying for permits to do test drillings in some of the most sensitive jewels of the Icelandic highlands, and if current plans go ahead the Reykjanes peninsula could get turned into a tip.

Of the twenty high-temperature geothermal areas in Iceland, sixteen have already been damaged by drilling and roadbuilding, the laying of pipes and power lines, power stations and overflow lakes, most of it solely to serve the demands of the aluminium industry. For the proposed new Alcoa smelter near Húsavík in the north, three huge areas of lava fields and hot springs have already been disfigured or destroyed. Those who know the areas and have studied the plans are quaking in fear: knowledge and respect for the land ceases to be a path to happiness and a deeper understanding of life, and turns into unmitigated sorrow. The only way of increasing energy utilization in this country is still further expansion of the aluminium industry. Everything comes down to that. If there are significant advances in deep drilling technology, how far is the aluminiumization of Iceland going to go? Perhaps we could use some of this energy to get Thjórsá running back in its old course again.

This is not a question of jobs or no jobs. There are high-tech companies in this country tearing their hair in frustration at government indifference and relocating abroad, while the industry ministry is ruled by a clique of old buzzards set on getting a fifty year old objective completed before bothering to acknowledge the present. Without any of the hullabaloo, without any of the government promotion, this country has managed to build up a decent range of technology-based industries in areas like computing, design and culture: Marel makes food processing machinery, Össur is a world leader in prosthetic limb technology. Citing these companies has almost become a cliché. Had many of this country's ablest technicians not been shut up in grey offices half their working lives in an unremitting wait for aluminium contracts, they would have been forced to come up with something different out of their own heads. Ambition would have found itself a channel where the opportunities and profits were greater. Some of them would be millionaires today. Icelandic engineering firms would be bigger and more powerful if they expanded into the international arena. The human resources of a medium-size engineering contractor, backed up by business managers, marketing experts, industrial designers, computer scientists and machine-tools builders, can take on any job that is going. The biggest, most complex constructions built by man today are software programs and computer code. If people had not had their minds so taken up by hydroelectric schemes, who knows? perhaps this country would now be the headquarters of JBjörnsson Sound Engineering, the leading competitors of Bang & Olufsen. Einar Ben Mountain Bikes? We might have had architects working on the new World Trade Center (they are Norwegian, Snæhetta), a 300-man software team designing the navigation system for the new Airbus. Perhaps even an Icelandic Space Institute. Or whatever.

Andri Snær Magnason

White knights in shining armour

In the *LOWEST ENERGY PRICES!!* brochure there is a photograph of a group of happy people sitting in a steaming hot pot and enjoying life, completely unsuspecting that at that very moment a benevolent bureaucrat has taken a conscious decision to crap into the water. The brochure was sent out to some of the most unprincipled companies in the world, together with an invitation to come and visit. People should have a look at the list; it makes scary reading. It includes multinational corporations in the chemicals industry, oil, metals and mining, many of them with long and disturbing histories of human rights abuses, environmental devastation and corporate corruption behind them. Among the lucky recipients, for instance, was Rio Tinto. In 1997 fifty-seven British MPs signed an early day motion in the House of Commons:

Source:
United Kingdom
Parliament, House of
Commons, Michael
Clapham, 'Rio Tinto
Corporation', Early
Day Motion 1194, 1
April 1998, http://
edmi.parliament.uk/
EDMi/EDMDetails.
aspx?EDMID
=15321&SESSION=701.

> *...this House condemns the activities of the Rio Tinto Corporation, which has been identified by the International Federation of Chemical, Energy, Mine and General Workers Unions as probably the most uncaring and ruthless company in the world judged by its appalling record of human and trade union rights violation, community destruction, environmental damage and disregard for the lives of indigenous people in many of the 40 countries where it operates.*

Source:
The United Kingdom
Parliament, House of
Commons, Session
2000-01, *Weekly
Information Bulletin*, 16
December 2000, http://
www.parliament.the-
stationery-office.com/
pa/cm200001/cmwib/
wb001216/edms.htm.

In December 2000, the motions tabled for discussion in the House of Commons included Motion 88: Rio Tinto plc and war crimes; and Motion 91: Rio Tinto plc: racial discrimination and environmental destruction.

Source:
'Biggest mining company
expresses interest', news
item in *Morgunblaðið*, 16
March 2004.

LOWEST ENERGY PRICES!! went out to companies that are not just famous, but world famous, world infamous, for the plundering of resources, destruction of rainforests and toxic pollution – companies with proven track records of intimidation and violence against trades unions and workers associations, abuse of human rights and culpable disregard for the health of working people in every corner of the earth, from Indonesia to Norway, from North America to Africa. The brochure went out to companies that have seized farming lands, flattened homes, destroyed, poisoned and abandoned. It went out to companies that under the protective wing of corrupt governments have used the police, the army and paid thugs to drive local people from the sites of prospective mines and dams. *LOWEST ENERGY PRICES!!* went out to companies that have violated shrines and holy places and jewels of nature, destroyed the societies of indigenous peoples and poisoned their environments and existence throughout the world. It went out to companies that have been singled out as 'the most hated companies in the world', or as a 'poster child for corporate malfeasance' for repeated breaches of contract and mistreatment of their employees.

If you believe that anywhere in the world there are gangs of hard-nosed, ruthless, rapacious sharks, then the offer went out to precisely such men. *LOWEST ENERGY PRICES!!* even went out to Russian companies embroiled in their 'aluminium wars' after the fall of the Soviet Union and the privatization of the state monopolies. Hostile takeovers were literally hostile takeovers. More than a hundred people were killed and, according to the New York Times, contract murders, savage beatings and general lawlessness were a regular feature of the industry at the time.

In the light of which, we can all wonder whether the sweet innocents who put together the *LOWEST ENERGY PRICES!!* brochure had any idea what they are doing or even want to live in the country they have set out to create. In a nutshell, it comes out like this: Paradise Requests Merger Talks with Hell.

To get a better idea of both sides of the issue, it is worth having a look at these companies' websites. There is an almost hypnotic feel to them. One plans to plant ten million trees. Another is funding research into a rare species of frog. There is a picture of a biologist surrounded by happy children. These things get more space than anything to do with gold mining operations in

Andri Snær Magnason

Indonesia. There are smiling employees in hard hats. Almost like a mural from the old Soviet Union. This is a place where it is good to work. I bet the chief executive is a really fine bloke. He got a bonus of 250 million last year. I take it all back what I said. The brochure went out to a group of caring international charity organizations. Remember none of us is perfect. A kitten was crushed under the wheels of a truck and only 0.5 per cent of the world's population was drowned.

Precisely because of their problems, companies of this type have become past masters in public relations, legal loopholes, image massaging and greenwashing. They know what works and what does not. They know you can use power to get your hands on resources, but you can also do it with a few well chosen words and promises. They know the weaknesses of democracy and democratically elected leaders. A pretty flower on your home page and a single act of charity has more impact than any number of statistics about thousands of square miles of flooded rainforest and 35,000 people driven from their homes to make room for a power plant to feed aluminium smelting in Brazil. The plans for still further devastation get lost among the flowers.

The brochure went out to companies that have made vast profits out of dealings with simple, venal and even well-meaning politicians, from military leaderships and third-world dictators to unsuspecting village headmen. Generally within the country there is some small interest group or power clique only too ready to smooth the company's path, even to use the police and army to clamp down on anyone that threatens its interests, whether it be trades unionists or the local inhabitants of some prospective area of operations.

We Icelanders have been inculcated with the idea that companies like Rio Tinto are so important because they will 'underpin living standards' in Iceland, act as 'pillars of the economy', maybe even pay for the education and welfare systems themselves. Their names appear in the papers on a regular basis and local trades unions quake at the knees. 'Chinese Alumina Plant for Húsavík?' 'Russians Consider Oil Refinery in Westfjords.' These companies are going to be the salvation of rural Iceland; they will be grounds for optimism, an end to years of waiting. They are going to save the atmosphere by 'making use of our clean, green energy reserves'. On the front page of one of our free newspapers, Fréttablaðið, we are told that talk of an alumina factory is 'raising hopes in Húsavík'. What the paper said nothing about was what this kind of operation actually entailed. No questions about reputations and past records.

And before anyone could open their mouth came the magic words: 2000 jobs! Once you have grabbed people's attention with a headline like this, nothing else matters. Not pollution. Not energy prices. Nothing. The enthusiasm is confirmed by a follow-up Gallup poll. People take it as read that things outside Reykjavík are so desperate that people will welcome the worst companies in the world with open arms. Their representatives are received like visiting heads of state. Best prostrate yourself to the very ground; our children's futures are in their hands. *Morgunblaðið*, 16 March 2004:

Source: 'Biggest mining company expresses interest', news item in Morgunblaðið, 16 March 2004.

> *Representatives from the world's biggest mining company, Rio Tinto, which owns and operates metal refining plants, factories and power stations throughout the world, have recently been engaged in talks with Landsvirkjun and the government aimed at exploring investment opportunities in this country. The representatives were here in Iceland in connection with the international aluminium conference held in Reykjavík at the beginning of this month.*

Morgunblaðið again, 16 July 2005:

Source: 'Representatives from Rio Tinto examine aluminium plant options', news item in Morgunblaðið, 16 July 2005.

> *TWO representatives from the Brazilian metal refining company Rio Tinto travelled around the north and east of the country last week to examine potential sites for aluminium plants and hydropower schemes. The company is one of several that have expressed an interest in establishing aluminium refineries in the north of Iceland.*

Rio Tinto. Lowest Energy Prices. 30 terawatt-hours. Were they having a look at waterfalls, sizing up Aldeyjafoss for example? Half the nation may look on aghast at the filth and mess created up at Kárahnjúkar, but no let up here. To pour oil on the flames we have representatives from 'probably the most uncaring and ruthless company in the world', coming at the invitation of Landsvirkjun and the industry ministry to have a look for themselves. And quite proper too for a government minister to be leading the welcome committee for world-famous people like these, while protesters are looked upon as terrorists.

Anyone reading *LOWEST ENERGY PRICES!!* now, ten years on, anyone looking at it through the eyes of a foreigner, will be totally lost as to why this affluent, healthy, long-living and innocent nation – a nation that describes

Andri Snær Magnason

itself as such – should voluntarily elect to go down this road. It is almost like watching a promising youngster getting drawn into drugs and bad company simply through a sense of inferiority and a lack of self-belief. 'Today's success is the outcome of a decade of promotional effort,' said the industry minister at the Federation of Icelandic Industries' conference in 2005. The power development interests are not going to go out of their way to protect things. Quite the contrary, they are willing to go to untold trouble, sacrifice and billions in costs to find some possible way of stripping money from the beauty of Iceland. And if that does not work, they put together a delegation to go and beg and plead. And if that does not work, the national coffers are opened up for subsidies. Morgunblaðið, 15 July 1998: 'Altogether the organization [EFTA] estimates that the state has supported the aluminium works to the tune of about 5.5 million dollars.' This figure does not take account of the land, the pollution and the low energy tariffs. Anyway, what the aluminium companies are paying for our electricity is classified information.

Source:
'Assistance for Norðurál declared legal', news item in Morgunblaðið, 15 July 1998.

In our naivety we have always thought of Iceland as being bigger on the inside than the outside – that the Icelandic highlands were an endless Siberia, a boundless America, the Himalayas. But we were wrong. We measure the distances in days' journeys, but a day's journey in the highlands is short for the simple reason that it lies through untracked wilderness and travelling speed is walking speed. The highlands are big because they exist in 'another time'. The rivers are amazing, but in reality they are few in number and tiny by world standards. The waterfalls are beautiful, but there are not so many of them either. Despite all we believe, the highlands are very small and very sensitive and very delicate. Iceland is not so big – 'slightly smaller than Kentucky', it says on the CIA World Fact Book website.

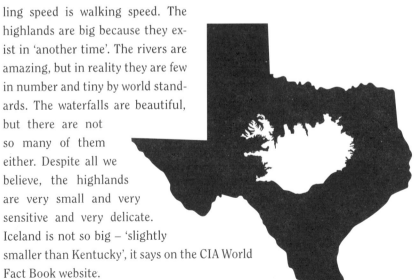

Map:
Texas and Iceland on the same scale.

A Self-Help Manual for a Frightened Nation

The whole picture has been there and available in documents and reports for years but never been laid out on the table for public viewing. The country has never been told exactly what lies behind these 30 TERAWATT-HOURS. The talk of submarine transmission lines has always centred on the cable itself; most people seem to have thought that this was just a question of sticking in a plug at Búrfell and laying a cable over to Britain. In fact, to make it pay, a submarine cable would require the harnessing of the three great glacial rivers of the north and the east, Jökulsá á Fjöllum, Jökulsá á Dal and Jökulsá á Fljótsdal, and diverting them down a single channel.

Icelanders who have travelled their own country in the last decades, who have marvelled at the beauty of Langisjór and come to think of it as a part of themselves, would be scandalized to realize that somewhere out in the wide world there was a deputation of bureaucrats in a desperate search for purchasers. I met an American engineer who shook his head when I said I was from Iceland. He had been at an international conference and witnessed these ambassadors of our country at the hotel bar trying to buttonhole the top brass of a well-known company with, to put in mildly, an appalling reputation. He put it like this: 'It was like seeing thirteen-year-old girls trying to get off with Mike Tyson.'

Places disappear. On the way out to the natural hot pools at Landmannalaugar, my family always used to stop at the Tröllkonuhlaup falls on Thjórsá and our parents told us the story of the place – about how the rocks in the middle were stepping stones set there by a troll woman so she could visit her sister on the other side. Then one year there was a fence up, and the river was gone and the falls had disappeared. Even so, you can still find the place listed in the guides and textbooks. Visiting a primary school one day I saw a poster on the wall where a child had written: 'Tröllkonuhlaup is on Thjórsá.' Perhaps the placename committee could issue a list of places that no longer exist. 'I combed your locks by Galtará' wrote Jónas Hallgrímsson, our poet of nature, our Wordsworth, our Whitman. Galtará no longer exists, lost somewhere beneath the waters of what is now the Blanda reservoir, helping to power the Norðurál aluminium plant in Hvalfjörður.

Langisjór is up for sale and has been for years. When the green line was plotted out on the map round the edge of Vatnajökull and the words 'National Park' pencilled in, they made a special detour to miss out Langisjór and the prospective Hálslón reservoir, despite these being some of the most remark-able parts of the whole that makes up Iceland's biggest ice cap. The arguments over Thjórsárver should come as a surprise to no one; Thjórsárver has been on sale for decades and up near the top of the Landsvirkjun hit list. The only thing that was lacking was a buyer.

Seen against the background of the industry ministry's plans to use Iceland's most beautiful places to power 'the most ruthless companies in the world ', there is something that leaves a rather nasty taste in the mouth about the NATO military exercises carried out in the Icelandic highlands in 1999 under the name Northern Viking. The premise behind these exercises was not defence against some threat from outside, but military action against nature conservationists. An environmental group called the Guardians of Unspoilt Nature is organizing protests against government policy but fails to attract popular support; as a result, a splinter group breaks off calling itself BLACK DEATH and turns to more extreme direct action and 'terrorist activities'. It is this threat that the might of NATO is launched against.

Rear Admiral David Architzel, the acting commander of the American Defense Force in Iceland, explained the rationale in an interview with *Morgunblaðið* on 23 June 1999:

> *The terrorist group in the exercises is an extremist group that has split off from a peaceful and well-intentioned environmental organization... The Icelandic government has received a tip-off about the extremists. The American Defense Force, at the request of the Icelandic government, is put on stand-by in preparation for operations against the terrorist group...*
>
> *Architzel says that the situation premised in these exercises is a very accurate reflection of conditions that might arise in the real world. The need for action of this kind is considerably likelier than defence against an attack on Iceland by a hostile power from out-side, as has been the case in exercises in previous years. 'Taking account of real conditions helps us to keep our eye on the fact that these exercises are a part of real life and modern society and not solely an "exercise",' said Architzel...*
>
> *Finally, Architzel said that an important element in the exer-cises this year is the involvement of the Icelandic government from*

Source: 'Exercises to take account of real-life situations', news item in Morgunblaðið, 23 June 1999.

207.

the outset. 'The government is a partner in the development of the operations, will share with us in the decision making over how the exercises are conducted, and work in close co-operation with the Defense Force and other forces from start to finish,' said Architzel.

In 1970 there was a plan to send torrents of muddy glacial water down the Laxárdalur valley, obliterating Iceland's most celebrated salmon river. After a funeral, around two hundred local farmers and their families gathered in the valley and dynamited a small dam in the river. Almost a hundred claimed responsibility. The scheme was dropped. Faced with this group of terrorists nowadays, we could just have called in the B-52s.

Seen in this light, war against the land takes on an entirely new meaning. Who knows, maybe we'll be able to equip our fighter jets with GoreTex sensors. But this is no laughing matter. It is terrifying. Military strategy is based on knowing your 'enemy', understanding how he thinks and feels, and predicting his responses. In view of the natural riches on the drawing board, one might quite reasonably expect fierce opposition from certain quarters, maybe even something along the lines of the reaction of the people of Mývatn in 1970 – all the more so when there has never been any intention to listen to what people were saying anyway. But that some of our politicians should have taken it this far...! 'The Defense Force, at the request of the Icelandic government, is put on stand-by in preparation for operations.' Press release from the foreign ministry, 18 June 1999:

Low-level flight exercises as part of NORTHERN VIKING 99

Source:
'Low-level flight exercises as part of NORTHERN VIKING 99', press release from the Ministry of Foreign Affairs, no. 057, 18 June 1999, www3. utanrikisraduneyti. is/frettaefni/ frettatilkynningar/ nr/1638.

On the days 19, 21, 22 and 23 June, low-level flying exercises by military aircraft are scheduled in a restricted low-level flying zone over the highlands in connection with the defence exercises NORTHERN VIKING 99. Low-level flights will be conducted by 6 Jaguar fighters from the British airforce and 4 F-15 fighters from the US air command.

It is difficult to imagine that the then foreign minister, Halldór Ásgrímsson, was seriously considering setting soldiers and fighter jets onto Icelandic and foreign tourist hill-walkers. Maybe it was some kind of joke.

Andri Snær Magnason

Photograph:
Langisjór.
(Photographer:
Jóhann Ísberg)

A military machine in existential crisis. It didn't seem quite proper to be exercising for an attack from Russia any more; the Russians might have been offended and kicked up a fuss in the Security Council. For the first time, the Icelandic authorities had got the chance to define the threat for themselves and deploy the army as they saw fit. And this was their choice. It is tragic, but fully indicative of the atmosphere nature conservation has had to live under in this country in recent years. The heavy-industry policy here is turning into a state within the state, answerable only to itself, and some politician comes up with the bright idea of ensuring the access of companies like Rio Tinto to an unspoilt and even protected land at *LOWEST ENERGY PRICES* by force of arms. Education is a heavy industry. Unspoilt is underutilized. The protection of the environment obstructs progress. Nature conservation is an act of terrorism. Let us note the language.

We in Iceland need to think seriously about whether Landsvirkjun, the old buzzards of the industry ministry and the National Energy Authority can be trusted with the custody of something as valuable as the highlands of Iceland and its rivers and scenery. Whether they can be trusted with the very lifeblood of the land. Whether this desire to harness the power of whatever moves does not amount to some kind of ideology, a blinkered obstinacy, a compulsion or disease, something to be seen as being in direct competition with other industries in Iceland rather than a reasonable force serving the interests of society. Even as a threat to the future and independence of this nation and the pride and self-esteem of its people.

Perhaps we ought to consider putting what remains of the waterfalls and wide open spaces of Iceland under the directorate of health as a designated and inalienable part of the national health service. By this, I mean health both physical and mental.

Fifty per cent of nothing

'Earth provides for man's need, not for man's greed.'
Gandhi

Looking at things from the global perspective provides no greater grounds for optimism. You find people acting as if our energy reserves are capable of saving the planet from coal, nuclear power, oil and gas:

> *Our energy resources are underutilized. We could produce about six times the electricity we do at present before the options start to decrease appreciably for environmental reasons. We need to want to use these renewable resources to our best advantage. And we have a moral responsibility to do so for the good of all mankind.*

Source: 'Misrepresentations on power development issues', article submitted by Thorkell Helgason, director general of the National Energy Authority, *Morgunblaðið*, 26 January 2003.

It is not malice that is bringing Rio Tinto to Iceland. No, no, no. The director general of our National Energy Authority considers it to be this nation's moral responsibility to bring in companies like this to come and produce more aluminium. But how important is Iceland in a global context? What would 30 terawatt-hours of hydropower get you on the world stage? This is approximately the amount of energy needed to power all the televisions in the USA for one year. This of course is a great and noble undertaking, but it does not tell the whole story. In 1999 a survey of energy use in American homes was carried out for the Lawrence Berkeley National Laboratory in California. The result was that electronic consumer durables such as TVs, alarm clocks, radios, videos and computers used about 110 TWh of electricity in a year. However, of these 110 TWh, 60 per cent went into the equipment at times when it was not actually being used! The devices were taking in current even though they were turned off; adapters were heating up, videos were on standby, TVs on remote control…

Source:
Meier, Alan, and
Rosen, Karen [no
date of publication],
*Energy use of U.S.
consumer electronics
at the end of the 20th
century*, report from
the Lawrence Berkeley
National Laboratory,
http://eetd.lbl.gov/EA/
Reports/46212/.

Which means, in a word, that all the usable water energy in Iceland would be enough to power a half of the household electrical equipment that is not in use in American homes. Or to put it another way: by harnessing every ounce of hydropower in Iceland, you get enough to provide for 50 per cent of NOTHING in the USA.

To quote the main finding: 'In all, consumer electronics consumed 110 TWh in the U.S. in 1999, over 60% of which was consumed while the products were not in use.'

Oh proud and mighty land of power! 'We still haven't managed to keep running more than ten per cent of the electrical equipment that isn't doing anything in the USA.' To give an idea, in 2001 electricity consumption in the United States was 3800 TWh. Loss and wastage within electrical supply systems is generally reckoned at about three per cent. Which means that energy loss in the US grid amounts to rather over 100 terawatt-hours a year.

In a recent article in *Morgunblaðið*, one of our power development enthusiasts said that people who did not want to harness our 'clean, green' energy reserves were suffering from 'environmental schizophrenia'. So that is our role in the world: if I look out of the window and see a stream running past my house, I am a schizophrenic if I choose not to make use of the 'clean energy' in this stream. If, however, I stick a generator in the stream and use the power to run three 40-inch televisions with a picture of a running stream,

Figure:
Untapped hydropower
reserves in the world (in
terawatt-hours a year),
rounded to the nearest
hundred.

Source:
www.grida.no
United Nations
Environmental Program

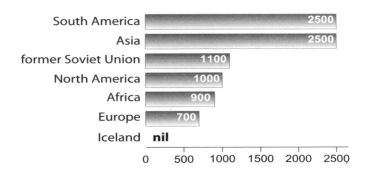

Andri Snær Magnason

I am rich, normal, healthy and sane, since I am saving the world by making use of the 'clean energy' of the stream.

Iceland is not the only country in the world with untapped reserves of water power. In North America, closer to home of the headquarters of the aluminium companies, there are unused reserves amounting to around 1000 TWh a year. Exploitable water power in Africa is somewhere in the region of 900 TWh/y, in South America around 2500 TWh/y, something similar in Asia. Europe, it is reckoned, still has about 700 TWh/y to go, the former Soviet Union about 1100. Altogether this comes up to around 8700 TWh/y of potential energy around the world that power engineers believe it would be economically viable to harness. Note that the figures are estimates and, in line with international practice, rounded to the nearest hundred. If you round Iceland's potential hydropower in the same way, it comes out as nil.

The experience of hydroelectric schemes around the world has been, not to overstate the case, patchy and in many cases tragic. As a rule, people advise against the maximal exploitation of hydropower sources. The very term 'underutilization' is downright misleading, since what we are talking about here is no more nor less than the very lifeblood of the planet, the earth's metabolic system that waters, nourishes and feeds a large part of the world's population. These veins and arteries are very much used, used to the full. However that may be, our water power does not even make it into the charts in an international context. We are not going to save the world. But we might very easily destroy ourselves.

The future in sheepskin shoes?

Our energy is not marked down for powering American televisions. It is marked down for powering American aluminium plants. What is all this energy needed for? It is needed to smelt aluminium. And why do we need to smelt aluminium? Because we have such enormous quantities of energy. We have to live off something. How much aluminium gets smelted in Denmark? Not one ounce. On the other hand, they export designer furniture for 3.5 billion dollars a year. And what do we need aluminium for? Now, that is the question. Is aluminium the 'foundation' for anything? Is the world's demand for aluminium fundamental to life in some way? And are we supposed to service this demand entirely unquestioningly?

How real, for instance, is an aluminium refinery? Is it the soil that nourishes the flowers? How big a base industry is it? How does it compare, say, with things that are not usually considered to be base industries, like TV stations, computer games, poetry books, Mickey Mouse and Britney Spears? How real is the need for electricity and the increased demand for energy?

About twenty per cent of the world's aluminium production goes into single-use containers and packaging, most notably drinks cans, food trays and 'tinfoil'. Since 1972 a thousand billion aluminium cans have been buried in landfill sites in the USA. Altogether around 17 million tonnes of aluminium. The equivalent of a hundred years' output from the Straumsvík smelter. In 2004 Americans threw away 800,000 tonnes of cans more than they recycled. If you add in the cartons and trays and foil and other packaging, the figure rises to 1.2 million tonnes a year. That is almost four times the projected annual production of the new Alcoa smelter at Reyðarfjörður. By burying the cans, energy is lost to the tune of three Kárahnjúkar schemes a year. If we take all the aluminium that goes into landfills in the USA as opposed to being recycled, the figure rises to 2.5 million tonnes a year. To refine this quantity of aluminium requires something like 30 terawatt-hours of electricity.

Recycling aluminium is not difficult: the metal does not degrade and making it reusable takes only a fraction of the electricity that goes into its original production. But aluminium is so cheap that people treat it as being infinitely disposable. The can costs as good as nothing. Soft-drinks and beer manufacturers in the USA oppose any attempt to introduce return charges on cans like we have in this country. Paul O'Neill, the former CEO and chairman of Alcoa, was treasury secretary during the first George W. Bush administration, so the aluminium companies have no shortage of political clout to stymie any moves aimed at reducing wastage: large-scale recycling has nothing in it for the aluminium companies while raw production produces perfectly adequate returns.

Looked at this way, are Icelanders saving the world with their 'clean energy'? Or are they perhaps encouraging waste and the squandering of resources by refusing to put any value on the land that goes into this industry? Are we saving the world? Or are we delaying progress and changes in patterns of consumption? Aluminium is just a commodity, one of a range of materials we can choose from – plastic, steel, glass, cardboard.

Is an aluminium plant an essential element of life, in the same way as fish and potatoes, electric lighting and the hot-water system? What are the laws that govern this new reality? Grass grows: I live; grass withers: I die? Sun shines: I live; sun vanishes: I die? No, this new reality obeys quite different laws. Image good: I live; image bad: I die. Consumption up: I live; consumption down: I die. Waste, profligacy, extravagance increase, I live, I prosper.

This is how the world works: Britney Spears signs an epoch-making deal with Pepsi and sales rise and there is a surge in demand for cans, up by ten per cent. The message filters out to the world market: Increased demand! 200,000 tonnes a year! At company headquarters the board decides to up production, open a plant in Iceland, close a plant in America. The papers in Iceland crow out the news: 'The aluminium plant will rise!' The industry minister flies around on his broomstick. ENERGY DEMAND UP! LET'S FLOOD THE COUNTRY!

Andri Snær Magnason

How real is this need for energy? What is it that calls for all this masculine labour and all these sacrifices? Is Britney Spears the equivalent of a fundamental force of nature, something comparable to the SUN that stimulates photosynthesis and fecundity to fatten the herds, or the WIND that moves the leaves, or the RAIN that sprinkles the earth? Is she a sister to the ocean current and the weather systems and the bloom of plankton in the seas that makes cod stocks swell by 200,000 tonnes? The star of Britney shines on the aluminium and life in the village prospers! Shouldn't we be falling to our knees and offering prayers to the blessed Britney? The goddess of fertility that creates demand through her seductive allure. The land of Iceland sinks beneath the waters, the króna strengthens, exporters suffer, the seaman sees his wages fall, trucks line up along the harbour side, the digger driver sings, the naturalist tears his hair out. Oh Britney! Turn your charms upon us and see our industry flourish!

Even if we do decide to save the world with our clean, green energy and turn the land over to aluminium production, it is not at all certain that the world will thank us for it. Our politicians, on the other hand, have repeatedly talked down the value and riches of Iceland, holding up to us instead a distorted image of the world and specious appeals to moral responsibility. At a meeting of the Icelandic Chamber of Commerce on the economic impact of the Kárahnjúkar hydro scheme, the chairman of Landsvirkjun said the following:

> I realize that people will fight against this power scheme and the disruption it will undeniably cause. To this there is nothing to say; there are many who feel that there is greater value to be had in keeping nature as it is. To the rest, however, we have argued that we have to live in this land; that it is not enough for people to live in foreign countries and have the opportunity to fly out in aluminium aeroplanes and then back when it suits them; and then tell us we should not be building obsolete factories that produce the aluminium they choose to travel in. These people would rather have everything as it was, so that we can stand around in sheepskin shoes and show them how the land used to be, full of the romantic feelings people have for the land and its people.

Source:
'Aluminium beverage can waste passes the "one trillion" mark – recycling rate drops to lowest point in 25 years', press release from the Container Recycling Institute, 24 May 2004, www.container-recycling.org/assets/pdfs/trillionthcan/UBC2004CRIPressRel.pdf.

A Self-Help Manual for a Frightened Nation

Source:
'Environmentalists
criticized', news item
in *Morgunblaðið*, 16
January 2003.

To this there is nothing to say. But to the rest of us who intend to live here, let us realize that we need to live with the same standards of living as our neighbours. For this we need to use our natural resources, and all our other resources and knowledge, in order to make the land inhabitable...

We want to be rational and whole and consistent. Of course it is hypocrisy to expect to fly about in aeroplanes and then refuse to do our part in producing the material used to make them. Least of all do we want to be seen as being alienated, as not doing our bit for the present and the *progress*. As failing to realize there is aluminium in aeroplanes and then being against aluminium.

The new long-haul Boeing 7E7 Dreamliner recently ordered by Icelandair has a fuselage made of carbon-fibre materials, with the aluminium content down to twenty per cent of the total weight, according to www.boeing.com. As a result, the plane is stronger, can have bigger windows, and uses less fuel than older aircraft. In the year 2005 ALCAN at Straumsvík produced 180,000 tonnes of aluminium – which means that ALCAN would be able to produce enough aluminium for around 10,000 of these planes a year. For a small nation, ALCAN represents a very generous contribution towards total world production. Yet even so there are people talking as if we were steeped in debt and calling it hypocrisy to want to save Thjórsárver and Langisjór against further schemes to make tin cans.

Note:
Alcan is since November
2007, Rio Tinto Alcan Inc.
Alcoa is now (jointly with
Chinalco, China's largest
aluminum producer) the
largest shareholder in
Rio Tinto Alcan.

Alcoa managed to plant a news item on the front page of *Morgunblaðið*: 'Most of the aluminium for the Airbus comes from Alcoa.' This went along with a piece about the output from the Reyðarfjörður aluminium smelter going primarily to serve the European aircraft industry. This was supposed make us feel proud about being part of the 'Alcoa community'. The main news from Airbus, however, was to the effect that the company had managed to reduce the use of aluminium by using carbon-fibre and plastic materials. There are about 3300 Airbuses in service around the world at present. The total quantity of aluminium in the entire Airbus fleet might be around 150,000 tonnes, based on modern production methods. That is, the entire fleet could have been built with less than half the projected annual output of the Reyðarfjörður plant. The world demand for aluminium does not come from the aviation industry; this is just a piece of wishful thinking concocted to be sneaked onto the front

Source:
'Airbus aluminium mostly
from Alcoa', news item in
Morgunblaðið, 28 April
2005.

Source:
www.airbus.com.

pages by public relations companies. The object is to make us Icelanders proud of a connection that has nothing behind it. On the www.alcoa.is website there is a list of Alcoa's customers. Pride of place at the top of the page goes to the aeronautical and aerospace industries. The message is clear: we are smelting spaceships and aeroplanes. So our sense of self-esteem is deflected away from the country, the waterfalls and the beauty, and onto paths that are built on what? Fallacies?

Every three months the people of America dump enough aluminium cans to renew the entire US airfleet. In one year, four times all the aeroplanes in the USA gets buried in landfills. At current production levels of aluminium we could travel by single-use planes every time we fly abroad. As the chairman of Landsvirkjun presents it, we are in debt to the world: we either produce aluminium, or we will be banished from the present. Driven back into the dark ages and sheepskin shoes.

It is so easy to hoodwink us. It is such a short time since life was raw materials. Meat was life. Fish was life. But aluminium is what? We have so little true knowledge of the world, we do not see how small we are. We do not look for information, do not ask questions, do not understand the broader context. We fail to see that just a tiny fraction of the rubbish tips of the world market could swamp Iceland and its economy in a matter of moments. At present it is one particular metal, one narrow possibility out of all the possibilities in the world.

'We need to produce aluminium,' they say. 'We want to have the next aluminium plant.' But why? Is there someone out there looking to manufacture wheel rims and Straumsvík cannot see to the demand? Anyone crying out for 100,000 tonnes of doorknobs? Is there a doctor who is going to do hip replacements on the whole of humanity? Is there someone with a big idea in their head who can't get any further for lack of an aluminium plant? No, that's not the way it is. We just want to be busy and to work hard and smelt. That is a job for men. It is that or sheepskin shoes.

Psychological warfare operates on people's insecurities, their lack of perspective. The advocates of power development in this country trot out the traditional metaphors of a 'base industry' and 'pillars of the economy' and play on our ingrained inferiority complex by conjuring up the humiliating symbol of our long years of national servitude – sheepskin shoes. It is easy to tell us to smelt aluminium so we can pay for our health and education systems and fly abroad in planes made of aluminium. But something strikes you as a bit odd when you read in the *LOWEST ENERGY PRICES!!* brochure that this country already has 'one of the world's best health care systems'. Is the million tonne nation really going to have an even better healthcare system? Thanks to Rio Tinto?

Is the Kárahnjúkar hydro scheme and the factory it supplies something *fundamental to life* in this country, like food, heating, light and aeroplanes? Or is it something more like a distraction, Mickey Mouse or Britney Spears? Each can answer this for themselves, and doubtless the answers will change according to circumstances. Sometimes cans, sometimes wire, sometimes car bonnets, building materials, chewing gum wrappers – and sometimes bombs. But in a world of distortion and misinformation, one thing is certain: that the Kárahnjúkar plant has more in common with Mickey Mouse than with jumbo jets, and is much, much closer to the rubbish tip than outer space.

And while we're on the subject of sheepskin shoes, how come you can go into a shop and pay almost 300 dollars for a pair of Nike trainers, but you can't get shoes from Dior made of sheepskin for love nor money anywhere? Just crocodile and snakeskin. Is it because no one has thought of designing a pair of shoes like this and giving them an image?

Thjórsárver: Terror Alert

Thjórsárver is a unique and precious work of nature of undisputed world value. The area is made up of wide tracts of rich highland vegetation, bogs and pools, criss-crossed by the upper reaches of Thjórsá as it flows its way down from the ice of the Hofsjökull glacier. At the end of July and the beginning of August the wetlands are an unbroken swathe of flowers that spreads around low hills and mounds, rising up to over 3000 feet above sea level on the slopes of Arnarfell. It is an oasis, an orchard in the desert, one of the few upland areas of Iceland not stripped bare by erosion. There among the turf is a major nesting ground for pink-footed geese, one of the few animal species entirely dependent on Iceland, with ninety per cent of the world stock breeding here. As a result, the pink-footed goose has a claim to being the most Icelandic of all birds; it is just a shame our 19th-century poets neglected to put it into their poems and so fix it in our national consciousness alongside the plover and the whimbrel.

Thjórsárver is on the Ramsar List of Wetlands of International Importance, and biologists who have investigated the conservation value of natural treasures throughout the world believe it merits inclusion on the UNESCO list of World Heritage Sites. There is no way to do justice to Thjórsárver in a few words – the place is material for a whole book, for an in-depth television documentary.

As we see from the articles of Halldór Laxness and Jakob Björnsson described earlier, there were plans afoot in the early 1970s to flood Thjórsárver in its entirety. The proposal was for a seventy-five square mile reservoir that would have stretched all the way from the low hill of Norðlingaalda up to the foothills of the Hofsjökull ice cap, thereby destroying the largest colony of pink-footed geese in the world. These ideas met with strong opposition but they remained on the table right up until 1981, when, after much to-ing and

fro-ing, a section of Thjórsárver was given protected status. However, the conservationists were forced to concede on their opposition to the flooding of
Eyjabakkar as part of the hydro plans for the east of Iceland.

The outlines of the Thjórsárver conservation area look a bit like the
borders of countries on a map of Africa – they are drawn up in straight lines
that take no account of river catchment areas and other ecological boundaries. All discussion of operations inside or outside the conservation area is
thus misleading. The protected area is too small; in a way it is like protecting
a tree but not its crown and roots. In any case, you do not need to be a biologist
or ornithologist to feel and understand the significance of the place. If Iceland
has any value at all, whether as a natural habitat or a work of creation, then
Thjórsárver ought to be the last place to be tampered with. Unfortunately,
Icelanders have never fully come into possession of this jewel of nature; it
has almost always had works hanging over it and the place has thus been
'politicized'. In the aforementioned declaration of protected status from 1981
there is a clause allowing the construction of a reservoir encroaching onto the
marshes so long as it 'does not detract unduly from the nature conservation
value of the wetlands'. The general public's understanding of the issues has
not been helped by the proposed reservoir at Thjórsárver being known not as
'the Thjórsárver Reservoir' but 'the Norðlingaalda Diversion'.

Now, it so happened that in the year 2002 Century Aluminum landed
a juicy contract and decided to expand its Norðurál smelter in Hvalfjörður by
a few thousand tonnes. Since we live in a world of infinite possibilities, the
alternative were clear:

Source:
'The Landsvirkjun
Norðlingaalda Diversion
plan', discussed on www.
lv.is/article.asp?catID=
180&ArtId=212.

*In order to meet Norðurál's electricity requirements within the
time requested it is essential to proceed with the construction of
the Búðarháls power station and the Norðlingaalda (Thjórsárver)
Diversion. No other options are to hand.*

Of all the potential hydroelectric sites in Iceland, this was the most controversial. An ornithologist interviewed said that, if it came to having to make
a choice between Gullfoss and Thjórsárver, it should be Gullfoss that went.
This time it was the locals of the Skeið and Gnúpverjahreppur districts, where

Andri Snær Magnason

Thjórsá flows into the southern lowlands, that led the campaign of action for the protection of Thjórsárver, alongside biologists and wetlands enthusiasts. The disputes that ensued should have surprised no one. The wetlands were up for sale, and had been so for years. They were part of the *LOWEST ENERGY PRICES!!* package. Some very conscientious men had put a lot of effort into trashing the place. Everything was more or less sorted. All that was needed was to start up the bulldozers.

The plans sparked off an enormously complex and intricate technical dispute in the media. The debate centred chiefly around the proposed works themselves and largely ignored questions such as why and whether they were needed in the first place. There were headlines with figures that meant even less to most people than TWhs – reservoir altitude 581 metres, 575, 578, references to article numbers in the 1981 conservation order. It was a complicated issue, a political issue, politicians came out for or against, at times in direct opposition to their own party lines. People wrote letters to the papers, everything moved at breakneck speed. The employment situation in the area was poor and so it was natural for journalists to be asking, What on earth is up with these people in Gnúpverjahreppur? What right does a little group of local farmers and a few naturalists think it has to stand in the way of progress, prosperity and the optimism building up around the aluminium industry in the west of Iceland? There were even mutterings along the lines of, For Geese, Against People. But there were also many who asked, Is there really reason to have Thjórsárver so high on the priority list? Isn't it possible to get the energy from somewhere else if the country is supposed to be so rich in it? No, it seemed there wasn't. At least, not at such short notice. And not so cheap:

> In order to meet Norðurál's electricity requirements within the time requested it is essential to proceed with the construction of the Búðarháls power station and the Norðlingaalda (Thjórsárver) Diversion. No other options are to hand.

Everything had to be done fast. Whether or not the Hvalfjörður aluminium works itself was going to provide the basis for economic prosperity and a multiplier effect, the future depended on STILL MORE EXPANSION. So far nobody was making cans, wheel rims or sheep pens out of the stuff. Local government officials in the west of Iceland joined forces with Landsvirkjun and started putting pressure on the people of Gnúpverjahreppur to stop this palaver about reservoir altitudes, 575 or 579, and allow the work to get under way immediately.

The urgency was a fiction, a smokescreen. 'Developing' Thjórsárver was absolutely in line with Landsvirkjun's prioritization programme; the simple fact was that the wetlands stood top of the list of preferred options. In an industry ministry report from 1996, the Norðlingaalda Diversion was scheduled next after the Búðarháls power station, and in 1998 Thjórsárver was earmarked for a magnesium refinery. Presumably the idea was to get all the contracts for the factory signed and sealed and then to announce the need for immediate action: 'In order to meet the electricity requirements of the magnesium plant within the time requested...'

Source:
Ministry for Industry and Commerce (1996), *Manpower needs and skills for power schemes and heavy industrial operations 1996-2002: committee report*, Ministry for Industry and Commerce: Reykjavík. Ministry for Industry and Commerce (1998), *Manpower needs and skills for power schemes and heavy industrial operations 1998-2005: committee report*, Ministry for Industry and Commerce: Reykjavík.

The beauty and uniqueness of the Icelandic landscape has been used to sell motor cars, mould images, unite the nation, adorn the national anthem, attract tourists and create not only spiritual wealth but also hard cash. Superlatives spring naturally to mind when we think of the beauty, riches and individuality of our country. People go to the mountains and come back renewed and refreshed. We have not needed to pay an advertising agency or a public relations consultancy to focus people's attention on what everyone can see with their own eyes; the country lives up to its image. Thjórsárver ought to be seen as our principal, our capital stock, objective proof of the country's worth. But in this instance the superlatives constituted a threat to the project and the future of the nation. Suddenly, just publishing and disseminating pictures, information and hard facts about Thjórsárver became a highly political act. The ministry for the environment made no attempt to provide information. If the people of Gnúpverjahreppur had asked to let schoolchildren know something about Thjórsárver, doubtless Landsvirkjun would have demanded equal time to present its side of the case. This situation has denied the nation the opportunity to acquire something of enormous value. Any proposal to submit the wetlands for inclusion on the UNESCO list of World Heritage Sites would probably have got blocked within the system.

Suddenly it was down to individuals and private initiative to persuade the nation you could not put a price on a conservation area purely in terms of cheap power for smelting 60,000 tonnes of aluminium. That Thjórsárver should not become the first hundred metres in some refinery potroom. The

Andri Snær Magnason

argument of the people of Gnúpverjahreppur was that there were other options available, that the people of their area had already accepted a fair number of power stations all the way up Thjórsá, and there was no need to disturb Thjórsárver if the country really had such large reserves of energy. They set out to draw attention to their cause, had literature printed, set up a website, collected money for a full-page advertisement in the papers and held a public meeting in Reykjavík. But all of this counted for little when placed against the TERROR ALERT in the economy:

> *There was singing of patriotic songs and reciting of poems, all because people were getting dewy-eyed at the prospect of a few blades of grass finishing up under water at Norðlingaalda... This place presents us with enormous possibilities and it is abundantly clear to everyone that Norðlingaalda is the most economical solution... This is the greatest piece of good fortune we could have if the intention is to stimulate economic growth and create a thriving economy. It is ready on the table and the terms have been agreed. We can do both these things. It is ours to decide, we are in a position to see that this country achieves high economic growth over the next years. We must do it. It is our duty to do it, because we bear a responsibility to the welfare of this nation.*

Source:
Einar Oddur
Kristjánsson, speaking in
parliament, 5 December
2002, *Alþingistíðindi*
(Icelandic Parliamentary
Gazette), 2002-03, 128th
legislative session B,
debates, p. 1791.

Terror Alert. Now or never. Economic growth comes down from above, not from the people themselves. It is the state that calls the tune. Thjórsárver or life. To be sure, Landsvirkjun agreed to have some research done into the area, but when in came to it the information gathered by the biologists proved too unpalatable to them. Uncomfortable findings were ignored and the picture was tarted up for the environmental assessment.

It is fair to say that public money has been used to attack Thjórsárver. Every penny that independent associations collected and used in their struggle to save the wetlands appeared to be met with a hundred from Landsvirkjun in an intensified 'public awareness' and image campaign that increased neither people's knowledge nor appreciation of the area. Considerably greater effort went into fostering perceptions of the inexhaustibility of our energy reserves. In the middle of its offensive against one of the greatest natural treasures of

Source:
Answer by the minister
for industry to a
question from Kolbrún
Halldórsdóttir on
company promotion by
Landsvirkjun, Iceland
State Electricity and
the Westfjord Power
Company, 5 December
2002, *Alþingistíðindi*
(Icelandic Parliamentary
Gazette), 2002-03, 128th
legislative session A,
parliamentary papers,
p. 2313.

Iceland, the company became the leading sponsor of the National Museum. To counter the powerful opposition and voluntary campaigning within the artistic community, the power company became an avid sponsor of the arts. A special initiative was set up, 'Art in Power Stations'. Between 1999 and 2002 it had an outlay of 300,000 dollars – of which 235,000 went on advertising. The best year was probably 2001; in that year, total expenditure amounted to 92,000 dollars, of which just short of 91,000 went to advertising companies. The image of a company supporting the arts means more than the art itself. By way of comparison, the National Gallery of Iceland has to make do with an annual acquisitions budget of just 125,000 dollars.

A compromise was sought, but the compromise still turned around how rather than whether. The minister for health put on his thinking cap and came up with a proposal: a small amount of vegetation would be lost but almost all the water would be diverted around Thjórsárver with ditches, protective walls, road-building works, blasting and general disruption to a fragile and unspoilt tract of land. In reality, the compromise was a rehash of a plan that had previously been rejected, only this time under a new name – 'countermeasures' – a magic word that sounded a bit like some kind of defence. On closer examination, the new proposal turned out to be even worse than the one people had been arguing about in the first place: it involved establishing a feeder reservoir right up against the base of Hofsjökull, with the accumulation of sediment and the siting of tipping areas directly above the wetlands themselves. What it really amounted to was a sop to people's sensibilities: the job would go ahead, but people would be spared the distasteful feeling that Norðurál was getting this precious gift from Iceland at rock-bottom prices.

The local council in Gnúpverjahreppur fought on and succeeded in delaying matters, a delay that proved significant because it emerged that there were other possibilities worth considering. The power could be generated from geothermal sources. Without going into all the ins and outs, the power company serving Reykjavík and the southwest peninsula reckoned it would be possible to supply Norðurál's energy requirements using geothermal sources, meaning that Thjórsárver could be spared. This would mean works and disruption on Hellisheiði, the moors you cross going east out of Reykjavík, but that was clearly a more acceptable option. More worrying was the air pollution

226.

in Hvalfjörður however the power is provided, and this is set to get worse in the coming years.

But why should the fate of an internationally significant site like Thjórsárver hang by such a slender thread that its future depends on a tiny group of motivated individuals? Would the wetlands now be under water if the people of Gnúpverjahreppur had not stood up and protested? What are we to make of the cultural sophistication of an affluent society where something like this becomes a possibility? To swap a jewel of nature on a UNESCO level for one sixth of an aluminium factory? Thinking back on it, it bespeaks a flagrant lack of respect for people, to say nothing of Iceland itself. There were people ready to trample Thjórsárver into the mud, and even to justify it as something wonderful and noble. The aluminium company was happy enough to accept this generosity. The contractors would not have given it a second thought.

April 20, 2004 was a big day for everyone who had fought for the protection of Thjórsárver. This was the day the contract was signed by which Norðurál would be supplied with power from geothermal boreholes operated by the Reykjavík Power Company. But even on this very day people could not breathe more easily, celebrate a temporary victory, and turn their minds to other things. One of those present at the signing was the managing director of Landsvirkjun. In an interview with *Morgunblaðið* he said he was hopeful that the Norðlingaalda (Thjórsárver) Diversion would get the go-ahead for the next expansion of Norðurál, in five to six years' time. The article goes on: 'Hopefully the works would be able to move forward quickly to the planning stage within the area, despite the majority on the local council being opposed to Landsvirkjun's plans. The managing director said he now sensed a greater readiness than previously on the part of council to come to an arrangement with Landsvirkjun...'

Source:
'Norðlingaalda
Diversion ready for next
stage', news item in
Morgunblaðið, 21 April
2004.

We can only hope the comments were taken out of context or poorly rephrased by the reporter. Only three days earlier, on 18 April, Morgunblaðið carried the news of the death of Már Haraldsson, chairman of the Gnúpverja- and Skeiðarhreppur district council, at the age of only 50, after a painful battle with cancer. In the obituary stood the following: 'He was leader of the majority

Source:
'Már Haraldsson', death
notice, *Morgunblaðið*, 18
April 2004.

group on the district council during the discussions and turmoils surrounding Landsvirkjun's plans for a Norðlingaalda Diversion. Már fought against these proposals right up until the last day of his life.'

The matter was not closed. Emissaries from Landsvirkjun travelled round the district, not to hold open and democratic meetings at which everyone could meet and take part in lively public debate, but calling on people one by one and talking to them behind closed doors. This led to mistrust and division within the community. Evening News, National Radio, 24 August 2005:

Source:
'Majority on
Gnúpverjahreppur
council overturned?'
Evening News, National
Radio, 24 August 2005.

Majority on Gnúpverjahreppur council overturned?

The majority on the Gnúpverjahreppur District Council, which recently emphatically rejected further operations at Thjórsárver, has possibly been overturned.

One of four members of the majority grouping has taken leave of absence for the remainder of his term and it has emerged that his deputy supports the attitude towards Thjórsárver of the minority on the council... This appears to have taken the members of the majority by surprise.

People can argue and get up in arms over this episode. What in the end matters most is where the real power lies:

Source:
'Harnessing unlimited
power and profits
from the world's most
progressive energy
program', *True Wealth*,
Stansberry & Associates
Investment Research, 17
August 2006.

The deal Century [Aluminum] struck with Iceland's power companies is smart... Century's power bill is simply a percentage of the price of aluminum on the London Metals Exchange. This arrangement works out great for both sides...

Century never has to worry that its energy cost will get too high as a percentage of what it sells. If Century's sales are great, then pays more for power, but it's happy to. If the price of aluminum crashes, Century's power cost goes way down.

It works out great for Iceland, too... It is very cheap for Iceland to deliver power to Century. The Icelandic power companies will make extraordinary profits on that power if aluminum prices stay strong. And if aluminum prices weaken, Iceland is not biting the hand that feeds it.

Andri Snær Magnason

Had Thjórsárver been carved up at the time in exchange for the first hundred metres of one of Norðurál's potrooms, the grief felt on a little island in the north Atlantic would have shown up as a minuscule increment on an account within another account, itself within another account, run by an accounts manager in a sub-department of the funds management section of the heavy-industry division of the Morgan Stanley investment bank. The final significance would have registered no deeper than this:

B. Klein: Just remind us again, the timing of the doubling of capacity in Iceland; when is that going to start?

C. Davis: Construction will start quite soon. The first metal should come out in the first quarter of '06.

B. Klein: Okay. And the cost, has it changed from what –

C. Davis: No. Jack, we haven't had anything that's more recent since my last number, have we?

J. Gates: No changes.

Moderator: We'll go to the line of Wayne Atwell, representing Morgan Stanley. Please go ahead.

W. Atwell: The expansion, has that been approved yet for Nordural?

C. Davis: We have all necessary permits in Iceland. We have the power. We basically presented the project to our board. The answer is fundamentally, yes.

Source: Transcript of a teleconference of investors on the first quarter's figures for 2004 of the Century Aluminum Company, 27 April 2004, www. centuryca.com/news/pdf/transcript042704.pdf.

Photograph: Thjórsárver. (Photographer: Jóhann Ísberg)

Ignorance is strength

There is consensus over the need for continued economic growth in Iceland, and it is abundantly clear that if we fail to utilize the country's energy resources there will be an appreciable downturn in economic growth as early as 2007 with an attendant rise in unemployment.

Halldór Ásgrímsson, prime minister,
Evening News, National Radio, 24 January 2006

Define the enemy and specify the alternatives.

A writer

I confess that I am frightened. These schemes are being pushed through at enormous speed and with inexorable determination, as if there is a competition on to get them up and running before anyone has a chance to consider the broader picture. No one knows where the battle lines will be drawn next. It is not possible to build one pyramid and it looks as if things are only just beginning. In November 2005, one of our free daily papers, Blaðið, reported our newly instated minister for finance as saying that 'we would require further development of energy-intensive industry in the future to support the living standards we wish to offer the Icelandic nation in the future.'

   If we deconstruct the semantics of this sentence and put it into human language, what he said was precisely this: 'If the aluminium companies are not interested in new projects, there will be no economic growth and everyone will get poorer, tourism will decline, educated people will forget whatever they've learned, business will stagnate, computers and washing machines will

Source:
'Aluminium works Iceland', news item in *Blaðið*, 5 November 2005.

work slower, our cars will get old and rusty, flow lines will hit the wall and medical research go kaput. I don't reckon there's anything to be gained by educating our young people and nothing unforeseen will ever happen again. For bulldozer drivers who have invested all their hopes in a summer's work for Rio Tinto, this will be the last chance they'll ever see. We'll have to shut down the elementary schools, the outpatients department at the children's hospital, the mentally ill will be on the streets, life-support systems will be turned off, childbearing will have to be limited, and a planned policy of emigration will need to instituted with immediate effect.'

Our entire well-being depends on things getting the nod from someone behind a desk at Morgan Stanley. But quality of life is not within the gift of individual companies, and no one in their right mind should believe that one company or one contract can deliver quality of life. The minister got his words from his predecessor, who doubtless got them from somewhere within the ministry. What these words imply is that Icelanders' lives and standards of living are directly linked to aluminium company investment and the demand for aluminium on the international markets. But if the impact of their operations is so great, then their power must be similarly great, and you won't see these companies pumping billions into our health and education services. Nobody is going to pay to keep us going.

Both of the aluminium companies currently operating in this country have changed ownership, and everything points to Alcoa running four plants in Iceland within a very few years. Alcoa is already building its smelter at Reyðarfjörður and is intending to decommission another in America and set up at Húsavík. Century Aluminum runs Norðurál at Hvalfjörður and wants to open another plant at Helguvík. Century Aluminum is a small company and already operates one factory in collaboration with Alcoa in South Carolina. There is every possibility that these two companies will merge at some point in the future. Doubtless many people would find it a bit excessive if Alcoa announced plans to build four aluminium refineries in Iceland, so the merger will probably be put off until Century has its two plants up and running, and Alcoa its two, and the power companies have put the nation in hock and linked repayments to aluminium prices up to the year 2050. Then they will be able to join forces and it will all be easier for us to swallow.

If quality of life is going to depend on the existence of these four Alcoa factories, then the minister's words must be taken to mean that people have to understand that life and living standards in Iceland are in some way bound up with the fortunes of this company. We will be the multiplier effect and be compelled to say when we go abroad, 'There's a health service in Iceland because Alcoa has four factories there.' The company will get to say the same thing on its website. If it was not for them, the situation would be 'much more worse than it is now'.

Alcoa could sell the whole complex on to Russal, in which case Russal would become the pillar of the economy and the basis for living standards. And then Russal could merge with Chinal and they could review the energy contract in line with current market rates for clean energy closer to the bauxite mines in Africa, and they would move their factories around the country to create bigger and more cost-effective units in response to hardening international competition.

It is a matter of the most fundamental importance for Icelanders that they should be able to approach their most important decisions of the present age not from a position of necessity and compulsion but on the basis of free choice. This is, above all else, a question of CHOICE. A temporary problem in the rural communities of Iceland has led to a peculiar struggle for unindependence that lacks any sense of ambition for the nation's future, in either the short or long term.

But it's OK. We can trust Alcoa. They have plenty of experience of acting the benevolent and informed dictator in towns and cities around the world. On the www.alcoa.com website there is a wonderful FAQ section:

What is Alcoa doing to respect the Hidden People of Icelandic folklore?

Alcoa has, in all places where we deal with a culture relatively unknown to us, shown proper respect for local customs and beliefs.

Well hallelujah, let's go out and do a rain dance in celebration. All very nice and well-meaning, to be sure, but the colonial mindset is there for all to

Source: 'Straumsvík – expansion or closure', news item on NFS, 3 March 2006. It goes on to say: 'If the Straumsvík aluminium plant is not able to expand it will have to be shut down and closed within a few years. This was the message from executives of Alcan in talks with the government, according to prime minister Halldór Ásgrímsson.'

see. The magnanimity of power can be even more revealing than its brutality. But is it true? Has the company really taken care not to mess with the elves and hidden people of Iceland? Those in touch with the supernatural world in this country say that everything in it is going crazy. Absolutely, stark staring crazy.

Source: 'Discussion committee concludes no basis for construction of ferrosilicon plant', news item in *Morgunblaðið*, 1 July 1987.

We are not a nation of chess players. We are a nation of ludo players. We hop around at the throw of a dice. For decades we have been talking about hydroelectric schemes, aluminium, aluminium refining, alumina and new factories without having any idea of the sizes and basic concepts involved, let alone the reputations of those who are supposed to be saving us.

There has been a lot of talk about the people of the Eastfjords having had to suffer a long wait for heavy industry, about it being their turn, about them deserving to get their aluminium plant at last after twenty years of waiting and having seen their hopes dashed again and again. At one time there was talk about a ferrosilicon plant at Reyðarfjörður but this eventually died the death in 1987. And what was the name of the company behind this proposed factory? The world-renowned Rio Tinto of course. 'Probably the most uncaring and ruthless company in the world.' Sore disappointment. Doubtless the innocent natives thought Rio was something to do with Duran Duran.

Source: 'Rio Tinto feels the pinch', news item in the *Guardian*, 13 May 1999. The article says: 'Rio Tinto's operation at Capper Pass was an environmental disaster, causing death and serious illness to many of its former employees.' In Indonesia Rio Tinto has a large stake in a company that is reported to have been razing villages to the ground and driving out the inhabitants to clear land for a proposed mine. Security patrols financed by the company are said to have used threats, rape, torture, kidnapping and murder against those who tried to protect their possessions and work tools or stand up against the poisoning of wells and water sources and the general destruction of farming lands, sacred sites and fishing grounds.

The Eastfjords of Iceland was not the only place to be disappointed by Rio Tinto in 1987. The company owned a tin smelter at Capper Pass near Hull in England. According to the Guardian it was accused of serious breaches of anti-pollution regulations which resulted in a discharge of heavy metals, arsenic, lead and radioactive materials into the environment. Employees and people living in the vicinity suffered serious damage to health, with cases of leukaemia, cancer and other serious diseases directly attributable to the plant. Litigation against the company went on for seven years, with the company employing the methods and arguments developed by the tobacco companies to delay and obfuscate the issues.

And how was the employment situation in the east of Iceland at the time when Rio Tinto wriggled itself off the hook? In a interview with *Morgunblaðið* on 1 July 1987 the head of the local council in Reyðarfjörður was quoted as saying that they 'would now have to find other ways to create employment in the Eastfjords, but as things stood there was absolutely no unemployment in the area; in fact there was a shortage of people to do the work'.

So, echoing Laxness, it might be fair to ask: It would be nice if someone could tell us where in the world there is a heavy-industrial working class that lives under better economic conditions than people do in Reyðarfjörður without any heavy industry. It is maybe worth noting that in 2001 Reyðarfjörður elementary school had the highest average exam results in the whole of Iceland. Reyðarfjörður has a population of only about 900. If the kids in a school of this size in Reykjavík had had the same amount of attention lavished on them by the country's authorities, engineers and media for the last twenty years, the first of them would just about now be completing their doctorates and landing huge international contracts for the Icelandic Space Institute, a multinational corporation involved in the design, development and construction of communications satellites serving the global TV and telecoms market. Or perhaps something more down to earth software, food mixers, resonance imaging equipment, drive shafts.

People have been pushing a heavy-industry policy for decades now and it is a tale of great expectations and bitter disappointments. Despite all that has happened in the Icelandic economy over the last fifty years, this policy has somehow always managed to keep its head above water. The state invested huge sums in the ferrosilicon plant at Grundartangi and lost just about everything it put in: the plant was supplied with power at way below cost price (and still is), and Iceland got bound in to regular payments to the Norwegians for technical assistance and advice, payments that continued even after Icelanders took over the running and started providing advisory services to the Norwegians.

Special committees and marketing agencies have been working for decades to attract heavy industry to this country, without success and to the detriment of any attempt by people here to stand on their own two feet. Politicians have driven around the farmlands, generally just before election time, telling eagerly expectant constituents that they are being eyed up by the worst company in the world – only for nothing ever to come of it. The most important piece of job creation of course concerned the politician, who got re-elected.

Decisions have been taken on new power development schemes based on the flimsiest of grounds. The hydroelectric plant on the river Blanda, for

Source: 'Extractive industries is not the answer for decent and sustainable livelihood: statement for the World Bank Extractive Industries Review (EIR)', statement from a group of Indonesian NGOs (the Indonesian Forum for the Environment (WALHI), the Indonesian Mining Advocacy Network (JATAM), and the Indigenous Peoples' Alliance of the Archipelago (AMAN)) and Australian NGOs (the Mineral Policy Institute, Friends of the Earth Australia, and the Asia-Pacific Unit, Australian Conservation Foundation): Bali, Indonesia, 26-30 April 2002, www.minesandcommunties.org/Charter/eirposit2.htm.

Source: Júlíus Solnes (2004), 'To harness power or not to harness power', Up in the Wind: the Journal of Civil Engineering Students, vol. 23, 2004, pp. 20-23.

Photograph:
Hydroelectricity
enthusiasts rode in to
parliament wearing
T-shirts bearing the
slogan 'Let's Harness
Blanda'. Loans were
raised with foreign
investors and the Blanda
hydroplant went up, even
though the electricity
generated was completely
surplus to requirements.
Job creation in the
neighbourhood proved to
be nil and even negative
in the longer term.

example, was built in the years following 1984 without there being any prospective purchaser for the power generated. The plant stood there for a decade and more capable of producing unwanted and unneeded electricity,

the country paid interest on its foreign loans without getting a penny in return, and Landsvirkjun lost a fortune. And yet for all this, we have people talking about this project as an example of mankind making good use of an 'underexploited resource' – rather than holding it up as a prime case of utter stupidity. We could have built twenty playschools a year for the money that haemorrhaged out of Blanda. In the end a buyer was found, at *LOWEST ENERGY PRICES!!*, though the actual rates of course remained classified information. Any kind of income was better than no income at all. The Blanda reservoir was filled and twenty-five square miles of varied vegetation was drowned. To compensate the farmers for lost grazing, schemes were introduced to fertilize and revegetate the blasted heaths above at a cost at the time of around 12.5 million dollars. The grass got eaten by the most expensive sheep in the history of Iceland. Ovine Rolls Royce. The dam also blocked off fish migration up to the Blanda heaths. 'A unique salmon stock that had previously existed there was wiped out; this must be regarded a major loss to the natural world as salmon migration so far above sea level is a rare and very special phenomenon.'

The Kárahnjúkar project would be worth a chapter of its own. The company is now hostage to an Italian contractor that is known for underbidding on projects and then going way over budget. So much has been spent there is no turning back. The position on the contracts is bad, to put it mildly, and any half decent lawyer can fill his pockets at the expense of the Icelandic nation.

Source:
Helgi Baldursson
(1995), *Democracy in
the fetters of power: the
Blanda dispute*, Land
Conservation Association
for the Blanda and
Héraðsvötn Drainage
Basins, [no place of
publication], p. 209.

Andri Snær Magnason

Of course this country needs power. It needs something under three terawatt-hours a year. To keep all the homes in Iceland lit and powered needs less than one terawatt-hour a year, and this one terawatt-hour a year could have been paid off long ago and now even maybe be coming free. The same goes for the one terawatt-hour used by general industry in this country. The heavy-industry policy seems almost to have become a sort of welfare system for the power development faction. The return on capital at Landsvirkjun has been around 0.9 per cent from the outset. The big companies have not become the kind of fount of gold that people expected, quite the opposite even: 'Since income from energy sales to heavy industry has been pegged to long-term contracts, the only way to break even has been to increase tariffs to companies supplying the general public.'

Source:
Jón Thór Sturluson
(2005), 'The performance
of Landsvirkjun and
the effects of heavy
industry on the national
economy', *Landsvirkjun
1965-2005: the company
and its environment*,
The Icelandic Literary
Society: Reykjavík,
p. 118.

All the electricity for Reykjavík and the surrounding areas could be got from a tiny patch of geothermal land up under Hengill to the south of Lake Thingvallavatn. The disruption involved would be on a par with the disruption caused by a skiing area. The various power companies – the Westfjord Power Co., the Reykjavík Power Supply Co., RARIK (Iceland State Electricity) and the Heating Company of Suðurnes – could easily have generated all the power this country needs and perhaps made a few dollars on the side. Little by little it would be possible to fuel the country's future car fleet from a few high-temperature boreholes. All these companies have served the nation well and lived in harmony with it. The assault by the ministry for industry, the National Energy Authority and Landsvirkjun on some of the pearls of Icelandic nature and their flirtation with the worst companies in the world have tarnished the image of the entire power sector.

If you go right down to the roots of the heavy-industry policy, the pot seems to have been cracked from the very beginning. There was a lot of banner waving about national interests, but perhaps certain more specific interests had a bigger part in what went on. Even in the earliest days patterns of behaviour could be observed that seemed to suggest that information and an open exchange of opinions were seen as a threat to the great plan:

With the scheme to use Urriðafoss now out of the picture, ideas about harnessing the river Thjórsá at Búrfell began to acquire greater prominence. The hydrographic survey had already shown

237.

that there might be a major problem with ice. The reset produced findings that demonstrated this conclusively. I found myself in the extraordinary position of witnessing direct attempts to prevent this research from being taken into account. People did not want any fuss being made about the ice on Thjórsá.

There were considerable financial interests at stake here. The Búrfell scheme was bound up with ideas for an aluminium smelter at Straumsvík. The envisaged company would be able to pay a certain price for the electricity and this needed to be factored in when assessing the cost of the hydroelectric scheme. Those who were fighting hardest for this new order in the industrial life of the nation needed to be able to demonstrate that the power scheme would be cost-effective on the basis of energy sales to the aluminium plant. The large costs of measures needed to deal with the problems of ice skewed the figures significantly. Taking them into account might make it appear that the project was simply not worth proceeding with…

There were political and financial interests at stake here too. It even happened that these parties were fully aware of the dangers posed by the ice but still preferred to keep quiet about it, at least at this stage of the proceedings. In their minds, the main thing appeared to be not to let anything detract from people's optimism over these projects.

I got phone calls at home in the evening that were tantamount to threats. I found these tactics so cheap and despicable that I chose to keep quiet about the whole wretched business. There was a struggle going on over directions in the working life of Iceland and it so happened that I had information that came out against one of these directions. One might say that I found myself caught in the crossfire.

Source:
Hermann Sveinbjörnsson
(1989), *Wade in! Sigurjón
Rist, hydrographer:
memoirs*, Skjaldborg:
Reykjavík, pp. 198-9.

Which presages our own times. On the day parliament was due to discuss the go-ahead for the Kárahnjúkar project, the geophysicist Grímur Björnsson submitted a memo on the subject of fault lines and earth fractures under the site of the proposed dam and the possible effects of the weight of the reservoir on volcanic activity in the region and the fault system:

Andri Snær Magnason

There is a considerable probability that the Kárahnjúkar dam itself will be built over an active fault zone. Thus the undersigned considers the risk assessment presented in the Landsvirkjun evaluation report to be totally inadequate: there are significant possibilities of the dam failing, and while this is the case this scheme has no place before parliament. The weight of the Hálslón reservoir will cause movements in the magma and may thus affect volcanicity in the vicinity of the reservoir.

Source:
'The Kárahnjúkar Hydroelectric Scheme: illusion and reality', essay by Grímur Björnsson, geophysicist at the National Energy Authority, addressed to the director general of the Authority, 14 February 2002, www. os.is/~grb/karahnjukar. html.

These are serious matters. So what was done to bring them to the world's attention?

On the Monday or Tuesday there was an in-house meeting at the National Energy Authority. The statement had now been put back into letter form but [the director general] had had anything that might linked it to the Energy Authority erased and had had it labelled confidential. I was not consulted on any of this... I received a message, an email from [the director general] in which he asked me to keep the matter to myself while he discussed it with Landsvirkjun. And then a month goes by, if I remember rightly, a month and a half, and then I'm called in to a meeting at Landsvirkjun. I think this was the day after parliament had agreed the proposal for the project to go ahead.

Source:
Grímur Björnsson in interview with Jón Ásgeir Sigurðsson, Evening Shift, Icelandic National Radio, Channel 1, 10 April 2005.

Major questions failed to find their way into the parliamentary chamber, nor out to the general public and thus not into the Gallup polls that govern the swings of political life in this country. The result is that the biggest earthfill dam in Europe stands directly on top of a geological fault. The dam was later redesigned with joints inserted because the criticism proved to be well founded. Whether these measure will do the job no one knows – and uncomfortable information will no doubt be kept well away from public scrutiny. When projects lie so much on the edge that any discussion of possible dangers is hushed up, you might as well turn to paranormal sources for your information:

Unwise men have taken many decisions on weighty matters... I have come to a churning river with a powerful current. It forms

Source:
'In the steps of
Nostradamus', front
page interview with the
French psychic Marcelus
Toe Guor in the Sunday
edition of Morgunblaðið,
29 July 1990.

a great waterfall that plunges down into an abyss. As far as my eye can see there is nothing but rocks and wilderness. The earth trembles beneath my feet. At this place, terrible things are happening… I see a flood wall, a dam on a great river that has been harnessed to produce electricity. The dam will break due to weaknesses in the cement.

Andri Snær Magnason

There are times you need to face unpleasant things

In the best case, the aluminium industry is a magnificent testament to the victory of the human spirit – earth being turned into spaceships and DVDs. In the worst case, the industry means pollution, breaches of human rights and the destruction of ecologies. Aluminium people have been invited to this country from all corners of the world, but we get to hear nothing about the background and records of their companies. This is both bad policy and highly dangerous. No country survives on Rio Tinto and putting one's faith in them should come with a large health warning.

Jamaica is an island of two and a half million people, about a tenth the size of Iceland. It is more than a luxuriant paradise of mountains and forests, the home of Rastafarians and reggae; it is also one of the world's leading exporters of bauxite and alumina. Aluminium is refined from alumina (Al_2O_3), which is itself processed from bauxite, an ancient soil type found particularly in tropical regions. The bauxite lies close to the surface and is extracted using

241.

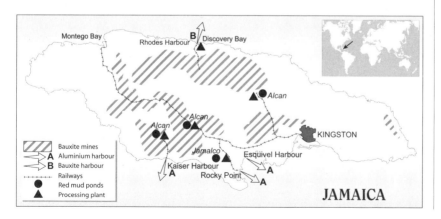

Map:
It is estimated that Jamaica's bauxite reserves will last another 150 years, but by then the island will have been stripped to the bone. (Based on a map drawn up by Prof. Robert J. Lancashire of the chemistry department of the University of the West Indies.)

shallow, open-cut mines extending over wide areas. To get at the bauxite the forest is stripped away, meaning that bauxite mining is responsible for a large part of Jamaica's chronic deforestation problem. The mines create dust and noise pollution. The roads leading to the mines open up untouched areas to tree felling and the plunder of natural resources. Fine dust from the factories gets blown over villages and farmlands and is washed into the sea during loading and unloading, causing damage to coral reefs. There is a constant need for new areas to mine and this is eating bit by bit into the delicate upland rainforest. The entire industry is coming under increasing scrutiny and becoming more and more controversial.

Source:
'Bauxite mining blamed
for deforestation', article
by Zadie Neufville, 6
April 2001, http://forests.
org/archive/samerica/
bauxmini.htm.

At current estimates, Jamaica has enough bauxite reserves to last perhaps another 150 years. This figure, however, may be a bit like Iceland's famous 30 terawatt-hours: by the time the bauxite has reached 'maximal exploitation' the whole island will have been pared down to the bone. By the ultimate technocratic vision, a third of Jamaica's total land surface is a potential bauxite mine. Even if the land is replanted afterwards it is not the same habitat; it is generally useless for cultivation, at best for grazing land.

Source:
'Jamaica bauxite case',
Case Study, American
University, www.
american.edu/TED/
bauxite.htm.

The bauxite is shovelled into alumina factories where it is leached with caustic soda, leaving a fine white dust, alumina. For each tonne of alumina thus produced the process creates one to two tonnes of a brownish red muck known simply as 'red mud'. Beyond the deforestation and the enormous energy demands, it is this red mud that constitutes by far the biggest problem associated with the aluminium extraction. The mud is contaminated with caustic soda and thus highly alkaline and hazardous to humans and animals. It is collected in ponds and lagoons, but the chemicals percolate into the environment and pollute groundwater, lakes and drinking water. For each million tonnes of aluminium manufactured there are around four million tonnes of this red mud somewhere in the world. For pictures of red mud ponds in Jamaica, see for example www.jbeo.com.

Bauxite and alumina are the 'leading exports' of Jamaica and one of the main 'pillars' of the nation's economy. Despite alumina production reaching around four million tonnes a year, the industry employs only about 5000 people. According to the Los Angeles Times, when Jamaica became independent from Britain in 1962, the new government took a decision to rely on mineral extraction as the route to living standards and future development, and the

Andri Snær Magnason

aluminium giants Alcoa, Kaiser and Alcan took over the role of colonial masters of the country.

The years in which the bauxite and alumina industry was being built up was a time of considerable boom and economic growth. But after around 1980 the market started to stagnate due to oversupply and the falling price of alumina, and the good times in Jamaica were succeeded by a long period of decline, which in reality continues to this day. The companies wield enormous power and have intimate links with the state authorities. Their interests are actively protected and promoted by legislation and government policy. Whether the lives of two and a half million Jamaicans count as a 'multiplier effect', or whether the industry represents a kind of neocolonialism, maintaining a ruling elite that profits from it and standing in the way of other kinds of development, I leave up to others to decide.

Source:
'Dust-up swirls around key Jamaica industry', article in the *Los Angeles Times*, 25 October 2004.

The article cited from the Los Angeles Times tells of the story a medical student who wanted to study the health of people living close to an alumina factory in Jamaica. Jamalco (a subsidiary of Alcoa) threatened to have the water supplies cut off to anyone who took part in the research. The authorities and spokesmen for Alcoa blamed the health problems on poverty and social deprivation and refused to look into the part played by pollution. So we will have to turn to another factory closer to hand.

Alumina is produced in Ireland, at Aughinish in County Limerick. In autumn 2005 the Irish Independent reported that residents in the vicinity of the factory were 'TERRIFIED' at plans to double the size of the mud ponds and waste tips. People were frightened of carcinogenic substances in the dust blown from the tips over their homes and farms and blamed this dust for causing death in livestock. If you go to the company's website, you won't find much about pools of red mud; but you'll be encouraged to learn that just outside the factory fence there is a butterfly nature reserve.

Source:
'"Red dust" application opposed over cancer fears', article in the Irish Independent, 31 October 2005. To quote: 'A TERRIFIED community has raised major cancer fears over plans to expand the giant "red mud" lagoons at the controversial Aughinish Alumina plant.'

Alumina processing is one of the most filthy, disgusting industries known to man on account half of its output being caustic red mud. So it should come as no surprise that an alumina plant stands high on the Landsvirkjun and industry ministry wish list, and that in 2003 a lot of preparation was actively carried out for a factory of this kind. According to the Invest in Iceland website, www.invest.is, steam power provides an ideal medium for aluminium

Source:
'Russians in heavy-industry talks with PM', news item in Fréttablaðið, 23 April 2002.
í Ríkisútvarpinu 17. desember 2005.

refining. The Chinese and Russians looked into Húsavík as a suitable location: according to www.atlantsal.is, the plan was to import bauxite from Guinea and Australia and process it here using 'clean energy' from the geothermal sources at Theistareykir, between Húsavík and Lake Mývatn. Newspaper reports talked about 'leading-edge technology' and two thousand jobs. One headline referred to 'optimism' among the people of Húsavík. But not a single unnecessary word, no discussion or explanation, about the two million tonnes of toxic red mud that would be coming out of the factory. That is fifteen times more than all the rubbish that gets picked up by the Reykjavík garbage collectors in a year. It is a fully laden truck of poisonous muck at three-minute intervals, every hour of the day and night. And where did they want to put this factory? According to www.atlantsal.is, on one of the headlands just outside the town, Héðinshöfði, Bakkahöfði or Gvendarbás. Gvendarbás? Gvendarbás stands right by the mouth of Iceland's most famous salmon river, Laxá in Aðaldalur, just as you enter the outskirts of Húsavík. This is how the Union of Icelandic Aircraft Maintenance Technicians website describes the place:

Source:
www.flug.is

The shoreline south of Húsavík – the Gvendarbás headland and Saltvík bay – has excellent sea-trout fishing, with the best conditions in the evening, in calm weather and at high tide. Fishing from the shore is free and no permit is needed. The coast offers something for everyone, even the most casual angler. All these community-owned fishing sites are within 5-10 minutes' walk of our holiday lodge in Aðaldalur.

Gvendarbás and free sea-fishing on a calm summer's evening do not feature in the figures for economic growth, nor in United Nations statistics for quality of life. I repeat: a conscious decision to crap into the water. The idea of an alumina factory and 200,000 truckloads a year of toxic slurry on the road between Húsavík and Laxá in Aðaldalur cannot be described otherwise. The details were thrashed out at meetings by people who like to see themselves as being cultured and educated; civil servants flew in great flocks from country to country on fact-finding missions; the company received planning

Source:
'Icelandic delegation examines Alcoa alumina refinery in Spain', news item in Morgunblaðið, 26 September 2002.

grants and assistance from the ministry for industry. In the news it was said that Straumsvík and Akureyri were also in the hat as promising places for these kinds of operations. We are plainly in good hands. The prime minister is

Andri Snær Magnason

always telling us that those who fear plans of this kind are 'against the future'. Perhaps it's time to return Stjórnarráðið, the elegant government offices in the centre of Reykjavík, back to its original form – as a Danish colonial prison, with bars at the windows and a big padlock on the door.

Ignorance is strength. Education is a heavy industry. People in Ireland are TERRIFIED. Here in Iceland the countryside smiles in celebration like Teletubbies every time someone goes to turn on the fan. Chinese alumina. A cancerous anode factory. 'Sustaining the health service.' Polycyclic aromatic hydrocarbons. A million tonnes of aluminium. 30 terawatt-hours. The cornerstone of living standards. The foundation of the economy. What are we supposed to live on? Probably the most uncaring and ruthless company in the world. Poison and murder. Where can I sign up for a dose of bubonic plague?

The Alcoa plant in Reyðarfjörður will in all probability smelt alumina from Jamaica, making us a link in that particular chain. Alcan also has mines in Jamaica. International competition is hard and there is little room for improving conditions, however much people may want to. If fifty per cent of the production of alumina is waste then there is every chance that the clean-up will prove to be more expensive than the production itself. Aluminium is a remarkable metal and serves its purpose amazingly well, where appropriate. But in other areas it is in direct competition with steel, timber, plastic, cardboard, glass, carbon fibre, or it is produced in poor countries that make fewer environmental demands. The companies seek out friendly governments, tax incentives, low wages, 'minimum environmental red tape', cheap energy – maybe even a population of remote and poorly informed islanders. There is always someone ready to underbid. The variables are simple. He who hesitates is lost. The Norwegian company Norsk Hydro had a survey done of the land to the north of the Vatnajökull ice cap. The conclusion was that this area was too valuable for its sacrifice to be justifiable. Alcoa signed its agreement with the Icelandic government on the promise of aiming to become 'the best company in the world'. The best company in the world is participating in the greatest premeditated piece of environmental devastation in Icelandic history. There is no point trying to sugar the pill; this is simply a fact. Iceland's gift to Alcoa is immense: we do not live by this company, but it is going to have the use of people whose strengths and abilities could have found a place in any company at all.

Seen in its ugliest light, the aluminium industry comes out like this: an ecologically sensitive forest is stripped away in Jamaica, clear forest pools are filled with red sludge and caustic soda, a ship sails off to Iceland, in Iceland a dam blocks off a valley, the land sinks under the weight of the water, clay is whipped up by winds from the mudflats beside a reservoir, electricity is sold at give-away prices by the people that sacrificed their land. There are always two sides to a story: there are some very pretty flowers on the website.

Aluminium is one of the most environmentally rapacious industries in the world. As a result, all around the world, on all fronts, it finds itself facing major problems. Sometimes things are done well, sometimes badly, but it's a dog-eat-dog world and life is tough on the international markets.

Source:
'Fresh investments in Orissa: sun god smiles again', article by Roy Pallavi, 27 September 2004, www. businessworldindia.com/ sep2704/news10.asp.

Source:
'The battle for bauxite in Orissa', news feature by Meena Menon, The Hindu, 20 April 2005.

The Indian state of Orissa has rich deposits of bauxite and the authorities have decided to turn the land over to mining and heavy industry in the hope of giving a rapid kickstart to industrial development. The Indian newspaper the Hindu reports on the threats to protected areas of jungle and the region's holy places. At one proposed mine site in Kashipur there is an impoverished group of inhabitants that has waged an unrelenting struggle for its very existence going back decades, an existence now threatened by an alumina refinery. In the year 2000 a group of villagers tried to shut off the roads leading to the bauxite mines in order to prevent their shrines and farming lands from being decimated. The police were called in and three of the villagers were shot dead. Workers at Alcan in Canada issued a statement saying they were boycotting work on alumina from Orissa, Alcan having acquired a 45 per cent stake in the project after Norsk Hydro withdrew in response to political pressure at home in Norway.

Source:
'Utkal Alumina confident of kicking off Rs 4,500 cr project soon', news item in the Hindu Business Line, 5 November 2003. http://www. thehindubusinessline. com/2003/11/06/stories/ 2003110602230200.htm

There are of course two sides to every story. In November 2003, the *Hindu Business Line* reported the disputes as follows: UTKAL Alumina International Ltd (UAIL), the 100 per cent export-oriented joint venture between Indal and the Montreal-based Alcan Company Ltd, is hopeful that its ongoing Rs 4,500-crore alumina project in Orissa will be completed without further delay. (...) The implementation of the project - to produce one million tonnes of alumina - has already been delayed due to resistance by local tribals [sic.] towards land acquisition. (...) The State Government has agreed to assist the company in getting physical possession of the required land.

246.

There is mess and filth and squalor in every corner of the world, in connection with all of mankind's activities. To every case there are many sides – though the contrasts here are particularly striking. The global picture is interesting, but it is not everything; the Icelandic side is quite enough, with its preposterous advertisements for our environmentally friendly 30 terawatt-hours. The energy authorities have a duty to explain to the nation just what lies behind this figure, and then formally beg the nation for its forgiveness.

I have made every effort to use only reputable sources: reports from the National Energy Authority and Landsvirkjun, the Hindu, the Los Angeles Times, the Irish Independent, the American University and the British parliament. I have kept silent over some of the vilest things in the histories of the companies involved – the destruction of the 'dreamlands' of the Australian aborigines, the damming of rivers and the bauxite stripping in the Amazon rainforests, the contracting company Bechtel currently setting up the aluminium refinery on the east coast of our country. Bechtel is one of the most notorious companies in the world for profiteering out of the miseries of war, the proud recipient, for instance, of the first big contract for the 'reconstruction' of Iraq. The close links between the owners of Bechtel and the Bush administration provide grounds for suspicion over the economic incentives behind the war. I have said nothing about Alcoa's sorry history 'as the worst polluter in the most polluted state in the United States'. The company says it wants to clean up its image: whether this happens in reality or just on its website remains to be seen.

This is all simply information that somehow fails to make it to public notice, despite our seeming set on becoming one of the biggest aluminium refining countries in the world. If you want to find out what is going on, if you want to see behind the glossy pictures of flowers and spaceships, you have to do it for yourself. Our politicians downplay the value and riches of Icelandic nature, they cow the public into acquiescence, they pick and choose what people are allowed to know, they sing the praises of companies of ill repute and expect us to be proud of them. The Airbus contract makes it to the front pages, but we are spared news like the piece below, even though the deal involved is every bit as big:

Source:
'And the winner is Bechtel', editorial in the New York Times, 19 April 2003.

Source:
Bob Herbert, 'Ask Bechtel what war is good for', International Herald Tribune, 22 April 2003.

Source:
'Alcoa set to clean up its Texas smelter', news item in American Metal Market, 23 June 2001.

247.

Source:
'Alcoa awarded contract
to produce aluminum
castings for tactical
Tomahawk missile
program', press release
from Alcoa, 1 December
2005, www.alcoa.com/
aerospace/en/news/
releases/tomahawk_
castings.asp.

Alcoa Awarded Contract to Produce Aluminum Castings for Tactical Tomahawk Missile Program

Alcoa announced today that its Alcoa Forged Products
and Aluminum Castings business has signed a five-year contract with Klune
Industries ... to manufacture high-strength aluminum structural
castings for the U.S. Navy's Tactical Tomahawk missile. The contract is
valued at nearly $30 million.

Source:
'Alcoa tour showcases
military', report in the
Pittsburgh Tribune
Review, 23 August 2005.
'Alcoa provides
aluminum for humvees
used in Iraq', posting
on www.alcoa.com, 18
November 2004.

Alcoa does well out of its military contracts. The company has close
working relations with the manufacturers of tanks, military vehicles, fighter
jets, helicopter gunships and bombs. Look up the word 'bomb' on their website
and you'll find yourself in a lot of stuff about dolphins.

The University of Akureyri is the heavy industry of Eyjafjörður. Hólar
School is the guided missile of Skagafjörður.

Every one of us ought to look up the information and judge things for
ourselves. It is striking how little the link knows about the chain. This ignorance is the more remarkable in view of the fact that the aluminium industry
is supposed to be set to become the basis for our future quality of life, and for
it people are prepared to hand over a beauty of world standards to companies
that have repeatedly violated everything we consider most sacred.

Photograph:
Tomahawk missile being
fired from the battleship
New Jersey.
(Photograph: US Navy).

Andri Snær Magnason

The people who are doing this do not see themselves as bad men. On the contrary, they believe they are acting out of pure benevolence. Well-intentioned men have taken it upon themselves to plan the future and save the country, and the world along with it. Well and good. But the project is so important that people have been forced to bend some of the ground rules on which our society is based: information, freedom of opinion, and democracy. The greatest threat to the drive for ever more power development in this country has proved to be the country itself: there is a risk it might achieve understanding, knowledge and the ability to stand up for itself.

Image and substance

The horse was all drenched with sweat, with water dripping from
every hair. He was caked in mud and panting furiously. He rolled
over six or seven times and then set up a great whinnying.
Hrafnkel's Saga

When the truth dies, very bad things happen.
Robbie Williams

When the people of Iceland need to be saved, it turns out that the greatest
threat to the nation's future is information and its own general knowledge
of itself. Science is the route to all progress, but what do you do when it
turns up unwelcome geological facts? Should they be put before people and
parliament like the figures for economic growth and the hope of maximum
profits? Biology is all very well, but what do you do about negative findings? If
one project is going to sustain the entire future well-being of the nation, is it
defensible to abandon it for some blades of grass and a few geese? How do you
deal with a people that is so hooked on the beauty of its country that it verges
on idolatry? Can such a people know what is best for it? Could Iceland's very
beauty prove a threat to the nation that lives in it? To some people, this might
sound absurd.

The following extract from the documentary film *Iceland in a New
Light* gives an insight into how people contend with a problem like the beauty
of Iceland. The film was shown on national television on the Thursday before
Easter 2003 and was excellent in many ways. One part dealt with the land that
is due to disappear beneath the Hálslón reservoir as part of the Kárahnjúkar
project:

Voice-over: If you look at a soil erosion map of the area, you might wonder whether the reindeer wouldn't be better off somewhere else.

Image: A reindeer is shot. A visual association is created with mink and hoverflies.

Voice-over: In the whole of Iceland there are few places more bleak and desolate.

Image: Drifting sand, little patches of soil clinging between bare rock.

Voice-over: This is the place idealists want to turn into a national park.

Image: Sand desert whipped by the wind.

Voice-over: Whenever the wind moves in dry weather in summer sand is blown up from the desert.

Image: Whirlwind, sandstorm.

Voice-over: Who can know for certain what effect a supply reservoir here might have on these parched soils and the region's water balance? Dust from the sand erosion can carry all the way down to Egilsstaðir. As you get closer to Mývatn it becomes impossible to see in front of your face.

Image: Sandstorm.

Voice-over: Is it necessarily right to look on human constructions that produce ecofriendly energy as the destruction of nature?

Image: Sinking oil tanker and burning sea.

Voice-over: Any damage to nature here is of a quite different order to the damage the world of man has to contend with in other countries that use oil or coal to produce energy...

Source:
Iceland in a New Light, documentary film directed by Hrafn Gunnlaugsson, National Television, 17 April 2003.

Iceland in a New Light received a grant of over a hundred thousand dollars from the ministry for the environment and a further sixty thousand from Landsvirkjun. 'In the whole of Iceland there are few places more bleak and desolate,' it said in the film. So the Vesturöræfi – the 'western wastes' – the reindeer trails, the Kringilsárrani nature reserve and the land around the river Jökulsá á Dal – are nothing more than blasted heaths, useless to anyone, and better off under water. The commentary and the images run directly counter to the knowledge of naturalists working for this same ministry. In the film the presenter asks, 'Who can know for certain what effect a supply reservoir here might have on these parched soils and the region's water balance?' The leading experts in this country believe the reservoir could set in train a vicious circle

Andri Snær Magnason

of soil depletion. The dangers of wind erosion from the bed of the reservoir are highlighted in a report by the University of Iceland Institute of Biology:

> *A large part of the fertile land to the northeast of the Vatnajökull ice cap could be in danger and lost to soil erosion. It should here be borne in mind that this is the best vegetated highland region in the country, the only one to have unbroken plant cover from the lowlands all the way up to the glacier and the only one that still has wide areas of dry-land vegetation that has elsewhere mostly disappeared as a result of erosion.*

Source:
Icelandic National Planning Agency (2001), *The Kárahnjúkar Hydroelectric Scheme up to 750 MW: Stage 1 up to 625 MW and Stage 2 up to 125 MW. Ruling of the National Planning Agency on the assessment of environmental impacts,* Icelandic National Planning Agency: Reykjavík, p. 206.

It is a strange feeling walking through this condemned country. Hjalladalur is not like other valleys in Iceland; it is almost a secret valley. The land is like a bowl, with the canyon of Dimmugljúfur a narrow crack in its rim. If you stand beside the canyon you do not realize that this twelve-mile cleft in the mountains broadens out and becomes greener as you move up towards the ice. This is the world of the Kringilsárrani nature reserve and the peculiar glacial moraines called *hraukar*, unique in the world, a line of low mounds produced when the Brúarárjökull glacier advanced down the valley in 1890, pushing the soil and vegetation before it and rolling it up like a carpet. The mounds are covered in emerald green grass where you can sit and watch reindeer grazing almost within touching distance. There are geese, birds and flowers right up against the roots of the ice cap. You can collect crowberries 2000 feet above sea level and watch Töfrafoss, 'the magic falls', plunging down

Source:
'Reykjasel rediscovered?' news report on National Radio, 11 August 2005. According to the report: 'Excavations have confirmed that the finds being investigated right up by the Kárahnjúkar dam date back to before the year 950. The site will be submerged in water with the creation of the Hálslón reservoir.'

Photograph:
Berjabrekka – 'Berry Slope' – and the river Kringilsá
(Photograph: Andri Snær Magnason)

Above the river Jökulsá á Dal archaeologists discovered ruins dating back to the earliest days of Icelandic history, believed to be Reykjasel, the summer farm mentioned in *Hrafnkel's Saga*. The site is considered to be one of the most important archaeological finds in Iceland in recent years. Excavations in the area were paid for by the Icelandic state through Landsvirkjun. These extraordinary remains could have helped us fill out our knowledge of living conditions in Iceland in ancient times. A few days after the picture on the left was taken, the area looked as in the picture on the right: a bulldozer had moved in and destroyed the site. It should be said that the

from the cliffs. Lower down the valley there are sites from the Icelandic sagas, where Einar Thorbjörnsson took the forbidden horse Freyfaxi and rode him in defiance of the orders of Hrafnkel the Priest. House remains have been uncovered here that go back to before 950, one of the most important archaeological finds in Iceland in recent years.

Along the course of Jökulsá á Dal there are extraordinary geological formations, towering basalt columns and platforms like the floor of some elfish church. There are river terraces that preserve 10,000 years of history of climate change. There are the Rauðaflúðir rapids where the river plunges screaming into a narrow channel before breaking up into atoms of spray. Lower down, the river runs over rocks that are so blood-red, bright orange and violet-purple you think your eyes are playing tricks. It is easy land to travel. I went walking there with a group of people, including a two-year old child

land here is much greener and more beautiful than what you can see from the Landsvirkjun observation platform at Sandfell. At the time in question, Landsvirkjun was one of the leading funders of the National Museum of Iceland.

From *Hrafnkel's Saga*: 'Then Hrafnkel went outside and saw his horse Freyfaxi and said, "I don't like you having been treated like this, my fosterling. But you knew what you were about when you told me of it and this shall be avenged. Now go to your flock."'

Photographers: Institute of Archaeology (left); Birgitta Jónsdóttir (right).

carried on his parents' backs, an elderly man and young children. There are warm springs in grassy hollows. There are gyrfalcons nesting. There are goose nests teetering on the edge of rocks overhanging the waters. Of whatever life flourishes in the highlands of Iceland, it is precisely here that this life is richest. And this life will be drowned.

But the land is not going to be allowed to rest decently to eternity in its watery grave. This land is going to rise again from the depths every spring, covered in mud and grey like a ghost. You will be able to compare it with the land that was there before. An area the size of Reykjavík that is now alive and green will stand dry on into the summer months, dead, covered in sand, fine dust, torn up soil and rotting vegetation.

Andri Snær Magnason

There is in fact something a bit misleading about the name itself – the 'Kárahnjúkar' project – so people can ask, 'Have you been there?' The name downplays the area affected: Kárahnjúkar is a mountain, and it is not a mountain that is being dammed and flooded. You cannot 'go there' and have a look over the worksite and think you have seen what is going to happen. But someone who has seen Lake Lagarfljót has 'been there'. The lake is going to be swollen by a whole big river of glacier-fed water; its mysterious green depths will go muddy brown; its temperature will fall; the surface will rise and tear away at the banks. 'Lagarfljót will become grimmer,' an old man who has lived by the lake all his life said to me. Kárahnjúkar is miles and miles away; he himself had never 'been there'. At the sea, the bay of Héraðsflói will lose the river that feeds it and the silt that nourishes its ecology and maintains its shoreline. The seal colonies along the shore will be destroyed. The shingles that guard the land will break up and within a few decades the sea will move in to flood over the lush green pastures of the natural paradise that is Húsey. You cannot see any of this from Kárahnjúkar. The line of waterfalls at the top of the Fljótsdalur valley will run dry. Kárahnjúkar nowhere near. Huge ranks of pylons will stretch down into Reyðarfjörður. Kárahnjúkar nowhere near.

Our environmentally sensitive minister for the environment revoked the protection order supposedly protecting Kringilsárrani and put the cost of a couple of Land Cruisers into a documentary telling the nation that a region that teems with variety, biologically, historically and archaeologically, is in fact ugly, barren and worthless. Any thoughts of establishing a national park are presented in such an unappealing way that the audience comes away convinced that this is absurd. The vast funds that went into *Iceland in a New Light* were handsomely repaid in the film itself by the following sequence:

> *Clip: Siv Friðleifsdóttir, the young and glamorous minister for the environment, going into the government offices in the centre of town.*
> *Voice-over: It must have taken real political courage to overturn the ruling of the national director of planning.*

There is something symbolic about the fact that around this time the ministry for the environment moved premises from Vonarstræti ('Hope Street') to Skuggasund ('Shadow Alley'). Tens of thousands of dollars went

Source:
Iceland in a New Light.
Author's note.
The national director of planning rejected the proposal for the Kárahnjúkar project on the grounds of its major environmental impact and its uncertain economic profitability; this ruling was subsequently overturned by the minister for the environment.

into a documentary disseminating ignorance to the nation at the very time that state-employed naturalists and other experts were being given explicit instructions not to express themselves publicly about the area and its nature, either on their own initiative or through their institutions, because their knowledge constituted a threat to the future of the project. To be sure, people were allowed to conduct research and write reports – reports on their own are harmless enough – but their findings were not to be passed on in language that any ordinary person might understand. The job of biologists was to count angiosperms, pteridophytes, bryophytes, compute numbers of goose nests, and draw up neutral comparative graphs and tables. But no, no, no if they wanted to talk like human beings and have their say about the value and importance of places in a broader context. Reports are forever being returned for revision for using 'language implying inappropriate value judgements'. A biologist shall first and foremost be an objective and value-free bioscience machine and very much second a human being. The official public view of the area shall remain: Worthless; bare rock and wasteland.

Landsvirkjun happily embraced the ugliness of Iceland as depicted in *Iceland in a New Light* when promoting the country to the world outside:

Source:
'Swedish crown princess presented with Icelandic stallion', news item in *Morgunblaðið*, 29 May 2003.

> ... *Jóhannes Geir Sigurgeirsson, chairman of the board of Landsvirkjun, hopes that he has managed to put across more positive messages to the people of Sweden than those that have appeared in the Swedish media on the subject of the Kárahnjúkar scheme. To this end, among other initiatives, a conference was held to coincide with Iceland Day, at which Icelandic power companies presented their views and a shortened version of Hrafn Gunnlaugsson's film Iceland in a New Light was shown. 'It came to our attention last winter that energy issues in Iceland were receiving negative coverage in the Swedish media and we felt this was based on lack of knowledge. We therefore decided to act and do something like this for Iceland Day. This is bearing results but there is still need for further promotional work...'*

The company seems to have developed an curiously acute eye for ugliness of late. People who have travelled with Landsvirkjun up to Thjórsárver

Andri Snær Magnason

come back with stories of how little value the place has. After a bit of sightseeing with Landsvirkjun around the highlands of eastern Iceland, the chairman of the parliamentary industry committee is reported to have described the area as 'nothing but sand and gravel with a few blades of grass, little in the way of life, nothing particularly impressive'. Beauty may be subjective, but the luxuriant grass and the goose and falcon nests most certainly are not.

Source:
Sigurður Kári
Kristjánsson, member of
parliament, in interview
with Thorfinnur
Ómarsson, National
Radio, Channel 1, 'At
the End of the Week', 23
July 2005.

The beauty of Iceland lies at the heart of our image of the country and the way this nation perceives itself. In opinion polls it rates as more important to us than God or our language, and for many they are all part of the same thing. This beauty became the main enemy of the project. Photographers were accused of exaggerating the beauty of Iceland. *Morgunblaðið* came under fierce criticism for publishing some glorious pictures of the landscape to the north of Vatnajökull. The photographer Ragnar Axelsson was accused of distortion in his series 'The Disappearing Land': the colours were said to be too powerful, the pictures too striking and not giving a true impression of the area. Too beautiful pictures, dismissed as propaganda!

Controlling the supply of information to the public has become an integral part of the Kárahnjúkar project. The Nature Conservation Agency was disbanded, its functions supposedly to be taken over by independent non-governmental organizations. Its funding appears to have been diverted into a documentary film used by Landsvirkjun to promote its own interests. The Icelandic Environment Association, Landvernd, is an umbrella NGO whose aim is 'to promote increased knowledge and awareness of nature and the country's environment'. This organization carried out an extensive review of all aspects of the Kárahnjúkar project and came out against it. This was not well received. ASÍ (the main trades union organization), SA (the employers' federation), Landsvirkjun, the local authorities' association and others resigned from the organization, leaving it bereft of funding and having to lay off staff.

Source:
'Conservation group in
financial difficulties',
Evening News, National
Radio, 18 May 2003.

So, preferably, Icelandic nature should have no paid advocate. The beauty of the country should not be overstated in public while the minister for the environment lies entranced by the romance of aluminium and sings hymns of praise to clean energy and shining fuselages. The following passage gives a good idea of how nervous public bodies have become about the public finding out what is happening:

Continuing Education Institute of the University of Iceland in propaganda war against the Kárahnjúkar project!

The University of Iceland has waged in with propaganda against the Kárahnjúkar project by setting up a special course with a clear message through its life education programme. The course is advertised in the Continuing Education Institute's prospectus and on its website. Due to be held in November this year, it goes under the title of 'Kárahnjúkar and Kringilsárrani'. Lecturer: Guðmundur Páll Ólafsson, naturalist and writer.

Source:
www.star.is
6 September 2001.

This piece of news appeared on a public website, www.star.is, run jointly by the Ministry of Industry and Landsvirkjun and managed by the PR company Athygli. These are the same parties as were also behind the website www.karahnjukar.is and the promotional campaigns in the Eastfjords pushing the benefits, benefits, benefits of the scheme. The item was followed up with a letter describing Guðmundur Páll as unqualified to run the course, a man widely known for his classic works *Birds in the Icelandic Landscape* and *The Highlands in the Icelandic Landscape*. So we see the same again: so long as a biologist remains a mechanical adding machine he is harmless, but once he steps forward as a human being and applies his knowledge to the context of society, history, the environment or language and interprets it for public consumption, then he becomes a threat that needs to be silenced.

www.star.is has now disappeared from the web, but a fragment from it, a kind of infoghost, showed up for many months afterwards if you went to Google and typed in the right words. Star.is was supposed to be somewhere the general public could go for various facts and reports on power development projects and aluminium works at the time the issues were still within the democratic process. Set up ostensibly as a forum for information and an open exchange of views, it ended up perpetrating some of the nastiest pieces of misinformation in Icelandic democratic history.

A publicly funded medium was used as a vehicle to discredit perfectly creditable people, both experts and general public. From star.is 'information' and 'news' was circulated to all the main media in the country through conventional PR channels. 'Opponents of Kárahnjúkar employ lies and deception' is a fair example of the kind of headline you got on star.is; it was the

Andri Snær Magnason

duty of star.is to 'draw people's attention to the tissue of lies put out against the Kárahnjúkar scheme'. One of the most respected naturalists in the country, Guðmundur Páll Ólafsson, is accused of 'falsehood' when he points to a connection between Kárahnjúkar and the possible damming of Jökulsá á Fjöllum. Guðmundur Páll's lies are said to be 'on a par with those perpetrated by member of parliament Kolbrún Halldórsdóttir on the TV current affairs show Spotlight when she referred to the reservoir site as a volcanically active area'. Ómar Ragnarsson – traveller, pilot, broadcaster, the most loved man on Icelandic television, a national institution brimming with infectious enthusiasm for everything he does – is said to be waging a 'holy war' against power schemes and heavy industry and is accused of talking 'constant claptrap'. Of all Icelanders alive today, Ómar probably knows the country better than anyone, making it hardly surprising the project saw him as one of its most dangerous enemies.

Star.is employed public money against democracy and the country's democratically elected representatives. It offered edifying pieces like: 'Greenleftist hopes dashed in parliamentary chambers. Green and Leftist politicians came out very much second best in the radio and TV debate on their proposal for a referendum on the future of the highlands north of Vatnajökull.' There was no name to the piece, nor to many others like it. Public officials kept up a campaign of unattributed vilification against members of parliament and accused ordinary citizens of lying, while at the same time forbidding the nation's experts from passing on their knowledge to the people who pay them.

The worst mauling was reserved for the chairman of the Iceland Nature Conservation Association. His statements were said to be 'empty and stupid'. There were headlines like 'Árni Finnsson still lying and that without shame'. 'Árni Finnsson, chairman of the Nature Conservation Association, has no qualms about straying a long way off the path of truth in his battle against hydroelectric schemes.' There is a quote from the chairman of Landsvirkjun to the effect that the Nature Conservation Association is a puppet of foreign activists and working against 'Icelandic interests'.

Democracy at home was travestied by appropriating the word 'easterner' and using it as a synonym for 'one nation, one will'. The conservationist point of view was presented as a threat to the east and to the rural areas in general. This distortion had its effect thanks to the politicians who laid down the terms and specified the options: aluminium or decay. Life became near intolerable for the minority in the east who did not want to watch on as people waged war against their land, because opposing the official line was portrayed as tantamount to treason against one's region and neighbours.

According to star.is, the Society for the Conservation of the Highlands of Eastern Iceland was 'out of step' with the views of the region as a whole and it was hinted that behind the society there were people other than easterners themselves. In August 2000 around sixty power development enthusiasts from Power for East Iceland covertly joined the Nature Conservation Association of Eastern Iceland (NAUST) with the idea of taking it over and subverting it with resolutions in favour of heavy industry. A hundred members of NAUST took out a whole-page advertisement in the papers urging protection of the highlands. This had no effect on the tone of the debate going on in all the media: there was much talk about 'the will of the east' and the like. When a little group of easterners floated candles on Lake Lagarfljót, star.is reported that 12,000 easterners had stayed at home. One can only wonder how many easterners simply did not dare to express their views publicly in this kind of atmosphere. The war against the land had started to take on the form of jingoism and moral blackmail.

The bellicosity is depressing, not least because the power needed to smelt the aluminium – if it really is just a matter of aluminium – could easily be generated from geothermal sources.

> *Asked whether there was any possibility of looking into the feasibility of creating a smaller aluminium plant in the east to be powered from geothermal power stations in the northeast, Valgerður said there was no question of abandoning the Kárahnjúkar development.*

The ministry's prioritization appears to have worked on the principle of starting off with whatever was most valuable, so that once this went through there would be nothing left to argue about. There seems to have been some kind of compulsion to get things done and dusted before time, technology or some new vision of the future made the dam redundant. This aluminium

Source: www.star.is. The website no longer exists and the domain is unused, and perhaps it will be impossible to prove that it ever existed. It would be curious to know whether and how information of this type will be preserved for the use of future historians. Many more people than those mentioned here were subjected to these attacks. Nor is it possible to prove all of the claims made here regarding the pressure put on naturalists to curb freedom of speech. But by phoning round a fair number of members of staff at the Icelandic Institute of Natural History and making other enquiries, I came across some extraordinary cases in which, for example, media interviews on the nature of Kringilsárrani were met with swift responses from the highest quarters in the power sector. It was the same thing over and over again: a naturalist as a human being was something that needed to be suppressed.

Source: 'Special think-tank appointed', interview with Valgerður Sverrisdóttir, minister for industry, in Morgunblaðið, 31 March 2002.

Andri Snær Magnason

plant was going to use four times as much electricity as all the conventional workplaces in Iceland combined and more than the aluminium plants at
Straumsvík and Hvalfjörður put together.

There were other ways of producing electricity, and many more ways of
creating jobs, but such considerations were simply not on the star.is agenda.
Choice did not come into it. The conservationist standpoint was a threat to the
east. Politicians set off one set of interests touching people's deepest emotions
against another and pretended there was an incompatible opposition between
them. The highlands or the home. Nature or community. Work or life. This
explains the bitterness, the civil cold war that cuts across bonds of family and
friendship. Huge amounts of public money has been poured into public relations to produce precisely this atmosphere. The victory of one would mean the
utter defeat of the other. It is all there in the language: people or geese. We
smelt aeroplanes. Education is a heavy industry. The highlands are rocks and
waste. Untouched and underutilized.

In all this turmoil nobody seems to have noticed that it was sharks
that were coming to save the drowning man. The lack of any kind of critical
analysis takes a surrealistic turn when star.is tells us that the 'crystal clear'
cooling water from the Alcoa factory might be used to create a warm-water
bathing beach next to the factory, and reaches its apotheosis in a quotation
from a spokesman for Alcoa:

> *It is right to remember the words of Jake Siewert, head of publicity
> at Alcoa, that in all its approach to the case Alcoa has taken full
> account of environment factors.*

Source:
www.star.is

The tough cookies of the Alcoa negotiating team appear not to have
met with any opposition. Some 4000 tonnes of sulphur dioxide (SO_2) will be
released over the fjord every year through the plant's gigantic chimneys. That
is already a fifth of what Norway aims to cut its total SO_2 emissions to by the
year 2010. In Norway there are 4.5 million people; in Iceland 300,000. The
chimneys will be some of the tallest structures in Iceland – over 250 feet high,
the same as a thirty-storey house, three times the highest apartment blocks in
the country. And therewith we will see the consummation of the ministry for
industry's fifty-year dream, the image of progress held out to us in *Geography
for Elementary Schools*, where 'belching factory smokestacks tower high over

the rooftops like a black petrified forest...' By way of comparison, the Norsk Hydro aluminium plant in Norway will release 200 tonnes of SO_2 into the air, a twentieth that of Alcoa.

Source:
V. Søyseth *et al.*
(1995), 'Relation of
exposure to airway
irritants in infancy to
prevalence of bronchial
hyperresponsiveness
in schoolchildren',
The Lancet, vol. 345,
28 January 1995, pp.
217-220.
V. Søyseth *et al.* (1996),
'Allergen sensitization
and exposure to irritants
in infancy', *Allergy*, vol.
51, October 1996, pp.
719-723.
V. Søyseth *et al.*
(1995), 'Bronchial
responsiveness,
eosinophilia, and short-
term exposure to air
pollution', *Archives of
Disease in Childhood*,
vol. 73, November 1995,
pp. 418-422.

One reason the Norwegians are aiming to cut SO_2 emissions is fear of acid rain. Another is the findings of comparative studies on the heath of children in clean fjords and fjords with aluminium works. Three major studies, in part funded by the Hydro Aluminium company, have shown that SO_2 pollution in the atmosphere causes allergic reactions in school children and an increased risk of lung disease. Those exposed to SO_2 pollution in infancy were shown to be more susceptible of breathing problems later in life than control groups in unpolluted areas.

This matters to us in Iceland because the pollution that caused these reactions in Norwegian children was within permitted SO_2 emission levels in Iceland. In a nutshell, the SO_2 pollution that had significant effects on the health of Norwegian schoolchildren would have been considered legal in Iceland, or within 'limit values' to use the technical term. Katrín Fjeldsted, the only doctor sitting in parliament and the only member of the government majority to vote against the aluminium plant, sounded a warning about SO_2 pollution. She cited the findings of the committee for heavy industry under the previous prime minister, which only ten years before had come out against siting aluminium plants in fjords:

> *Weather conditions in fjords are such that cold air sinks to the bottom, with warmer air on top: this is simple physics. Sulphur dioxide (SO_2), produced as a pollutant in the emissions from aluminium works, collects between these layers in a fjord, the cold layer and the warm layer. There it builds up, especially in calm weather. Reyðarfjörður has prevailing calm weather conditions 46 per cent of the time. By way of comparison, Reykjavík is calm, I believe, about 7 per cent of the time...*
>
> *The aforementioned siting committee examined the possibility of building an aluminium works in Eyjafjörður. It was reckoned that within an eight mile radius of Akureyri it was fairly certain that young children, asthma sufferers and the old would show symp-*

Andri Snær Magnason

toms of lung conditions after two to four days' calm... In a calm fjord such as Reyðarfjörður, in which the distances are even less, viz. three miles, it seems clear – at least, this is what I conclude – that the proximity of an aluminium plant could make Búðareyri uninhabitable. I therefore say to the people of Reyðarfjörður: if you get an aluminium plant, then you will have to leave.

Source:
Katrín Fjeldsted,
speaking in parliament,
28 January 2003,
Alþingistíðindi (Icelandic
Parliamentary Gazette),
2002-03, 128th
legislative session B.
debates, p. 2718.

The Icelandic Meteorological Office investigated conditions in Reyðarfjörður in 2002 and came to the following conclusion:

A reentry over the smelter is also possible in summer when light westerly wind, having blowed over the smelter during late night, suddenly changes to become easterly during the early morning. Fumigation can then follow when the air near the ground becomes unstable due to heating by the rising sun, and polluted air is partly brought down to the surface.

However, the most unfavourable conditions are probably periods with very low wind velocity and variable wind direction. Multiple entries of the same air over the smelter and the population center Búðareyri are then occasionally possible.

Source:
Flosi Hrafn Sigurðsson
et al. (2003), 'Wind and
stability observations
in Reyðarfjörður,
July 2002–May 2003,
Icelandic Meteorological
Office: Reykjavík.
www.vedur.is/utgafa/
greinargerdir/2003/
03032.pdf, p. 27. Quoted
verbatim.

In other words – if the weather is good, then it is bad; and if it is bad, then it is good. According to the Meteorological Office model, long-term pollution over the course of months and years will probably remain within 'acceptable' limits, but short-term pollution might on occasions go comparatively high. Here we again run into a technical term on a par with terawatts: air pollution is measured in micrograms per cubic metre, or $\mu g/m^3$.

...predicted 1-hour values are occasionally quite high. The 350 $\mu g/m^3$ 1-hour guideline and the 50 $\mu g/m^3$ 24-hour guideline are predicted reached at Budareyri, although only on very rare occasions. However, this seems very high compared with the generally very low background values for SO_2 in Iceland.

Source:
Flosi Hrafn Sigurðsson
et al. (2003), 'Wind and
stability observations
in Reyðarfjörður,
July 2002–May 2003,
Icelandic Meteorological
Office: Reykjavík.
www.vedur.is/utgafa/
greinargerdir/
2003/03032.pdf, p. 23.

There are probably very few of us who understand these figures, but the mean value that affected the health of babies in Norway was in the range

20-40 micrograms per cubic metre. In view of this, the figure of 350 seems incredibly high, even if only as a short-term value; similarly the figure 50. At Reyðarfjörður, fluorine pollution will be less than in Norway, so the studies are not fully comparable. But if fluorine pollution is in normal proportion to SO_2 pollution, short-term values are likely to reach fairly high levels. The apparent lack of concern on the part of our leaders seems incomprehensible but is fully in line with their attitudes elsewhere: 'Is anybody seriously going to claim that one can live a good life here on clean air alone?' However, we can safely go along with the prime minister's closing comments in the same article: 'But we must also never forget that man is a part of nature; if he destroys his environment, then he also destroys himself.'

Source:
'Employment issues
at the start of a new
century', article by
Halldór Ásgrímsson,
Dagur, 7 April 1999.

We have to live off something. People or geese. People or children. What was it that the *LOWEST ENERGY PRICES* brochure was offering? 'Iceland is nature at its purest. The freshest air you will ever breathe and the purest water in the world are goals worth striving to maintain.' In passing, star.is was an acronym for 'the Site Selection Committee for an Aluminium Plant at Reyðarfjörður'. On the basis of the pieces posted on its website, one would hardly expect vast amounts of balanced reasoning from that quarter.

Perhaps the matter was investigated. And perhaps some public official was instructed to keep his mouth shut. We have no way of knowing. The information presented was said to be based on a misunderstanding. Disputed. Misinterpretation. So that's the way it has to be. I reserve the right to understand nothing and to believe nobody.

Good men learned to harness nature and got locked up inside a closed world of their own professional expertise. Good men were supposed to serve the nation and it ended up with the nation being expected to serve them. Good men were supposed to make our lives easier, provide us with light, power, quality of life and health, and they ended up going to war against the very qualities of life they themselves had had a part in creating. A single technological possibility, a single source of power, became an ideology. Information, truth and the nation's sense of beauty became enemies of the great objective; military strategy came in place of creative flexibility and resourcefulness. After years of stagnation, the policy shifted back into gear for the sole purpose of presenting

Andri Snær Magnason

the country's shipwreck formally to the eyes of the world, professionally and morally. A dam rises up directly athwart the rules society plays by; the geological faults are merely symbolic of a much greater and more serious rift. When the truth has to be hidden and opinions suppressed, nothing can be trusted. However many good men there may be working on the project, however well and professionally they do this work, there has never been more truth in the words, 'except the Lord build the house, they labour in vain that built it'.

Source:
Job 127:1
King James Bible

Iceland – from independence to sustainability

Nothing is more dangerous than an idea – if it is the only idea.
Émile-Auguste Chartier (1868-1951)

The newspapers feed us with a daily diet of pieces about the aluminium company and the power company and, above all, the politicians rescuing the east of Iceland from collapse. A double-page spread in Morgunbladið in August 2001 gave it in a nutshell. Under the headline 'Anxious easterners still live in hope', a businessman was reported as saying that if nothing came of the aluminium plant 'we might as well order a bus to come out east and pick up the people'. There was an interview with a disappointed lad of sixteen who had been planning to do a training course that would have fitted him for a job in an aluminium factory. A middle-aged man said, 'An aluminium plant is of course not God almighty. But we need something to create jobs… I can't see how we can just go out and collect herbs and grasses. There is no future in that.' A garage owner said he could not see any other job opportunities in the region. It was all the talk of the town: 'I don't know anything about these archaeological remains you're a supposed to be able to see up there in the canyons. I haven't notice them in all those pictures they've been showing of the region. If we don't get some mass industry, this place is going to become a ghost town, little by little.' A woman who had moved to Egilsstaðir from Fáskrúðsfjörður reckoned the whole of the Eastfjords would turn into a ghost town if nothing came of the hydropower and aluminium smelting schemes.

Source:
'Anxious easterners still live in hope', article in *Morgunbladið*, 3 August 2001.

In the article no less than four people talked about the area being abandoned. No belief in the future, no faith in other possibilities. Man's whole future, man's whole happiness, appeared to depend on a single aluminium company. To read the article, there was nothing within the community itself,

A Self-Help Manual for a Frightened Nation

nothing in the skill and knowledge and expertise of the easterners, or of the Icelanders in general, that might be able to keep society afloat. Nothing except an aluminium plant. And that was it, so far as the people were concerned, regardless of whether this picture was right or wrong. Maybe it is worth looking at it from a wider perspective: How much should you have to pay for a house in an area that markets itself in such a negative way?

The problem is that the people did not have the capital, the technology or the manpower to set up the hydro scheme for themselves. They had no bauxite mines, no aluminium works, no processing companies, and no alumina. People were waiting for a company to come and save them, without any notion of its history or reputation or the methods it used, let alone anything about 4000 tonnes of sulphur dioxide. People wanted a dam, but no one knew whether this was economically or technologically viable. It was not until a year and a half after this article in Morgunblaðið, in December 2002, that people had any clear idea of the deal they had got themselves into. There was only one bid for the Kárahnjúkar contract within the planned budget, from Impregilo. Now finally, for the first time, people could look at the bid and ask themselves: 'So who are Impregilo? Why is their tender so low? Are they expecting people to work for free?'

Sociological studies, on the other hand, seemed to support the view that the decision on the aluminium plant was the right one:

Eastfjords: Population Set to Rise With Arrival of Aluminium Plant

The population of eastern Iceland is set to rise by up to 2000 as a result of the aluminium plant at Reyðarfjörður and there will be a substantial increase in jobs for women throughout the region. This is one of the findings of a report released today by the Research Centre of the University of Akureyri.

Among other things, the report predicts that the population of eastern Iceland will pass 13,500 in 2008, with an increase attributable to the arrival

Source:
'Population set to rise with arrival of aluminium plant', report on National Radio, 3 December 2005.

Andri Snær Magnason

of the aluminium plant of 1500 to 2000. It is predicted that the aluminium plant will produce 414 new jobs directly, with a further 468 in secondary industries, giving a total of 882 new jobs.

So, the number of new jobs in secondary industries as a result of the multiplier effect or the trickle-down effect or whatever will be precisely 468. It is that easy to manipulate a community, to plan and calculate things down to the last individual. The soul is material. Man is a machine. The metal shapes the man. We can't live on air.

After the multiplier effect comes the lemming effect. The Eastfjords have provided a model that every other rural politician longs to emulate. Local government officials from the east have travelled the land, preaching the faith and bearing witness to the success. Everyone deserves an aluminium plant. The northerners are blessed with everything they need for a second Alcoa factory – geothermal power sources, the great glacial rivers flowing north to the ocean. Straumsvík can have the lower reaches of Thjórsá and expand from 180,000 tonnes to 460,000 tonnes, and then it will be really, really, really enormous. The Reykjanes peninsula down in the southwest is estimated to have hidden reserves of geothermal energy enough to power an aluminium plant at Helguvík. Norðurál expands apace and fume clouds lace Mt Esja's face. Landsvirkjun is currently looking for a buyer for Langisjór. Southerners? There's enough in the Torfajökull ice cap, Markarfljót, Hvítá and Gullfoss, for an aluminium smelter of their very own. To stave off any threat of recession, there is always Jökulsá á Fjöllum and the thundering cascade of Dettifoss, plenty for another one all by itself. And we can dust down the old plans for channelling streams to flood out Thjórsárver. Altogether, that gives us enough for five new aluminium plants. 2070 new jobs. Precisely. So that is it: Iceland harnessed to the hilt, with all the attendant disputes, propaganda, pollution and sorrow, would provide work for less than 0.7 per cent of the country's population. The nation's entire attention would be monopolized for decades, opinions divided according to people's attitudes towards something that is in reality nothing. The country would be mortgaged to the tune of billions for fifty years and its performance directly linked to the price of aluminium on the world market. 'It is our moral responsibility to use our clean, green energy for the good of all mankind.'

There are real, working public servants in Iceland who genuinely see this future like a mirage. Someone came up with the name 'Einarsver' for the proposed aluminium works at Húsavík, in honour of Einar Benediktsson. Which makes it interesting to see what one of the Einar Bens of our own times has to say about this policy. Here is Ágúst Guðmundsson, chairman of the Bakkavör group, the biggest supplier of ready-made meals in Britain:

Source:
'Ágúst Guðmundsson:
heavy-industry policy out
of date', news item on the
Morgunblaðið website,
www.mbl.is, 8 February
2006.

I am convinced that, even if Iceland managed to establish itself as one of the leading aluminium producers in the world and harnessed all the most cost-effective electricity generation options in the country, the returns from this and its benefits to Icelandic society would never amount to more than the contribution of a single successful conventional company expanding into international markets.

It is a myth that the economy needs aluminium refineries in order to grow. People who believe this are in fact exhibiting a lack of faith in Icelandic business and its ability to create new value for the nation in the future.

The heavy-industry policy is deflecting the nation's attention from the vastly superior possibilities that reside in HUMANITY, our children and their education, and their potential to create infinitely greater wealth for us, both material and spiritual. A maximally exploited Iceland will not be enough to keep us going. The economy will become dependent on the building of more and more dams and more and more power plants and aluminium works, on new electricity lines constantly rising, and the land sinking ever deeper and deeper under the weight. A heroin economy, an unremitting cycle of addiction, that each government passes on to the next. We will never know what ideas are passing us by, what companies are withering on the vine, and how far we are trailing behind our neighbouring countries in ways of thinking and technological development. The danger signs are there already:

Source:
'High-tech industry
abandoning the
country?' news item
on National Radio, 17
December 2005.

High-tech industry accounted for 4 per cent of GDP last year, heavy industry 1 per cent. The high-tech industries employ around 6500 people, heavy industry a few hundred. There are high-tech companies like Össur, Actavis, DeCode, Medcare Flaga, Marel and CCP

Andri Snær Magnason

developing and producing everything from pharmaceuticals to computer games, and all of them are now aiming, to a greater or lesser extent, to relocate their operations abroad.

A varied and creative flora of Icelandic companies is disappearing, its seeds unable to take root. Fishing companies are failing, tourism is languishing, and on top of this the land is being corrupted. Spontaneously propagated and independent companies are being starved to make room for what? Four Alcoa factories? Our national image is going down the plughole for what? Isn't this perhaps what we might call 'malignant economic growth'? The future vision is all worked out and, according to the prime minister, there is only one way to go:

> *...it is abundantly clear that if we fail to utilize the country's energy resources there will be an appreciable downturn in economic growth as early as 2007 with an attendant rise in unemployment.*

Source:
Halldór Ásgrímsson, prime minister, on the planned expansion of heavy industry up to the year 2012, Evening News, National Radio, 24 January 2006.

The pattern repeats itself. Be afraid. Dam your rivers or die. The leader has no faith in the future and the country's limitless opportunities. The leader identifies the danger and lays down the hard conditions. You can only go on past experience and bring the future of the Eastfjords down to the lowest common denominator:

> *The ministry considers that it has been sufficiently demonstrated that, if nothing comes of the proposed power-generation schemes...,* the negative development seen in the populated areas of eastern Iceland in recent years is likely to continue, and also that there are no apparent signs of any change in this trend in the foreseeable future.

Source:
Ruling of the ministry for the environment on the environmental assessment of the Kárahnjúkar hydroelectric scheme, case no. 01080004, 1 January 2001, www. rettarheimild.is/ Umhverfis/UrskurdirR aduneytisins/2001/01/0 1/nr/836.

Against this, there was only hopelessness and decay. It is an admission of inferiority, dependence and brutality. Landsvirkjun was presented as the only hope for *humanity* in the east. The future of the east is at the beck and call of the international corporations, a by-product of their operations. A news network from Trinidad and Tobago talks about Landsvirkjun and Alcoa and their ambitious *'sustainability programme'* for Iceland. The hydroelectric scheme as such will not be sustainable or self-sufficient, rather maybe just a

271.

link in a chain reaction leading to destruction. But the companies are going to keep a watchful eye over the interests of *humanity* and attend to everything that touches us; they will see to our healthcare, education system, the environment, the road system, public security, cultural levels, gender roles, age concerns, house prices, wage trends, as well as, presumably, as before, the media and public relations. This is what they mean by *'social sustainability'*.

Source:
'Alcoa seeking the best for T&T', news item in the Trinidad & Tobago Express, 4 December 2005.

The aluminium sickness is set to spread across the land, and with it more and more 'sustainability programmes'. If you are looking for a neat way of summing up the history of 21st-century Iceland, how about: 'Iceland – from independence to sustainability'? Just recently we have had the people of Húsavík celebrating their independence in the form of a new smelting plant. Instead of running with the herd, the best option is always to head in the opposite direction. The aluminium plant did not save the Eastfjords; it was just one of many possibilities. One of a thousand. But still everyone is asking, 'But what could we have done otherwise?'

What can one do in Iceland? Would the east become a ghost town if Alcoa went bust tomorrow? Might the population of the region go up to 20,000 in the next twenty years anyway? Was the distress and poverty and hopelessness of the east real? Or was it just a tactic that politicians employed to engender public sympathy and justify a danger like the Kárahnjúkar dam, the thirty-storey chimneys and the 4000 tonnes of sulphur dioxide at subsidized energy prices?

The beauty of Icelandic nature became a threat to the project. But isn't that true, too, of the nature of mankind, its creative spirit, its resourcefulness and ability to think for itself? Instead of feeling insulted when experts from Reykjavík produced reports to say that all hope was lost, we have allowed this sense of utter powerlessness to pass for established fact.

The whole debate has been based on a false picture of the east of Iceland. There were and are successful companies there, and people wanted to live there and young people moved back there when they had finished their studies long before the aluminium business got going. There were people with all kinds of ideas that received no support because they failed to fit in with THE IDEA, the big solution that was going to change everything. The chapter about the lamb and local produce at the beginning of this book is not fiction. It has happened. Go to www.austurlamb.is and have a look. For a really good

Andri Snær Magnason

cut of meat, there are a couple of farms I can personally recommend: Unaós on the shores of Héraðsflói, for instance, and Hákonarstaðir up in the Jökulsá valley.

There are flourishing fishing companies in the east of Iceland, and Iceland has trained biotechnologists, chemists, food scientists and business managers who could double the value of the cod or capelin catch. To star.is, ideas like these merited nothing but contempt: 'Are Eastfjorders supposed to mess around with teaspoonfuls of microbes?' Healthcare, pharmaceuticals, herbs and spices and complementary medicine are global industries worth billions. And what were people taught to say about them? 'Are Eastfjorders supposed to go out and gather Iceland moss?'

Tourists come to Iceland, and Egilsstaðir is an international back-up airport. Egilsstaðir is every bit as much Iceland as Keflavík – more so, many would say. To tens of thousands of tourists arriving by charter flight to drink in the beauties of Icelandic nature, it makes no difference whether you drive round the country starting from Egilsstaðir or Keflavík. Egilsstaðir is a stone's throw from some of the biggest tourist attractions in the country, two hours from the major cities of Europe. If some part of the tourists landed here, it would spread the benefits more evenly around the country. In every part of Iceland there are investments that need to bring in a return. If we could manage that, there would be economic growth in all the rural areas. Behind every 50,000 tourists there are around a thousand work years and 60 million dollars in added value distributed through all parts of society. That is twice as many jobs, and considerably more varied jobs, and a wider flora of companies than you get from 200,000 tonnes of aluminium. Direct links alone between the Eastfjords and Europe would make it easier for people to live there. Ten thousand passengers a year arriving by plane and passing through would create a demand for buses, accommodation, car rentals, tourist guides, leisure facilities, services, shops, pilots, air hostesses, baggage handlers, air traffic controllers and more and more. Loads of jobs. Hundreds of Icelanders have run air services all round the world but the possibilities inherent in this have never been taken seriously. Instead, we have an airport with no view of the future and with no finance to promote itself.

I know a German woman who did a horseriding holiday around Snæfell, in what they are now calling 'the Kárahnjúkar region'. She spent a week on horseback in the mountains and then flew on to Reykjavík and I took her to the ancient assembly site at Thingvellir, the Gullfoss waterfall and the hot springs at Geysir. She wasn't particularly impressed. 'I saw much better things out east,' she said. I thought she was joking until I went there myself. On Jökulsá á Fljótsdal there are waterfalls over a hundred feet high, Faxi and Kirkjufoss, some of the most impressive in all Iceland. By way of comparison, the lower, main part of Gullfoss is only about 65 feet. All that is needed to make some money out of it is a visit from one of our leading photographers. Our holiday companies could educate children in the wonderworld of the rivers and the reindeer of Kringilsárrani. And what do the politicians have to say about ideas like these? 'Are the Eastfjorders supposed to put on dances in sheepskin shoes and bake pancakes for tourists?'

One of the most extraordinary experiences I have ever had was lying on my back in the pitch dark in the swimming pool at Lýsuhóll on Snæfellsnes, looking up at the northern lights weaving and dancing in the heavens. It was a feeling almost like floating in space. This is an experience that can be sold in every part of the country in the darkest days of winter. Every year in December half a million people go to Rovaniemi in Finland to see Father Christmas, and we think Iceland does well with its 300,000 visitors a year. Reindeer, darkness and northern lights could make a powerful attraction, and you don't need half a million dollars to provide the locals with plenty to keep them busy. A few planeloads a week would be enough to keep the hotels, guesthouses, shops and restaurants up and running. That would be economic growth, because this way we would get better use out of our underutilized investments. It would even benefit the people of Hornafjörður, Vopnafjörður, Seyðisfjörður and other parts of the east that have been bypassed in the current wave of investment.

Local councils can invite more than just politicians and representatives from Rio Tinto to drop in and raise a few glasses and see things for themselves. They could invite ordinary people, point to the advantages of living down by a real harbour, encourage them to sell their second car and buy themselves skis and a kayak because these are something you never get tired of. Good for the kids, everyone home for lunch, fun to be alive. Why not the village as the social unit of the 21st century? This is no pipe dream; there are people in my family who have chosen to live this way. There are provincial dumps with populations of millions out there in the world and there are centres of world culture with a thousand. Detroit is palookaville. Seyðisfjörður is a world city. Culture has nothing to do with numbers.

Andri Snær Magnason

The Eastfjorders could have looked at all the new jobs and industries that have taken off in recent years and set out to get themselves a piece of all the alienation in the country. They could have created communal centres for the self-employed and those who can work wherever the like, a community where engineers, architects, computer scientists, graphics designers, accountants and people like that could set up and work for companies in the great world outside. As four per cent of the population, they could have demanded four per cent of all the jobs that people do here in Iceland, and perhaps an even bigger slice of the job market that is not restricted by time or place. One goldsmith, a thirty man stockbroking firm, a fifty man computer company, an advertising agency with a staff of fifteen, five people operating Radio Eastfjords, two TV programmes, three professional actors dubbing shows for children, a ten man fertility clinic attached to the Healthcare Trust of Eastern Iceland and the geothermal pools at Mývatn promising:

Floating on your back in the warm water
with the northern lights streaming over you,
is a certain path to ovulation.

The ever-growing number of affluent Europeans with fertility problems – why not them as a significant pillar of the economy?

In the east of Iceland there were not just opportunities, there were more opportunities than almost anywhere else in Iceland. If people had worked undaunted and with a long-term belief in the future, rather than in fear and despair, buildings would have risen, community spirit flourished, companies been founded, and people moved in to take their part in society – and they would have owed thanks to no one, no government minister, no company, no one but themselves as individuals and others like them, people who live through people, people as the pillars of the economy. That is how jobs are created, and this is how the world keeps turning.

Taming the machine

Man is free. The machine is there to serve man. And if the machine fails to do this, it is best to switch it off. Over the last few years we have watched on as a machine has run out of control. We Icelanders have received much from our country in recent decades without repaying its bounty in kind. As this is written, Thjórsárver is on ice. That is the limit of our generosity to our country as we make our way into the 21st century. The country's beauty has given its people a huge start in life, raising them farther and higher than the 300,000 people who live here have any right to expect. The world outside confuses us the people of Iceland with Iceland the island in the northern seas. The world confuses the strength of the land with the people that come from it, and it is in our interests to keep it that way.

If the land to the north of Vatnajökull sinks beneath the waters, the international media will be here to report it. The media are always on the look-out for dramatic pictures, and who knows what kind of image they will present? For many it will be a symbol of Iceland defeated. Perhaps the world will see it in this light: if the richest country on earth cannot protect and pre-serve its heritage, what hope is there for the rest of us? Iceland's reputation is fragile and vulnerable. It is like integrity, honesty, rectitude. These are things you cannot buy. I want my children to enjoy the respect of the world outside this country; I want the name of Iceland to give them a head start, to open doors that would otherwise have remained locked. I want them to be literate in the beauty of their country and I want this country to have a rich assort-ment of prosperous and creative industries. I do not believe the present policy of land destruction is in the interests of this nation. Iceland is destined for something greater and deeper than being merely a link in a chain of squander and waste on the international markets. I want my children to be free to use their knowledge and talents as human beings, not as machines or cogs in the service of a cause that runs directly contrary to their convictions.

I am writing this book because I fear the world will start to dissociate Iceland from the people that live there – Iceland as a symbol of beauty, the Icelanders as a symbol of what threatens beauty and fears it and does not understand it. The quality of life we enjoy we owe to democracy. This democracy brings us in over 6 billion dollars a year in direct income. You can work this out by comparing us with a dictatorship that is rich in resources. People's freedom to have ideas and think new things is an absolute condition for change and progress in all areas of life, and it for that reason that we have freedom of speech and freedom of opinion. It is because we decided to fend for ourselves that we enjoy the quality of life we do. Democracy can be infuriating, it can slow things down and hold things back, but it has proved better than any other system known to man.

Democracy is not dull and boring. It is when it fails that the mistakes occur. It is a fundamental principle that all voices should get a hearing, that everyone in this country should have the opportunity to say what they think as human beings about matters that are going to touch us for all eternity. Whatever happens, there is a chance the project will fail: the tunnels may collapse, the reservoir may leak, the dam may break. Alcoa may go bust. There could be a revolution in Jamaica. 'The will of the Eastfjorders,' say the politicians. That is not right. What people there wanted was to live and grow and have a future. On the banks of Lagarfljót there are men and women who consider this the biggest mistake in Icelandic history:

Source:
'There are few things more lovely than a freshly ploughed field', interview with Eymundur Magnússon, farmer at Vallanes in Fljótsdalur, Blaðið, 17 February 2006.

We had the chance to save a big piece of land in a polluted world from this kind of devastation, and we messed it up. For the future, there would have been great value in it if we had decided otherwise, but quick profit came out on top. It seems the authorities think that the two things can go together, destroying the country and hanging on to an image of a pure and untouched nature. I believe this to be the biggest mistake in Icelandic history.

Andri Snær Magnason

278.

The GDP of Iceland is 12.5 billion dollars a year. 1.25 billion is not so much if we think of it as a ransom, that by sacrificing this sum we have reclaimed our country from the hands of people who do not know how to treat it. That way we can put a price tag on land that has always been seen as worthless. The place can become the heart in the national park that is Iceland, and the dam will stand there ready but unused, a monument to man's capacity to control the machine – to the fact that technology exists to serve man and not the other way round. Man tamed nature, and then the machine tamed man, until man got a grip on the machine, and on himself. 1.25 billion is not a lot to pay; on the contrary, it implies a necessary commitment.

The project has left a legacy of great value. A road has been built up the Fljótsdalur valley and forty miles into the highlands to the site of the dam. A gigantic cavern has been scooped out of the mountain above Fljótsdalur. In this cavern we could install Ólafur Elíasson's *Sun* (a part of his *Weather Project*), a work that once filled the Turbine Hall of the Tate Modern in London and probably the most famous piece of visual art ever produced by an Icelander. The most famous piece of visual art ever produced by an Icelander. The publicity alone should be worth the billion and a quarter dollars, because the dam and the sun will stand as symbols that there is hope for us and for humanity.

We will save ourselves millions by not polluting the waters of Lagarfljót. We will save millions if we allow the estuaries of Héraðsflói to stand in peace. We will save ourselves millions upon millions if we preserve the Hjalladalur valley and allow the river to enrich the sea, sustain the carbon cycle and nourish the algae and fish spawn. The waterfalls along Fljótsdalur will one day be worth as much as Gullfoss. And as for the soul – that is something no one can put a price on.

I believe the future will be amazing, and after that the whole world will become a better place. If we cannot make that happen, then no one can.

Publisher's Note

Dreamland was published early in 2006, made record sales and appealed to remarkably disparate reader groups. The young radicals' web site recommended the book while it was also awarded the freedom prize by the young libertarians. Dreamland was seen to put the debate on the environment in a new perspective. Dreamland uses Iceland as an example to understand the world and why so much goes wrong despite the fact that people have democracy, free press and general prosperity. Andri writes about many of the major topical issues and found new facets on many.

In 2006 the closure of the American cold war base in Keflavík was imminent. Up to 2000 people were in danger of losing their jobs. When the first copies of Dreamland were being delivered from the printers, the American government announced their withdrawal of their army, which came as a surprise to most people. Suddenly the book's deliberations on the future of the base location became an acute political issue. An initiative was launched immediately to find a use for the buildings the army had left behind. An international university was founded at the location and apartments rented to students. A film studio is planned, a data centre and various other activities. The price of housing did not drop in neighbouring municipalities. The population has grown and jobs have also increased. Over six hundred jobs were lost but a year after the departure of the military there were only 50 people registered as unemployed.

Regardless of whether big companies are good or bad, the book was a cry for help. Every day one could hear news of new smelters and requests for licences for preparatory studies or for power stations with attendant sacrifices of Iceland's most sensitive areas. Newsmen and politicians seemed to take it as read that ability in man to create an occupation for himself and to find a way through life was an exception, rather than a rule. People seriously asked: what other possibilities are there?, - and saw nothing unusual in a community of 300,000 becoming the world's biggest aluminium smelter.

The book concludes by posing a question, whether the dam should not be allowed to stand as a memorial to an accident that almost happened. Fifteen thousand took part in a protest march, calling for a halt to the project. The government did not accede to the request. On the morning of 28 September 2006 the dam locks were closed, marking the start of the slow drowning of 50km2 of land – all for one Alcoa smelter. The same evening all lights in Reykjavík and vicinity were switched off when the City enacted an idea from the first chapter in the book. Two days later the military finally left after 6 months of preparation.

Alcoa is pressing hard for another smelter in North Iceland, thus threatening sensitive high geothermal heat areas in the North and possibly using two more glacial rivers. Should this come to fruition, Alcoa will be by far the largest company in North and East Iceland and will use almost all the potential energy with the exception of that in the glacial river Jökulsá á Fjöllum.

Sources

Genesis 3:17-19, King James Bible

Elín Aradóttir and Kjartan Ólafsson (2004): Community spirit and innovation: research into selected rural areas, Institute for Regional Research: Akureyri, p. 115.

President Bush welcomes Iceland prime minister to White House,' transcript of conversation between the US president and the prime minister of Iceland, 6 July 2004. www.whitehouse.gov/news/ releases/ 2004/07/20040706-2.html.

Guðjón Friðriksson (1999), Einar Benediktsson: a biography, Vol. 2, Iðunn: Reykjavík, pp. 6-7.

Landsvirkjun (2004), The environment in our hands, Landsvirkjun: Reykjavík, p. 12

Hákon Aðalsteinsson (2002), 'Energy policy considerations for the people of southern Iceland', lecture by the director general and project manager of the National Energy Authority at the general meeting of SASS (Association of Local Authorities in Southern Iceland), 30 August 2002, www.sudurland.is/sass/ Hugleiding.pdf.

Jakob Björnsson (1970), 'On nature conservation, with particular reference to hydroelectric development in Iceland', p. 25

'Now to tame the waterfalls of Iceland', article in Living Science, vol. 8, 2004, pp. 50-55.

United Kingdom Parliament, House of Commons, Michael Clapham, 'Rio Tinto Corporation', Early Day Motion 1194, 1 April 1998, http://edmi.parliament.uk/EDMi/EDMDetails. aspx?EDMID =15321&SESSION=701.

The United Kingdom Parliament, House of Commons, Session 2000-01, Weekly Information Bulletin, 16 December 2000, http://www.parliament.the-stationery-office.com/pa/cm200001/cmwib/wb001216/ edms.htm.

International Federation of Chemical, Energy, Mine and General Workers Union (ICEM) (1998), Rio Tinto – tainted titan: the stakeholders' report, ICEM: Belgium.

'Biggest mining company expresses interest', news item in Morgunblaðið, 16 March 2004.

'Representatives from Rio Tinto examine aluminium plant options', news item in Morgunblaðið, 16 July 2005.

'Assistance for Norðurál declared legal', news item in Morgunblaðið, 15 July 1998.

'Exercises to take account of real-life situations', news item in Morgunblaðið, 23 June 1999.

'Low-level flight exercises as part of NORTHERN VIKING 99', press release from the Ministry of Foreign Affairs, no. 057, 18 June 1999, www3.utanrikisraduneyti.is/frettaefni/frettatilkynningar/ nr/1638.

'Misrepresentations on power development issues', article submitted by Thorkell Helgason, director general of the National Energy Authority, Morgunblaðið, 26 January 2003.innan fárra ára. Þessu lýstu forráðamenn Alcan yfir við ríkisstjórnina, -segir Halldór Ásgrímsson forsætisráðherra."

Meier, Alan, and Rosen, Karen [no date of publication], Energy use of U.S. consumer electronics at the end of the 20th century, report from the Lawrence Berkeley National Laboratory, http://eetd.lbl.gov/ EA/Reports/46212/.

Andri Snær Magnason

www.grida.no, United Nations Environmental Program

'Aluminium beverage can waste passes the "one trillion" mark – recycling rate drops to lowest point in 25 years', press release from the Container Recycling Institute, 24 May 2004, www.container-recycling. org/assets/pdfs/trillionthcan/UBC2004CRIPressRel.pdf.

'Environmentalists criticized', news item in Morgunblaðið, 16 January 2003.

'Airbus aluminium mostly from Alcoa', news item in Morgunblaðið, 28 April 2005.

www.airbus.com.

'The Landsvirkjun Norðlingaalda Diversion plan', discussed on www.lv.is/article.asp?catID= 180&ArtId=212.

Ministry for Industry and Commerce (1996), Manpower needs and skills for power schemes and heavy industrial operations 1996-2002: committee report, Ministry for Industry and Commerce: Reykjavík. Ministry for Industry and Commerce (1998), Manpower needs and skills for power schemes and heavy industrial operations 1998-2005: committee report, Ministry for Industry and Commerce: Reykjavík.

Einar Oddur Kristjánsson, speaking in parliament, 5 December 2002, Alþingistíðindi (Icelandic Parliamentary Gazette), 2002-03, 128th legislative session B, debates, p. 1791.

Answer by the minister for industry to a question from Kolbrún Halldórsdóttir on company promotion by Landsvirkjun, Iceland State Electricity and the Westfjord Power Company, 5 December 2002, Alþingistíðindi (Icelandic Parliamentary Gazette), 2002-03, 128th legislative session A, parliamentary papers, p. 2313.

'Norðlingaalda Diversion ready for next stage', news item in Morgunblaðið, 21 April 2004.

'Már Haraldsson', death notice, Morgunblaðið, 18 April 2004.

'Majority on Gnúpverjahreppur council overturned?' Evening News, National Radio, 24 August 2005.

'Harnessing unlimited power and profits from the world's most progressive energy program', True Wealth, Stansberry & Associates Investment Research, 17 August 2006.(2001): Kárahnjúkavirkjun allt að 750 MW – Fyrri áfangi allt að 625 MW og síðari áfangi allt að 125 MW. Úrskurður Skipulagsstofnunar um mat á umhverfisáhrifum. Skipulagsstofnun: Reykjavík, bls. 206.

Transcript of a teleconference of investors on the first quarter's figures for 2004 of the Century Aluminum Company, 27 April 2004, www.centuryca.com/news/pdf/transcript042704.pdf.

'Aluminium works Iceland', news item in Blaðið, 5 November 2005.

'Straumsvík – expansion or closure', news item on NFS, 3 March 2006. It goes on to say: 'If the Straumsvík aluminium plant is not able to expand it will have to be shut down and closed within a few years. This was the message from executives of Alcan in talks with the government, according to prime minister Halldór Ásgrímsson.'

'Discussion committee concludes no basis for construction of ferrosilicon plant', news item in Morgunblaðið, 1 July 1987.

'Rio Tinto feels the pinch', news item in the Guardian, 13 May 1999. The article says: 'Rio Tinto's operation at Capper Pass was an environmental disaster, causing death and serious illness to many of its former employees.'
In Indonesia Rio Tinto is reported to have been razing villages to the ground and driving out the inhabitants to clear land for a proposed mine. Security patrols financed by the company are said to have used threats, rape, torture, kidnapping and murder against those who tried to protect their possessions and work tools or stand up against the poisoning of wells and water sources and the

A Self-Help Manual for a Frightened Nation

general destruction of farming lands, sacred sites and fishing grounds.

'Extractive industries is not the answer for decent and sustainable livelihood: statement for the World Bank Extractive Industries Review (EIR)', statement from a group of Indonesian NGOs (the Indonesian Forum for the Environment (WALHI), the Indonesian Mining Advocacy Network (JATAM), and the Indigenous Peoples' Alliance of the Archipelago (AMAN)) and Australian NGOs (the Mineral Policy Institute, Friends of the Earth Australia, and the Asia-Pacific Unit, Australian Conservation Foundation): Bali, Indonesia, 26-30 April 2002, www.minesandcommunties.org/Charter/eirposit2.htm.

Júlíus Solnes (2004), 'To harness power or not to harness power', Up in the Wind: the Journal of Civil Engineering Students, vol. 23, 2004, pp. 20-23.

Helgi Baldursson (1995), Democracy in the fetters of power: the Blanda dispute, Land Conservation Association for the Blanda and Héraðsvötn Drainage Basins, [no place of publication], p. 209.

Jón Thór Sturluson (2005), 'The performance of Landsvirkjun and the effects of heavy industry on the national economy', Landsvirkjun 1965-2005: the company and its environment, The Icelandic Literary Society: Reykjavík, p. 118.

Hermann Sveinbjörnsson (1989), Wade in! Sigurjón Rist, hydrographer: memoirs, Skjaldborg: Reykjavík, pp. 198-9.

'The Kárahnjúkar Hydroelectric Scheme: illusion and reality', essay by Grímur Björnsson, geophysicist at the National Energy Authority, addressed to the director general of the Authority, 14 February 2002, www.os.is/~grb/karahnjukar.html.

Grímur Björnsson in interview with Jón Ásgeir Sigurðsson, Evening Shift, Icelandic National Radio, Channel 1, 10 April 2005.

'In the steps of Nostradamus', front page interview with the French psychic Marcelus Toe Guor in the Sunday edition of Morgunblaðið, 29 July 1990

'Bauxite mining blamed for deforestation', article by Zadie Neufville, 6 April 2001, http://forests.org/archive/samerica/bauxmini.htm.

'Jamaica bauxite case', Case Study, American University, www.american.edu/TED/bauxite.htm.

'Dust-up swirls around key Jamaica industry', article in the Los Angeles Times, 25 October 2004.

'"Red dust" application opposed over cancer fears', article in the Irish Independent, 31 October 2005. To quote: 'A TERRIFIED community has raised major cancer fears over plans to expand the giant "red mud" lagoons at the controversial Aughinish Alumina plant.'

'Russians in heavy-industry talks with PM', news item in Fréttablaðið, 23 April 2002.
í Ríkisútvarpinu 17. desember 2005.

www.flug.is

'Icelandic delegation examines Alcoa alumina refinery in Spain', news item in Morgunblaðið, 26 September 2002.

'Fresh investments in Orissa: sun god smiles again', article by Roy Pallavi, 27 September 2004, www.businessworldindia.com/sep2704/news10.asp.

'The battle for bauxite in Orissa', news feature by Meena Menon, The Hindu, 20 April 2005.

'Utkal Alumina confident of kicking off Rs 4,500 cr project soon', news item in the Hindu Business Line, 5 November 2003.
http://www.thehindubusinessline.com/2003/11/06/stories/ 2003110602230200.htm

Andri Snær Magnason

'And the winner is Bechtel', editorial in the New York Times, 19 April 2003.

Bob Herbert, 'Ask Bechtel what war is good for', International Herald Tribune, 22 April 2003.

'Alcoa set to clean up its Texas smelter', news item in American Metal Market, 23 June 2001.

'Alcoa awarded contract to produce aluminum castings for tactical Tomahawk missile program', press release from Alcoa, 1 December 2005, www.alcoa.com/aerospace/en/news/releases/tomahawk_ castings.asp.

'Alcoa tour showcases military', report in the Pittsburgh Tribune Review, 23 August 2005.
'Alcoa provides aluminum for humvees used in Iraq', posting on www.alcoa.com, 18 November 2004.

Icelandic National Planning Agency (2001), The Kárahnjúkar Hydroelectric Scheme up to 750 MW: Stage 1 up to 625 MW and Stage 2 up to 125 MW. Ruling of the National Planning Agency on the assessment of environmental impacts, Icelandic National Planning Agency: Reykjavík, p. 206.

'Reykjasel rediscovered?' news report on National Radio, 11 August 2005. According to the report: 'Excavations have confirmed that the finds being investigated right up by the Kárahnjúkar dam date back to before the year 950. The site will be submerged in water with the creation of the Hálslón reservoir.'

Iceland in a New Light.

'Swedish crown princess presented with Icelandic stallion', news item in Morgunblaðið, 29 May 2003.

Sigurður Kári Kristjánsson, member of parliament, in interview with Thorfinnur Ómarsson, National Radio, Channel 1, 'At the End of the Week', 23 July 2005.

'Conservation group in financial difficulties', Evening News, National Radio, 18 May 2003.

www.star.is, 6 September 2001.

www.star.is. The website no longer exists and the domain is unused, and perhaps it will be impossible to prove that it ever existed. It would be curious to know whether and how information of this type will be preserved for the use of future historians. Many more people than those mentioned here were subjected to these attacks. Nor is it possible to prove all of the claims made here regarding the pressure put on naturalists to curb freedom of speech. But by phoning round a fair number of members of staff at the Icelandic Institute of Natural History and making other enquiries, I came across some extraordinary cases in which, for example, media interviews on the nature of Kringilsárrani were met with swift responses from the highest quarters in the power sector. It was the same thing over and over again: a naturalist as a human being was something that needed to be suppressed.

'Special think-tank appointed', interview with Valgerður Sverrisdóttir, minister for industry, in Morgunblaðið, 31 March 2002.

www.star.is

V. Søyseth et al. (1995), 'Relation of exposure to airway irritants in infancy to prevalence of bronchial hyperresponsiveness in schoolchildren', The Lancet, vol. 345, 28 January 1995, pp. 217-220.
V. Søyseth et al. (1996), 'Allergen sensitization and exposure to irritants in infancy', Allergy, vol. 51, October 1996, pp. 719-723.
V. Søyseth et al. (1995), 'Bronchial responsiveness, eosinophilia, and short-term exposure to air pollution', Archives of Disease in Childhood, vol. 73, November 1995, pp. 418-422.

Katrín Fjeldsted, speaking in parliament, 28 January 2003, Alþingistíðindi (Icelandic Parliamentary Gazette), 2002-03, 128th legislative session B, debates, p. 2718.

Sources

Flosi Hrafn Sigurðsson et al. (2003), 'Wind and stability observations in Reyðarfjörður, July 2002–May 2003, Icelandic Meteorological Office: Reykjavík, www.vedur.is/utgafa/greinargerdir/2003/ 03032.pdf, p. 27. Quoted verbatim.

Flosi Hrafn Sigurðsson et al. (2003), 'Wind and stability observations in Reyðarfjörður, July 2002–May 2003, Icelandic Meteorological Office: Reykjavík, www.vedur.is/utgafa/greinargerdir/ 2003/03032.pdf, p. 23.

'Employment issues at the start of a new century', article by Halldór Ásgrímsson, Dagur, 7 April 1999.

Job 127:1, King James Bible

'Anxious easterners still live in hope', article in Morgunblaðið, 3 August 2001.

'Population set to rise with arrival of aluminium plant', report on National Radio, 3 December 2005.

'Ágúst Guðmundsson: heavy-industry policy out of date', news item on the Morgunblaðið website, www.mbl.is, 8 February 2006.

'High-tech industry abandoning the country?' news item on National Radio, 17 December 2005.

Halldór Ásgrímsson, prime minister, on the planned expansion of heavy industry up to the year 2012, Evening News, National Radio, 24 January 2006.

Ruling of the ministry for the environment on the environmental assessment of the Kárahnjúkar hydroelectric scheme, case no. 01080004, 1 January 2001, www.rettarheimild.is/Umhverfis/UrskurdirR aduneytisins/2001/01/01/nr/836.

'Alcoa seeking the best for T&T', news item in the Trinidad & Tobago Express, 4 December 2005.

'There are few things more lovely than a freshly ploughed field', interview with Eymundur Magnússon, farmer at Vallanes in Fljótsdalur, Blaðið, 17 February 2006.

WEBSITES:
www.airbus.com
www.alcan.is
www.alcoa.com
www.alcoa.is
www.atlantsal.is
www.austurlamb.is
www.boeing.com
www.bookcrossing.com
www.dansihfurniture.dk
www.flug.is
www.globalsecurity.org
www.grida.no
www.invest.is
www.jbeo.com
www.karahnjukar.is
www.memorialspaceflights.com
www.miljostatus.no
www.rikiskassinn.is
www.star.is
www.wheresgeorge.com
www.whitehouse.gov

Andri Snær Magnason

A Self-Help Manual for a Frightened Nation

Andri Snær Magnason

ICELAND - From the CIA Factbook

Background: Settled by Norwegian and Celtic immigrants during the late 9th and 10th centuries A.D., Iceland boasts the world's oldest functioning legislative assembly, the Althing, established in 930. Independent for over 300 years, Iceland was subsequently ruled by Norway and Denmark. Fallout from the Askja volcano of 1875 devastated the Icelandic economy and caused widespread famine. Over the next quarter century, 20% of the population emigrated, mostly to Canada and the US. Limited home rule from Denmark was granted in 1874 and complete independence attained in 1944. Literacy, longevity, income, and social cohesion are first-rate by world standards.

Geography

Location:	Island between the Greenland Sea and the North Atlantic Ocean, northwest of the UK
Area:	*total:* 103,000 sq km, *land:* 100,250 sq km, *water:* 2,750 sq km, *coastline:* 4,970 km
Maritime claims:	*territorial sea:* 12 nm, *exclusive economic zone:* 200 nm
Climate:	temperate; moderated by North Atlantic Current; mild, windy winters; damp, cool summers
Terrain:	mostly plateau interspersed with mountain peaks, icefields; coast deeply indented by bays and fiords
Highest point:	Hvannadalshnukur 2,110 m (at Vatnajokull glacier)
Natural resources:	fish, hydropower, geothermal power, diatomite
Land use:	*arable land:* 0.07%, *permanent crops:* 0%
Total renewable water resources:	170 cu km (2005)
Natural hazards:	earthquakes and volcanic activity
Environment - current issues:	water pollution from fertilizer runoff; inadequate wastewater treatment

People

Population:	304,367 (July 2008 est.). Pop. Growth rate: 0.783% (est.)
Infant mortality rate:	*total:* 3.25 deaths/1,000 live births *male:* 3.39 deaths/1,000 live births *female:* 3.1 deaths/1,000 live births (2008 est.)
Life expectancy:	*male:* 78.43 years, *female:* 82.76 years (2008 est.)
Total fertility rate:	1.91 children born/woman (2008 est.)
Ethnic groups:	mixture of descendants of Norse and Celts 94%, population of foreign origin 6%
Religions:	Lutheran Church of Iceland 85.5%,
Languages:	Icelandic, English, Nordic languages
Literacy:	*(definition:* age 15 and over can read and write) *total population:* 99%

Government

Government type:	constitutional republic
Legal system:	civil law system based on Danish law; has not accepted compulsory ICJ jurisdiction
Suffrage:	18 years of age; universal
Legislative branch:	unicameral Parliament or Althing (63 seats; members are elected by popular vote to serve four-year terms)

Economy

Economy - overview:	Scandinavian-type, basically capitalistic economy, yet with an extensive welfare system (including generous housing subsidies), low unemployment, and remarkably even distribution of income. In the absence of other natural resources (except for abundant geothermal power), the economy depends heavily on the fishing industry, which provides 70% of export earnings and employs 6% of the work force. The economy remains sensitive to declining fish stocks as well as to fluctuations in world prices for its main exports: fish and fish products, aluminum, and ferrosilicon. Substantial foreign investment in the aluminum and hydropower sectors has boosted economic growth which, nevertheless, has been volatile and characterized by recurrent imbalances. Iceland's economy has been diversifying into manufacturing and service industries in the last decade, and new developments in software production, biotechnology, and financial services are taking place. The tourism sector is expanding, with the recent trends in ecotourism and whale watching. The 2006 closure of the US military base at Keflavik had very little impact on the national economy; Iceland's low unemployment rate aided former base employees in finding alternate employment.
GDP :	$19.52 billion (2007 est.)
GDP - per capita:	$39,400 (2007 est.)
GDP - by sector:	*agriculture:* 5.3%, *industry:* 26.3%, *services:* 68.4% (2007 est.)
Labor force:	180,000 (2007 est.), *agriculture:* 5.1%, *industry:* 23%, *services:* 71.8% (2005)
Unemployment:	1% (2007 est.)
Agriculture :	potatoes, green vegetables; mutton, dairy products; fish
Industries:	fish processing; aluminum smelting, ferrosilicon production; geothermal power, tourism
Industrial production growth rate:	9% (2007 est.)
Electricity -	8.533 billion kWh (2005)
Electricity -production by source:	*fossil fuel:* 0.1%, *hydro:* 82.5% *nuclear:* 0%, *other:* 17.5% (geothermal) (2001)
Electricity -consumption:	8.152 billion kWh (2005)